IN THE NAME OF

ALLAH

THE ALL-COMPASSIONATE, ALL-MERCIFUL

HEALING
Body & Soul

- TITLE: *HEALING BODY & SOUL*
- AUTHOR: DR. AMIRA AYAD
- ENGLISH EDITION 1 (2008)
- NEW REVISED ENGLISH EDITION 2 (2013)
- REVISED AND EDITED BY: JAMILA HAKAM
- LAYOUT DESIGN: IIPH, EGYPT BRANCH
- COVER DESIGN: SAMO PRESS GROUP

HEALING
Body & Soul

Your Guide To Holistic Wellbeing
Following Islamic Teachings

غذاء الروح والبدن

Dr. Amira Ayad

Revised and Edited by
Jamila Hakam

الدار العالمية للكتاب الإسلامي
INTERNATIONAL ISLAMIC PUBLISHING HOUSE

Copyright © 2013 International Islamic Publishing House
King Fahd National Library Cataloging-in-Publication Data

Ayad, Amira
Healing Body & Soul / Dr. Amira Ayad 2. - Riyadh, 2013

582 pp ; 21 cm

1- Islam and self-improvement   2-Islam and medicine
I- Title

214.61 dc   1433/1244

Legal Deposit no. **1433/1244**
ISBN Hardcover: 978-603-501-202-7

International Islamic Publishing House (IIPH)
P.O. Box 55195 Riyadh 11534, Saudi Arabia
Tel: 966 1 4650818 / 4647213 — Fax: 966 1 4633489
E-mail: iiph@iiph.com.sa — iiphsa@gmail.com
www.iiph.com | www.iiph.com.sa

CONTENTS

Chapter 3
Intellectual Body 217

Chapter 4
Emotional Body 259

Chapter 5
Spiritual Body.. 369

Pronunciation and Transliteration Chart

Arabic script	Pronunciation	Trans-literated form
أ	short 'a', as in *cat*	a
آ — ئ	longer 'a', as in *cab* (not as in *cake*)	â
ب	/b/ as in *bell*, *rubber* and *tab*	b
ت	/t/ as in *tap*, *mustard* and *sit*	t
ة	takes the sound of the preceding diacritical mark sometimes ending in h (when in pausal form): ah, ih or ooh; or atu(n), ati(n) or ata(n) when uninterrupted	h or t (when followed by another Arabic word)
ث	/th/ as in *thing*, *maths* and *wealth*	th
ج	/j/ as in *jam*, *ajar* and *age*	j
ح	a 'harsher' sound than the English initial /h/, and may occur medially and in word-final position as well	ḥ
خ	as in *Bach* (in German); may occur initially and medially as well	kh
د	/d/ as in *do*, *muddy* and *red*	d

Arabic script	Pronunciation	Trans-literated form
ذ	as in *this*, *father* and *smooth*	dh
ر	/r/ as in *raw*, *arid* and *war*; may also be a rolled 'r', as pronounced in Spanish	r
ز	/z/ as in *zoo*, *easy* and *gaze*	z
س	/s/ as in *so*, *messy* and *grass*	s
ش	as in *ship*, *ashes* and *rush*	sh
ص	no close equivalent in English, but may be approximated by pronouncing it as /sw/ or /s/ farther back in the mouth	ṣ
ض	no close equivalent in English, but may be approximated by pronouncing it as /d/ farther back in the mouth	ḍ
ط	no close equivalent in English, but may be approximated by pronouncing it as /t/ farther back in the mouth	ṭ
ظ	no close equivalent in English, but may be approximated by pronouncing 'the' farther back in the mouth	dh
ع	no close equivalent in English: a guttural sound in the back of the throat	'
غ	no close equivalent in English, but may be closely approximated by pronouncing it like the French /r/ in 'rouge'	gh

Arabic script	Pronunciation	Trans-literated form
ف	/f/ as in *fill*, *effort* and *muff*	f
ق	no close equivalent in English, but may be approximated by pronouncing it as /k/ farther back in the mouth	q
ك	/k/ as in *king*, *buckle* and *tack*	k
ل	/l/ as in *lap*, *halo*; in the word Allah, it becomes velarized as in *ball*	l
م	/m/ as in *men*, *simple* and *ram*	m
ن	/n/ as in *net*, *ant* and *can*	n
ﻫ — ﻪ — ه	/h/ as in *hat*; unlike /h/ in English, in Arabic /h/ is pronounced in medial and word-final positions as well	h
و	as in *wet* and *away*	w
و	long 'u', as in *boot* and *too*	oo
ي	as in *yard* and *mayo*	y
ي	long 'e', as in *eat*, *beef* and *see*	ee
ء	glottal stop: may be closely approximated by pronouncing it like 't' in the Cockney English pronunciation of *butter*: *bu'er*, or the stop sound in *uh-oh!*	(omitted in initial position)

Diphthongs

Arabic script	Pronunciation	Trans-literated form
أَو، وَ	long 'o', as in *owe, boat* and *go*	au, aw
أَي، يَ	long 'a', as in *aid, rain* and *say*	ay, ai, ei

Diacritical marks (tashkeel)

Name of mark	Pronunciation	Trans-literated form
´ fathah	very short 'a' or schwa (unstressed vowel)	a
´ kasrah	shorter version of ee or schwa (unstressed vowel)	i
´ dammah	shorter version of oo	u
´´ shaddah	a doubled consonant is stressed in the word, and the length of the sound is also doubled	double letter
° sukoon	no vowel sound between consonants or at the end of a word	absence of vowel

ARABIC HONORIFIC SYMBOLS USED IN THIS BOOK

(﷾): *Subḥânahu wa Ta'âlâ* — Glorified and Exalted is He

(ﷺ): *Ṣalla Allâhu 'alayhi wa sallam* — *Blessings and peace be upon him*

(﷡): *'Alayhi as-salâm* — Peace be upon him

(﷠): *Raḍiya Allâhu 'anhu* — May Allah be pleased with him

(﷠): *Raḍiya Allâhu 'anhâ* — May Allah be pleased with her

Hadith grade terms in this book

Sound:	*ṣaheeḥ*
Reliable:	*ḥasan*
Weak:	*ḍa'eef*
Odd:	*ghareeb*
Authentic:	includes sound, reliable, or any grade in between
Acceptable:	*sakat 'anhu*; the grader of the hadith did not comment on it, meaning that he found noth ing unacceptable in it

A WORD ABOUT
THE WORD *LORD*

$\mathcal{T}$he word lord in English has several related meanings. The original meaning is 'master' or 'ruler', and in this sense it is often used to refer to human beings: 'the lord of the mansion' or 'Lord So-and-So' (in the United Kingdom, for example). The word *Lord* with a capital L is used in the lexicon of Islam to refer to the One and Only God — Allah. In Islam, there is no ambiguity about the meaning of this word. While it is true that one may occasionally use the word *lord* (whether capitalized or not) to refer to a human being, in Islamic discourse the reference of this term is always clear from the context.

The Editor

PUBLISHER'S NOTE

*A*ll praise and thanks belong to Allah alone, the One, the Almighty, and All-Merciful. Blessings and peace be upon Prophet Muhammad, the last of His Messengers and Prophets, his family, his Companions and all those who follow in his footsteps until the end of time.

One frequently hears the phrase 'Islam is a complete code of life,' but how often is this concept actually put into practice by Muslims themselves? In many cases, we tend to focus on the ritualistic aspects of our religion, without realizing that we have to give time and attention to the whole person that Allah created. Each of us is made up of a body, a mind and a soul. Each of these aspects of the human being has needs, which if left unfulfilled, may weaken and sicken it.

Amira Ayad has written a book that addresses the needs of all these components of the human from a holistic, Islamic perspective. Packed with practical advice from the Qur'an, the Sunnah, and traditional and alternative healing practices — both ancient and modern, handy tables and reference guides like her 'Health problems and suggested dietary intervention', and a comprehensive Index, *Healing Body & Soul* is a timely and timeless reference manual for the modern Muslim family or individual.

May Allah bless the efforts of all who contributed to the production of this book, and may it be acceptable to Him.

Muhammad Abdul Mohsin Al-Tuwaijri

Managing Director
International Islamic Publishing House
Riyadh, Saudi Arabia

To my dearest Mother,

With a great debt of love and gratitude for all the wisdom, patience, ethics and morals you taught me, and for all the support, encouragement and love you gave me. May God bless you and grant you the peace of mind, body and soul.

PREFACE AND ACKNOWLEDGMENTS

When I was in school, my teacher used to write a note on my creative writing work stating: "Very good ideas, but badly expressed!" As I have always loved books, I admire authors, but I never dared to even dream of becoming one. I knew I had a science-oriented mind, whereas I do not have much talent for talking. It was after my presentation for the Master's degree when a former student of mine, who then became my colleague, told me: "Congratulations, very elegantly presented, as you used to teach us, easy and to the point." This was my inspiration to start this work which I hope will also be elegant, easy and to the point.

First and foremost, all praises and thanks are due to Allah for helping me fulfil this work and may peace and prayers be upon our **Prophet Muhammad** who guided us to Islam, upon his Family and his Companions who worked so that Islam could rise and shine on the whole world.

Second, I want to express my deepest gratitude to all my teachers, to all the authors of the books I learnt from, to all Muslim scientists and scholars throughout the years and to all my friends and family members. I would not have written this book if not for the encouragement, help and support from my dear friend Dr. **Pansee**. The editors at **IIPH** have been very helpful and patient — I cannot thank them enough.

I would also like to express my gratitude to my brother, Dr. **Ahmed Ayad** for his valuable help. I am thankful to my parents, **Adel** and **Soheir** for all their teaching and support. Special thanks to my children, **Youssof** and **Janna**, who taught me patience, dedication and unconditional love. Most of all, I would like to thank my husband, **Ihab**, for being there for me.

﴿ ... رَبَّنَا لَا تُؤَاخِذْنَآ إِن نَّسِينَآ أَوْ أَخْطَأْنَا ... ﴾ ۞ ﴿ (سورة البقرة: ٢٨٦)

﴾...O Allah! Do not condemn us if we forget or fall into error...﴿

(Qur'an 1: 286)

Disclaimer

This book is intended as a general guideline for a healthy lifestyle. Any suggested treatments or preventative measures mentioned in this book are not meant to take the place of treatment and/or advice by qualified health practitioners. Neither the author nor the publisher can be held responsible for any loss, injury or claim arising from the use or misuse of the information contained in this book.

INTRODUCTION

When I began studying alternative therapy and holistic well-being, I read about the centuries-old Indian, Chinese and Japanese traditional practices of herbal and therapeutic medicine. It made me wonder, why are we following practices derived from polytheistic belief systems? Do we have no Islamic alternative? WHY? Did not our dear Prophet — (ﷺ) (peace and blessings of Allah be upon him) — say:

«I left among you what if you hold on to, you will never go astray, the book of Allah and my Sunnah (life practice).»[1]

This does not apply only to acts of worship ('ibâdât), for Islam covers all aspects of life. The wellbeing of the whole person — emotionally, physically, spiritually and mentally — is necessary for the believer to participate fully in life, fulfilling his or her duty towards Allah and towards society.

A brief history of Western medicine

Since the beginning of recorded history, Western medical practitioners have adopted one or the other of two opposing paths: 'rationalism' (acquiring medical skills through reason) or 'empiricism' (acquiring medical skills through experience). Empiricism is an approach that respects the integrity and individuality of the whole person; it aims to stimulate, enhance and/or support the person's vitality, immunity and inherent healing powers. In this philosophy, each individual is looked upon as a special case, with his/her own combination of thoughts, emotions, and (religious) belief, whose physical health, lifestyle (such as eating habits), and environmental conditions all contribute to that individual's well-being or illness.[2] In contrast, the philosophy of rationalism concentrates on attacking illness by alleviating the symptoms of disease, rather than searching for the causes behind it.

The Greek Hippocrates is considered to be the father of 'traditional' western medicine. He lived around 1000 years before the Hijrah[3] or 400 years before the birth of Jesus (BC), and built his medical practice on observation and experience using the natural world as a teacher that helped him to better understand how healing is achieved. His type of practice persisted for centuries as the standard approach to methods of healing. The Hippocratic Oath (a vow containing a code of ethical behaviour that is still taken by Western-trained medical students all over the world) is said to have been written by him. An approach diametrically opposed to empiricism was advanced by a fellow Greek, Aristotle (who lived in the ninth century before the Hijrah or 384-322 BC). Aristotle made major contributions in anatomy and biology; he also studied and taught philosophy, physics and metaphysics and advocated the rationalist way of thinking. Over two centuries later another Greek, the physician Galen, (who lived about five hundred years before the Hijrah, in the second century after Christ's birth, or Common Era — CE), also adopted the rationalist philosophy. He was one of the first experimental physiologists, and strongly supported observation and reasoning. The vast body of knowledge left by Galen was later to be used by European and Muslim Arab physicians alike as a base for further scientific inquiry and development.[4]

In the tenth century after the Hijrah (H)/sixteenth century CE, Paracelsus, a Swiss chemist and physician, revived empiricism by combining theory and practice and by treating the patient as a human being — a whole entity, a combination of spirit and matter, and not just a physical body.[5] Paracelsus' philosophy was soon eclipsed, however, for in the eleventh century H/seventeenth century CE, the ideas of the philosopher René Descartes became popular. Descartes, who was also a physicist, physiologist and mathematician, was a rationalist who doubted everything and believed that experience does not lead to primary knowledge and information.[6] Western scientists subsequently began to study the body in terms of the structure and function of its organs, tissues and cells. In the eighteenth century, scholars of medicine no longer looked at the body as a whole; they saw it as a machine with separate parts that could be fixed by the 'proper' intervention, which came in the form of poisonous drugs and harsh, sometimes even bloody treatments and surgery. This concept still operated till very recently: I remember when I was a student at the faculty of pharmacy, the lesson they gave us when we entered the morgue for the first time was: "Do not get overwhelmed by what you see; look at these corpses as if they were cars, and the internal organs are the engines that need to be fixed."

In 1263 H/1847 CE, the American Medical Association (AMA) was founded with the intention of elevating the standard of medical education in the United States.[7] The philosophy of the AMA counteracted empiricist philosophy and en-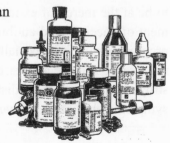

couraged the rational approach to medicine. The efforts of the AMA were given the support of the emerging pharmaceutical industry. During that period, the American civil war started. This extremely bloody conflict required 'miraculous' rapid cures to be provided by now well-known pharmaceutical companies. Along with the medicines they provided, the pharmaceutical companies supplied physicians with a detailed explanation of each disease and the methods of treatments with, of course, 'patented drugs'. This was to the economic benefit of both parties: the companies, which made a fortune as well as gaining a strong political influence; and the physicians, who saved time and money spent on learning and experiencing new technologies and gained the trust of desperate patients who found easy and rapid ways of treatment that required no effort on their part. However, they missed the point that it does not constitute a radical cure, as we shall see.

Soon afterwards, the AMA started evaluating and validating medical schools in the United States. As expected, the results of this project were proclaimed in the favour of *allopathic*[8] methods of treatment, which is known to us now as 'modern medicine'. Many schools that taught 'alternative medicine' were forced either to shut down or to follow the new 'scientific medicine' path.

The work of Robert Koch and Louis Pasteur, the two founders of modern bacteriology, further strengthened the move towards modern 'orthodox' medicine. Both considered the human body to be at the mercy of extraneous organisms.[9] With the development of vaccines and antibiotics, the idea of the 'miracle cure' progressed rapidly, especially during World War II, and medicinal science became a disease-oriented practice, focusing on 'destroying' the cause of the disease and 'suppressing' the undesired symptoms, and both interventions, as you can see, are accomplished with pharmaceutical medications which might not be in the best interest of the patient.

A clear example before our eyes is the chemotherapeutic treatments of cancer: the side effects of the 'medication' given are usually much more serious than the disease itself; using poisonous drugs adds to the toxic load of the organism and delays its effort to fend off the disease. Surgery is another method of treatment according to the allopathic philosophy. Allah did not create any organ or cell in our body that does not have a specific and important role — whether we have already discovered it or not. Furthermore, since a person is one and a whole organism, one cannot injure one part without affecting in some degree the entire organism. Taking the same analogy used by my pharmacy teachers, this resembles the first time German and American cars were introduced to my country, Egypt. The Egyptian mechanics, who had until then been used only to Soviet and Italian cars, found lots of parts in the engine 'useless additions', and reacted to an engine problem by scrapping these 'extra parts'. No wonder the new cars did not survive for long under their 'treatment'. Surgery in general weakens the organism and saturates the tissues with poisonous antiseptics and anaesthetics, rendering the affected parts and the body as a whole less resistant to deterioration and disease. I cannot deny that, in some cases, surgery is a necessity and a lifesaving intervention, but in most cases, especially nowadays, it is taken very lightly, and not at all as the last resort that it ought to be.

Today, after many years of following the path of medical 'rationalism', we should ask: What is the success rate of modern synthetic drugs against diseases like schizophrenia, Parkinsonism, autism and so many others? Is the high tech, high cost of modern

Western medicine really useful in treatment and diagnosis, or is it a placebo that is more of a 'feel-good' factor for both patients and doctors? Do we rely too much on drugs for treatment?

With the failure of 'up to date' medical technology to prove effective against prevalent modern-day ailments like obesity, hypertension, heart disease, diabetes, and the increased incidence of cancer in many societies, people are starting to refer once again to what is often called 'alternative' therapy. This therapy, as we shall see, is actually the original medicinal approach to health, once called 'holistic medicine'.

Islamic medicine

Islamic medical knowledge started with a base collected by Muslims in the early phase of Islamic history mainly from Greek sources, in addition to medical knowledge from Persia, Syria, India and Byzantine Rome.[10] This information was then assimilated and greatly expanded. The physicians of the time contributed to this work with their observations, practice, experience and experiments, helping to develop a flourishing medical science which gave priority to the preservation of health over the curing of ailments.

It is important to note here that, as stated by Ibn Khaldoon (the well-known medieval Muslim jurist, sociologist and historian) in his *'Muqaddimah'*: this Islamic medicine was "definitely no part of divine revelation but was something customarily practiced by the Arabs".[11] Nevertheless, the Qur'an mentions the beneficial effects of some natural foods like honey and dates, and orders abstinence from others such as flesh of swine (pork), alcohol and intoxicants. The second main reference of Islamic studies, the *Sunnah* [the recorded sayings and traditions of Prophet Muhammad (ﷺ)] also includes many guidelines regarding food intake and general lifestyle. In addition, it has taught us prophylactic measures and the management of simple physical problems as fever, headache, diarrhoea and constipation. Prophetic medicine places great stress on cleanliness, oral hygiene and the moral, emotional and spiritual aspects of human life.

According to Islamic medicine, physical ailments were thought to arise mainly as a result of the accumulation of excess waste substance in the body. Overeating, improper food choice and an unhealthy lifestyle in general were regarded as the sources of the accumulated morbid matter, and it was believed that when the digestion process became overwhelmed, disease resulted. The most important feature of Islamic medicine, though, is the fact that it regards the human being as a sacred entity consisting of a body and a soul (the latter is called *rooh* in Arabic). This *rooh*, which originates from the Divine Spirit, was regarded by the physicians as the driving force behind the body. Attaining the purity of the soul is the ultimate aim of the healer.[12] In much of the original Islamic literature, we can find a special section on the methods of purifying the heart. The Muslim scholars referred to modern psychological ailments such as hatred, envy, attachment to material life, anger and hostility as 'diseases of the heart' or 'soul ailments' that should be managed first before attending to the ailments of the physical body.

Islamic medicine passed through three stages: first came the translation of the Greek and Persian medical books into Arabic, which took place mainly during the first two centuries after the Hijrah (the seventh and eighth centuries CE). The second stage started when Muslim physicians, after studying and assimilating the foreign work, added to this body of knowledge from their own observations, research and experience. During this stage, many physicians contributed to the flourishing of Islamic medicine. One of the most famous among them was Al Razi (226-313 H/841-926 CE). Al Razi stressed the importance of the will or the desire of the patient to get well. He listed certain principles for the preservation of health which included moderation and balance in one's food, drink, physical activity and rest, improvement of the surrounding environmental conditions, adopting an active, healthy lifestyle, avoiding sins and evil acts, and balancing one's ambitions with one's will-power and ability.[13]

Al Razi's fame started with the establishment of a hospital in Baghdad. To select the best location for the hospital, he ordered that some pieces of meat be hung in different places around the city and examined these pieces daily for any signs of spoilage; the site where the meat had undergone the least degradation was chosen for the new hospital.[14]

Ibn Sina (369-428 H/980-1037 CE) was another famous Muslim physician. He was known to the West as 'Avicenna', and widely recognized for his famous book of medicine, *Al-Qânoon* or 'The Law'. Like most of the physicians of his time, Avicenna was also educated in the sciences of the Qur'an, Islamic law, mathematics, anatomy, logic and philosophy.[15]

Books written by Ibn Sina and Al Razi brought together the Greek and Islamic principles of medicine. Their works and those of many other Muslim scientists later made their way to the rest of Western Europe.[16] Their writings were translated into Latin and other languages, and used as textbooks by European scholars and scientists for several centuries.[17]

As a direct result of this Islamic influence, the knowledge of the ancients was discovered, preserved, expanded upon and improved, and finally given back to the West.[18]

The second stage lasted until the seventh century H/thirteenth century CE, after which came the stage of decline. By that time the whole Islamic *Khilâfah* (Caliphate) was deteriorating gradually, and sadly so (along with it) were the branches of science and other knowledge in which Muslims had excelled for centuries.[19]

During the eighth century H/fourteenth century CE, a new type of medical writing emerged, called 'Prophetic medicine'. This was intended as an alternative to the Greek-based body of medical science. The authors were religious scholars, rather than physicians. They revived the traditional medical knowledge applied and practiced by the Arabs during the Prophet's (ﷺ) time, and advocated Qur'anic teachings and those of the Sunnah over Greek medical practices, thus producing a new way of practice that was eagerly accepted by religious Muslims.[20] Most famous among them were the writings of Ibn al-Qayyim Jauziyah and Imam Dhahabi, which form the basis of Islamic medicine as known to us today.

In Islamic medicine, the mode of practice started with physiotherapy and nutritional assessment; if those did not produce the required healing, the physician then resorted to drugs.[21] The Arabs at that time had a refined and mature knowledge of food and nutrition, and were aware that food deficiencies and proper dietary schemes were important elements of diagnosis and treatment. It was generally agreed that whenever healing could be achieved through nourishment and diet, medicine ought to be avoided. Physiotherapy included exercises, proper breathing, ablution and water baths.

Finally, medicines, if used, should be similar or related to regular food and should contain no noxious or harmful substances.[22] Pharmacological drugs were classified as either simple or compound. Since the physicians of the time were highly knowledgeable in chemistry, pharmacology and the study of drug interaction, they used simple drugs first; if these failed, they referred to compound drugs. Honey was widely used as medicine; many herbs were prescribed for various ailments, and some herbs were even recommended for aromatherapy. In addition, cupping was widely practiced, but cauterization was generally disliked and avoided.[23]

Ibn al-Qayyim's statement, "Prophetic medicine has a divine element to it"[24] is indicative of the overall approach. As noted above, physicians were knowledgeable about the 'sickness of the heart and soul' and methods of treatment; they realized the effects of stress, mood and feelings on the physical body, and used positive affirmations to increase hope and strengthen the will to be healed. Moral values such as love, courage, patience, kindness, and altruism were prescribed as the best remedies for the inner self, and prayer was practiced for maintaining the connection with Allah, preserving the health of the body and soul, strengthening faith, bringing happiness and energizing the body against ailments.

In the early tenth century H/seventeenth century CE, Islamic medicine began to be challenged by the rapidly spreading science of modern allopathic medicine, which finally took over the core of the health care systems in most Islamic countries.[25] Islamic medicine still enjoys a wide popularity among Muslims. This has caused a recent revival of this ancient knowledge which is now practiced by physicians who derive their mode of healing from both modern medical practice and old Islamic traditions. Thus, it is common to find physicians in India, Malaysia and throughout the Middle East giving advice and treatment from Islamic medicine, in addition to more conventional Western-derived treatment.

The Holistic approach to health

Unlike conventional medicine, holistic or alternative therapy does not concentrate solely on the physical body. It views the human being as a combination of five 'bodies':

➤ The physical body, which includes the muscle and bone structures, in addition to different functional systems and organs such as the heart, lungs, and digestive system.

➤ The biochemical body, which is concerned with all the chemical compounds and chemical reactions that occur inside the organism, including its nutrition, the enzymes and hormones that are synthesized, and the body's environment as well, whether affected by airborne pollution, dust, foreign bodies or other factors.

➤ The intellectual body, concerned with one's mind.[26] The mind is the centre of thoughts, the driving force of human action and behaviour; it is the centre of intellect, the power of human choice. The intellectual body also involves the subconscious mind, sometimes called intuition or human instinct.

➤ The emotional body, which is concerned with one's psychological state, responses to stress, feelings and interaction with other human beings, whether in close relationships such as one's parents, spouses, and children, or with one's friends, neighbours and co-workers; or to do with one's co-existence in the society in general, the level of cooperation, humanitarian beliefs and brotherhood concept.

➤ The spiritual body: the soul or the higher self. This is the part we usually neglect in our daily routine. This is the body which connects us with our Almighty Creator and which acquires its driving energy directly from this sacred connection.

According to the holistic approach, health is not only the absence of illness, but also the balance between these five bodies. The World Health Organization (WHO) describes *health* as "a state of complete physical, mental and social wellbeing" — and this is exactly what Islamic teachings are all about.

As I mentioned earlier, holistic therapy was the origin and the norm for the practice of medicine; this is how therapy started in ancient Egypt, Greece, India and China. Therapists back then treated each person as an individual case: they looked beyond the symptoms of disease. They were there to help the patients to understand and combat their own illnesses by restoring their body's natural defences.

Hippocrates applied his golden rule in treating all his patients, "Primum non nocere," which translates as 'Above all, do no harm.' This is the same rule applied in Prophetic medicine as in a hadith narrated by Abu Dâwood and reported by Abu Hurayrah that the Prophet (ﷺ) forbade treatment with noxious substances.[27]

In an ancient work compiling Hippocrates' rules, called *Corpus Hippocraticum*, that famous therapist stressed the importance of taking into account the eating habits, emotional and psychological conditions and even the faith and spiritual connections of the patient.

Holistic Islamic teachings

Prophet Muhammad (ﷺ) used different types of remedies (natural or divine) for various ailments. The Prophet's law was that drugs should only be used when needed. Ibn al-Qayyim recommended spending more time and energy to purify the heart and inner self and preserving health by adopting a moderate, sensible lifestyle, avoiding unhealthy habits, and improving the surrounding environment.[28] It is a fact that curing the ills of the physical body without curing those of the heart and soul does not benefit much.

Ibn al-Qayyim's opinion regarding the best way to treat a medical problem demonstrates the wisdom of the Islamic approach to health; this opinion can be summarized in the following recommendations he made to doctors:[29] First diagnose the disease and search for the true cause behind it. The patient should be checked to determine if s/he is strong enough to fight the disease without the need for medication. The patient's age, habits, origin, mood and any changes in his/her state should be taken into consideration. The physician should also consider the condition of the patient at the time s/he caught the disease and remember the environmental and seasonal effects on health. Before prescribing any medicine, the physician should investigate the options of food and diet. If medicine is a must, the simplest one possible should be selected. Last but not least, the doctor should be knowledgeable about the sicknesses of the heart and soul and the effects of stress, mood and feelings on the physical body, and should know how to deal with them appropriately.[30]

When you buy a telephone, a television or a computer, first you read the manufacturer's guide. If not, either you will cause the breakdown of your instrument or you may use it without difficulty, but you will not get the full benefits out of it: you will not be able to explore fully all its capacities, powers and potential. The same goes for us human beings: our 'manual' has been sent down by our Creator Himself. In many verses of the Qur'an, Allah reminds us to follow His way, to learn and adjust our lives according to the rules and advice in that Glorious Book He has given us:

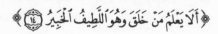

(سورة المُلك: ١٤) ﴿ أَلَا يَعْلَمُ مَنْ خَلَقَ وَهُوَ ٱللَّطِيفُ ٱلْخَبِيرُ ۝ ﴾

❨Should not He Who has created know? And He is the Most Kind and Courteous [to His slaves] All-Aware [of everything].❩

(Qur'an 67: 14)

(سورة الأنعام: ٣٨)   ﴾ ... مَّا فَرَّطْنَا فِى ٱلْكِتَـٰبِ مِن شَىْءٍ ... ۝ ﴿

❨...We have neglected nothing in the Book...❩   *(Qur'an 6: 38)*

﴾ ... وَنَزَّلْنَا عَلَيْكَ ٱلْكِتَـٰبَ تِبْيَـٰنًا لِّكُلِّ شَىْءٍ وَهُدًى وَرَحْمَةً وَبُشْرَىٰ لِلْمُسْلِمِينَ ۝ ﴿

(سورة النحل: ٨٩)

❨...And We have sent down to you the Book [the Qur'an] as an exposition of everything, a guidance, a mercy, and glad tidings for those who have submitted themselves [to Allah as Muslims].❩

(Qur'an 16: 89)

The guidance and enlightenment contained in these teachings ensure not only our happiness in this earthly life, but in the after-life as well. It is the way for eternal comfort, relief, bliss, felicity and prosperity.

Allah created the human race and specified its role. He says in the Qur'an:

﴾ ... وَإِذْ قَالَ رَبُّكَ لِلْمَلَـٰٓئِكَةِ إِنِّى جَاعِلٌ فِى ٱلْأَرْضِ خَلِيفَةً ... ۝ ﴿

(سورة البقرة: ٣٠)

❨...And [remember] when Allah said to the angels: I will create a vicegerent on earth...❩   *(Qur'an 2: 30)*

According to Ibn Mas'ood, who was one of the Companions known for his deep understanding of the Qur'an, being vicege-rents on earth means we are appointed by Allah in a position of responsibility to apply His laws on earth. Prophet Adam u and his descendents are responsible for establishing Allah's law on earth and ruling according to that law, keeping it ordered and peaceful as Allah wants it to be. This role requires good manners, considerate behaviour, purity, correct faith and strong belief. In short, we have to adjust our emotional and spiritual bodies to better perform this task.

Still, just inhabiting earth is not enough, we are also ordered to develop and make this land flourish:

﴿ ... هُوَ أَنشَأَكُم مِّنَ ٱلْأَرْضِ وَٱسْتَعْمَرَكُمْ فِيهَا ... ۝ ﴾ (سورة هود: ٦١)

﴾...He brought you forth from the earth and settled you therein...﴿
(Qur'an 11: 61)

The process of settling requires work to make the earth a better place to live. That work includes exploration, action, dedication, intellect and good health, all of which requires us to work on our physical, biochemical and intellectual bodies. Yet, to fulfil these roles perfectly we have to perceive and comprehend the true meaning of all of this — the real purpose of our creation:

﴿ وَمَا خَلَقْتُ ٱلْجِنَّ وَٱلْإِنسَ إِلَّا لِيَعْبُدُونِ ۝ ﴾ (سورة الذاريات: ٥٦)

﴾And I [Allah] did not create the jinns and humans except that they should worship Me [Alone].﴿ *(Qur'an 51: 56)*

In other words, the aim of developing the earth and the intention of hard work and positive actions is Allah's worship. We should seek only Allah's approval; we should always supplicate for His guidance and praise Him for His blessings.

Nowadays, many practicing Muslims live uncomfortably with a struggle between their religious and spiritual practice on one side and their professional and social life on the other. They end up choosing between them or leading a parallel existence that ruptures their inner peace and creates a continuously stressful internal conflict. The nature of everyday life seems to impose on us a certain type of compartmentalization. We have a working life, a home life, a religious life, and often many more. In each compartment we change clothes, behaviour, even personalities. This is so confusing and disconnecting from the self. The best way to connect all of these together — to reach inner peace and satisfaction — is to remember the purpose of our creation:

﴿ وَمَا خَلَقْتُ الْجِنَّ وَالْإِنسَ إِلَّا لِيَعْبُدُونِ ۝ ﴾   (سورة الذاريات: ٥٦)

﴿And I [Allah] did not create the jinns and humans except that they should worship Me [Alone].﴾   *(Qur'an 51: 56)*

Following this guidance, we can change each and every habit into worship. By faithful intentions and true devotion to Allah, even exercising, working, cooking, playing or any other daily routine can be turned into an act of worship. The intention is the crucial factor that gives true meaning to life and to work, that turns a mere mechanical ritual into a true spiritual enlightenment. According to Professor 'Abdullah 'Ulwân, good intentions and sincerity are the primary conditions for our work to be accepted by Allah.[31] These should be the true driving forces behind any Muslim's action. Allah (ﷻ) says:

﴿ قُلْ إِنَّ صَلَاتِي وَنُسُكِي وَمَحْيَايَ وَمَمَاتِي لِلَّهِ رَبِّ الْعَالَمِينَ ۝ لَا شَرِيكَ لَهُۥ وَبِذَٰلِكَ أُمِرْتُ وَأَنَا أَوَّلُ الْمُسْلِمِينَ ۝ ﴾   (سورة الأنعام: ١٦٢–١٦٣)

﴿Say [O Muhammad]: Verily, my ṣalât [prayer], my sacrifice, my living, and my dying are for Allah, the Creator and Master of the Universe]. He has no partner. And this I have been commanded, and I am the first of the Muslims.﴾   *(Qur'an 6: 162-163)*

Allah (ﷻ) also says:

﴿ قُلْ إِنِّي أُمِرْتُ أَنْ أَعْبُدَ اللَّهَ مُخْلِصًا لَّهُ الدِّينَ ۝ ﴾   (سورة الزُّمَر: ١١)

❨Say [O Muhammad]: Verily, I am commanded to worship Allah [Alone] by obeying Him and doing religious deeds sincerely for Allah's sake only and not to show off, and not to set up rivals with Him in worship.❩

(Qur'an 39: 11)

Islam, a complete code of life

Prophet Muhammad (ﷺ) was the last of the prophets; he was sent by Allah to all humankind. That is why his message had to be complete and inclusive of all aspects of life on both individual and societal levels. The Qur'an is explained and applied by the Prophet's Sunnah. Prophet Muhammad (ﷺ) was not only the leader of the Nation, the commander of the army and the teacher of all Muslims; he was also a husband, a father and a grandfather. Studying his whole life gives us a complete example of all we need to live a peaceful, prosperous and productive life. The Prophet's teachings organize our relations with Allah, ourselves, our bodies, our parents, children, relatives, neighbours and co-workers — even with our guests and our enemies. Islam clearly establishes our duties and rights; it establishes a perfect system of life that includes everything — literally everything: what to eat and drink, what to wear, how to behave within the marriage and the family; it organizes prayers, work and even relaxation. Allah says in His Holy Book:

﴿ لَّقَدْ كَانَ لَكُمْ فِى رَسُولِ ٱللَّهِ أُسْوَةٌ حَسَنَةٌ لِّمَن كَانَ يَرْجُواْ ٱللَّهَ وَٱلْيَوْمَ ٱلْأَخِرَ وَذَكَرَ ٱللَّهَ كَثِيرًا ﴿٢١﴾ ﴾ (سورة الأحزاب: ٢١)

❨Indeed in the Messenger of Allah [Muhammad] you have a good example to follow for him who hopes in [the Meeting with] Allah and the Last Day and remembers Allah much.❩   *(Qur'an 33: 21)*

Islamic teachings are not restricted to the mosque; they are guides for all aspects of life, whether social, ethical, emotional, spiritual, economical, or political.

Balance and Moderation

Islam is totally compatible with human nature. It establishes a wonderful harmony between the requirements of the soul and the demands of the body. Muhammad Ghazâli observed rightly that the nature of Islam links the universe with life, the human body with its behaviour, science with morality, and the intellect with supplication (*du'â'*).[32] It is clear that Islam does not dissociate the physical body from the soul — it sees them as an integrated whole.[33] The Qur'an stresses the importance of moderation and balance between worldly desires and Allah's Straight Path:

(سورة البقرة: ١٤٣)   ﴾ ... وَسَطًا أُمَّةً جَعَلْنَكُمْ وَكَذَلِكَ ﴿

﴾Thus, have We made of you an Ummah [community of believers] justly balanced...﴿   *(Qur'an 2: 143)*

﴾ ... ٱلدُّنْيَا مِنَ نَصِيبَكَ تَنسَ وَلَا ٱلْأَخِرَةَ ٱلدَّارَ ٱللَّهُ ءَاتَىٰكَ فِيمَآ وَٱبْتَغِ ﴿
(سورة القصص: ٧٧)

﴾But seek, with that [wealth] which Allah has bestowed on you, the home of the Hereafter, and do not forget your portion of legal enjoyment in this world...﴿   *(Qur'an 28: 77)*

﴾ فِي ءَامَنُوا لِلَّذِينَ هِيَ قُلْ ٱلرِّزْقِ مِنَ وَٱلطَّيِّبَتِ لِعِبَادِهِ أَخْرَجَ ٱلَّتِي ٱللَّهِ زِينَةَ حَرَّمَ مَنْ قُلْ
(سورة الأعراف: ٣٢)   ﴾ ... ٱلْقِيَمَةِ يَوْمَ خَالِصَةً ٱلدُّنْيَا ٱلْحَيَوٰةِ

﴾Say [O Muhammad]: Who has forbidden the adoration with clothes given by Allah, which He has produced for his slaves, and good and lawful] things of provision? Say: They are, in the life of this world, for those who believe, [and] exclusively for them [believers] on the Day of Resurrection...⟩   *(Qur'an 7: 32)*

The Prophet's Sunnah (code of life) clarifies this idea and never demanded humans to go beyond their natural limits, as he (ﷺ) said:

> "Indeed, I swear by Allah that among you I am the most fearful of Allah and the most pious. However, I fast and break my fast, I pray and sleep; and I marry women. So, whoever refrains from my way is not among my followers."[34]

Neither exaggeration nor negligence is accepted by Islamic law — whether in one's duties towards Allah, oneself, one's family or one's community.[35] Allah says:

(سورة البقرة: ٢٨٦)   ﴿ ... لَا يُكَلِّفُ ٱللَّهُ نَفْسًا إِلَّا وُسْعَهَا ۚ ﴾ ﴿٢٨٦﴾

⟨Allah burdens no person beyond his scope...⟩   *(Qur'an 2: 286)*

The Almighty also says:

﴿ ... يُرِيدُ ٱللَّهُ بِكُمُ ٱلْيُسْرَ وَلَا يُرِيدُ بِكُمُ ٱلْعُسْرَ ... ﴾ ﴿١٨٥﴾

(سورة البقرة: ١٨٥)

⟨...Allah intends for you ease, and He does not want to make things difficult for you...⟩   *(Qur'an 2: 185)*

Professor Yusuf Qardawi sees Islam as a "balanced formula of rights and duties," where people are not given so many rights that they infringe on those of others, nor are they taxed with more obligations than they can carry out.[36]

Quick preview

During the course of this work, I try to explain how you can combine the rich tradition of Islamic teaching with beneficial contemporary scientific knowledge in order to lead a holistically healthy and happy life.

The book is divided into five chapters, each concerning one of our five human 'bodies', clarifying in each chapter how to look after that body and keep it healthy. During the course of the book, you will notice how these bodies are interconnected; the health of one is highly dependent on the wellbeing of the others, so that a happy, healthy life entails a balance between all of them.

> It is important to note that the translation of the Qur'an into another language is not a simple process. It involves translation of the meanings of the Qur'an, and however accurate the work may be, it falls short of conveying the wealth of meanings that the miraculous text of the original conveys. For this reason, the Arabic text of the verses is always presented before any explanation/translation in English in this book. In addition, it should be noted that it is often necessary to look at several different translations[37] and explanations in order to arrive at a clearer understanding of the meaning. It is with this goal of clarity and understanding in mind that the wording of many of the translations of the verses that are mentioned in this book has been changed slightly.

A word also about the hadiths in this book: wherever possible, only sound and authenticated hadiths are used, and most of these can be found in any translation of Nawawi's *Riyâdh aş-Şaliheen* (included in the references for this book), A few hadiths that are considered by Islamic scholars to be weak (not verifiable) have been included not as hadiths, but as wise sayings; this has been done only where they help to explain a point, and do not contradict the authentic Sunnah or the Qur'an.

CHAPTER 1

PHYSICAL BODY

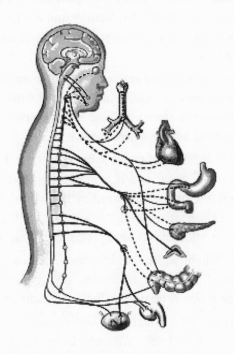

$\mathcal{T}$he health of our physical body is vital to our entire well-being. Illnesses of the physical body are quite obvious to most people, and their symptoms are the main focus of orthodox medicine. The physical body is made up of all our structural elements, like bones, muscles, joints, and tendons, as well as the different functional systems: the cardiovascular, respiratory, gastrointestinal and immune systems and others. The key to a balanced, healthy physical body is to live an active and virtuous life conforming to the teachings of the Qur'an and the Sunnah.

Prophet Muhammad (ﷺ) said: «The strong believer is more loved by Allah than the weak one, and there is benefaction in both.»[38] This hadith demonstrates the importance of taking good care of your body, keeping it fit, healthy and strong, as a strong body holds the potential for a powerful soul, a sound personality and a wise intellect.

Islam teaches us many ways to protect, empower and preserve our bodies, both through prophylactic (preventative) measures that include abstinence from vice, and by referring to physicians and seeking medical advice when needed.

«Jâbir (ﷺ) related that the Prophet (ﷺ) said: There is a cure for every disease, and if a medication overcomes a disease, then (the patient) is cured by the will of Allah Almighty."[39] He (ﷺ) also said: "Ask Allah for forgiveness and health, for after faith nothing is better than health."»[40]

However, Dhahabi wrote that it is forbidden to use any non-permitted medication for our treatment, saying that healing will only be attained if one is treated by halal (legitimate) means.[41]

Before discussing the effects of Islamic teachings on different body systems, we should note two important rules in Islam meant to ensure a healthy physical body.

The first rule is 'No harm'

*P*rophet Muhammad (ﷺ) said: «No harm and no reciprocating harm.»[42]

Allah (ﷻ) says in the Qur'an:

$$ \text{﴿ ... وَيُحِلُّ لَهُمُ ٱلطَّيِّبَٰتِ وَيُحَرِّمُ عَلَيْهِمُ ٱلْخَبَٰٓئِثَ ... ۝ ﴾} $$

(سورة الأعراف: ١٥٧)

﴿...He allows for them as lawful *ṭayyibât* [all good things, deeds, beliefs, persons, foods, etc.], and prohibits for them as unlawful *khabâ'ith* [all evil and unlawful things, deeds, beliefs, persons, foods, etc.]...﴾
(Qur'an 7: 157)

Smoking and tobacco use

Smoking tobacco is without doubt a highly harmful habit. According to the World Heatlh Organization (WHO), the number of people smoking tobacco has decreased in the developed Western world while the habit is prevailing in developing countries. Smoking causes 90% of the cases of lung cancers and 85% of the other pulmonary diseases such as chronic bronchitis, emphysema and asthma, in addition to 35% of the cases of heart attacks and embolism (blockage) of the coronary arteries. Smoking is also associated with cancers of the mouth, pharynx, larynx, oesophagus, stomach, pancreas, cervix, kidney, ureter, and bladder. The US Environmental Protection Agency (EPA) has classified environmental tobacco smoke as a class A (known human) carcinogen (cancer-causing substance).[43]

Why is it so harmful?

First of all, cigarette smoking is found to paralyze the *cilia*.[44] When the cilia are prevented from doing their job, the lungs become clogged with mucous secretions, leading to regular coughing. The function of the cilia can be permanently damaged if smoking is continued for years, leaving the lungs and all the respiratory system without proper protection against environmental hazards. Smoking has also now been highly linked to impotence, penile erectile dysfunction and male infertility. The cause was attributed to the effect of smoking on the nervous, hormonal and vascular (blood vessel) systems; in addition to its role in reducing the motility (ability to move) and density (in numbers) of sperm.

Furthermore, there are thousands of different chemicals in cigarette smoke, including many known carcinogenic and toxic chemicals and their compounds, examples of which are: ammonia, acetone, benzene, cadmium, nickel, formaldehyde, lead and mercury. These toxins are spread around and stored in every tissue and cell in the body where they can speed up the growth of cancer cells and various degenerative diseases. Filters do not remove most of these deadly toxins; they are used by the advertising companies to convince smokers that cigarettes are somehow safe.[45]

Nicotine

When you inhale smoke, nicotine enters your lungs where it is quickly absorbed into your bloodstream and carried to the heart, brain, liver, and spleen. Nicotine is an addictive poisonous alkaloid: if a person consumed half a gram of it, s/he would die in less than a minute due to the paralysis in his or her respiratory muscles. Nicotine stimulates both the central and the autonomic nervous systems; this causes raised blood pressure (by constricting the blood vessels), increased pulse rate and loss of appetite. Some studies indicate that nicotine activates the release of adrenaline while inhibiting the release of insulin. This puts smokers at high risk of developing hyperglycaemia (increased blood sugar levels), which is a precursor to diabetes[46].

Passive smoking

Smoking hurts many people who live around smokers. 'Passive smoking' is when you breathe other people's smoke; it is also known as 'second hand' smoking. One of the major hazards of passive smoking is that the non-smoking person is actually inhaling unfiltered cigarette smoke. As mentioned earlier, although filters do not guard smokers from tobacco's harmful effects, they offer a little protection. However, studies show that passive smokers can be exposed to carcinogen levels up to 100 times higher than those that smokers inhale directly through a cigarette. Children are the most common victims; children exposed to second hand smoke are more susceptible to — and thus likely to develop — asthma, bronchitis, pneumonia and other respiratory tract dysfunctions.[47] Do we really want to harm our loved ones in this way — all for the sake of enjoying a cigarette?

WHO has classified tobacco and cigarette smoking as 'addictive weakening substances'[48] We know that Umm Salamah reported:

«The Prophet (ﷺ) prohibited every intoxicant and weakening agent.»[49]

Allah (ﷻ) says:

(سورة البقرة: ١٩٥)   ﴿ ... وَلَا تُلْقُوا بِأَيْدِيكُمْ إِلَى ٱلتَّهْلُكَةِ ... ۝ ﴾

﴿...And do not throw yourselves into destruction...﴾ *(Qur'an 2: 195)*

So according to Islam, tobacco is prohibited as it is an addictive, harmful, weakening substance; and smoking slowly kills its user and often even those who live and work with him or her.

In addition, Prophet Muhammad (ﷺ) said:

«Allah has prohibited you from wasting money.»[50]

Without doubt, smoking is a shameful waste of money. First of all, there is the money spent by smokers on cigarettes, teeth whiteners, and breath fresheners — and air fresheners for their homes and cars. Less obvious, but even more expensive, is the high price that society must pay for medical treatment for the serious and debilitating diseases discussed above — not to mention the cost to the economy of all the days taken off the patient's job due to smoking-related illness.

Alcohol

Allah (ﷻ) says in the Qur'an:

﴿يَٰٓأَيُّهَا ٱلَّذِينَ ءَامَنُوٓا۟ إِنَّمَا ٱلْخَمْرُ وَٱلْمَيْسِرُ وَٱلْأَنصَابُ وَٱلْأَزْلَٰمُ رِجْسٌ مِّنْ عَمَلِ ٱلشَّيْطَٰنِ فَٱجْتَنِبُوهُ لَعَلَّكُمْ تُفْلِحُونَ ۝ إِنَّمَا يُرِيدُ ٱلشَّيْطَٰنُ أَن يُوقِعَ بَيْنَكُمُ ٱلْعَدَٰوَةَ وَٱلْبَغْضَآءَ فِى ٱلْخَمْرِ وَٱلْمَيْسِرِ وَيَصُدَّكُمْ عَن ذِكْرِ ٱللَّهِ وَعَنِ ٱلصَّلَوٰةِ فَهَلْ أَنتُم مُّنتَهُونَ ۝﴾

(سورة المائدة: ٩٠-٩١)

❨O you who believe! Intoxicants [all kinds of alcoholic drinks], gambling, stone altars [used for sacrificing to idols] and arrows [for seeking luck or decision] are an abomination of Satan's handiwork. So avoid [strictly all] that [abomination] in order that you may be successful. Satan wants only to excite enmity and hatred between you with intoxicants [alcoholic drinks] and gambling, and to hinder you from the remembrance of Allah and from *ṣalât* [the prayer]. So, will you not then abstain?❩   *(Qur'an 5: 90-91)*

Alcohol is definitely not good for you. In her book *The Holistic Doctor*, Dr. Deborah McManners summarized the effects of alcohol on the human body under the heading "What's your poison?" She pointed out that too much alcohol ages the brain, increases the risk of breast cancer, damages the liver, kidney and pancreas, leads to many cardiovascular problems and heart diseases, causes a burning sensation in the chest, erodes the stomach lining (gradually inducing ulcers), raises the blood pressure, and increases the risk of impotence — it "provokes the desire but takes away the performance." In addition, alcohol raises the risk of miscarriage and increases the chance of birth defects if consumed during pregnancy, and women who drink regularly are more prone to premenstrual mood swings and cravings.[51]

Some people think that drinking alcohol in cold weather warms the body. What alcohol actually does is to dilate the superficial blood vessels causing the blood to rush towards them, which gives a temporary feeling of warmth. This feeling is soon dissipated by heat transfer from the body to the surrounding environment due to the continuous blood circulation. In addition, alcohol causes temporary numbness of the *hypothalamus* (the region of the brain responsible for giving you warnings if your body feels cold, hot, hungry or thirsty). This causes the intoxicated person not to feel the cold, and this is the reason one hears about people who froze to death on Christmas Eve (when a lot of people drink alcohol and go outdoors) without even noticing that they were cold.[52]

People used to think that alcohol had some health benefits, and they refer to the verse in the Qur'an that says:

﴿ ۞ يَسْـَٔلُونَكَ عَنِ ٱلْخَمْرِ وَٱلْمَيْسِرِ قُلْ فِيهِمَآ إِثْمٌ كَبِيرٌ وَمَنَـٰفِعُ لِلنَّاسِ وَإِثْمُهُمَآ أَكْبَرُ مِن نَّفْعِهِمَا ... ۝ ﴾ (سورة البقرة: ٢١٩)

◆They ask you [O Muhammad] concerning alcoholic drink and gambling. Say: In them is a great sin and [some] benefit for men, but the sin of them is greater than their benefit...▶ *(Qur'an 2: 219)*

Actually, this verse was one of the steps Allah prescribed for those who had been drinkers before they became Muslims to completely give up alcohol. As we know, alcohol is addictive, so stopping it in one step would have been impossible for some of them to bear.

The total prohibition of alcohol even as medicine is clear in the following hadith of the Prophet (ﷺ).

«Tariq ibn Suwaid al-Ja'fi asked Prophet Muhammad (ﷺ) about alcohol manufacture and he prohibited him from doing it. So he said: O Messenger of Allah, I manufacture it for medicines, to which the Prophet replied: It is not a remedy, but a disease.»[53]

Anas (ﷺ) said that the Messenger of Allah (ﷺ) cursed ten categories of people who deal with wine (and any alcoholic drink): the one who manufactures it and who orders (or pays for) it to be manufactured, the one who drinks it, the one who delivers it and the one to whom it is delivered, the one who serves it, the one who sells it, the one who gains money from it, the one who buys it and the one for whom it is bought."[54] He (ﷺ) also told us:

«The days and nights will pass and a group of my people will drink alcohol, calling it by other names.»[55]

So whatever you call it: wine, spirit, vodka, or beer — all are ḥarâm!

Drugs

«Anything causing inebriation is considered intoxicant and all intoxicants are prohibited (harâm).»[56] Opium, heroin, cannabis and all other recreational drugs have disastrous effects on both the mind and body. Some are hallucinating agents that give a temporary feeling of euphoria, but soon the drug abuser will end up in a vicious cycle of depression, dependence and addiction.

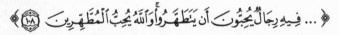

The second rule is Cleanliness

*I*n this chapter, we are concerned only with the physical cleanliness, while the purification of the heart, mind and inner self will be dealt with in other parts of this book.

Body hygiene

Allah (ﷻ) says:

﴿ ... فِيهِ رِجَالٌ يُحِبُّونَ أَن يَتَطَهَّرُوٓاْ وَٱللَّهُ يُحِبُّ ٱلْمُطَّهِّرِينَ ﴿١٠٨﴾ ﴾

(سورة التوبة:١٠٨)

﴿...In it are men who love to clean and to purify themselves. And Allah loves those who make themselves clean and pure.﴾

(Qur'an 9: 108)

The Prophet (ﷺ) said: «Cleanliness (ritual purity) is one half of faith."[57] He also said: "Whoever sleeps with dirty hands without washing them and something befell him, let him blame only himself."[58] Islam also requires that for the prayer to be accepted, a Muslim should perform ablution. Prophet Muhammad (ﷺ) taught us: "Ablution is the key to prayer.»[59]

We learn from the Qur'an:

$$﴿يَـٰٓأَيُّهَا ٱلَّذِينَ ءَامَنُوٓاْ إِذَا قُمْتُمْ إِلَى ٱلصَّلَوٰةِ فَٱغْسِلُواْ وُجُوهَكُمْ وَأَيْدِيَكُمْ
إِلَى ٱلْمَرَافِقِ وَٱمْسَحُواْ بِرُءُوسِكُمْ وَأَرْجُلَكُمْ إِلَى ٱلْكَعْبَيْنِ ۚ وَإِن كُنتُمْ جُنُبًا
فَٱطَّهَّرُواْ ... ٦﴾$$

(سورة المائدة: ٦)

﴿O you who believe! When you intend to offer ṣalât [the prayer], wash your faces and your hands [and forearms] up to the elbows, rub [by passing wet hands over] your heads, and [wash] your feet up to the ankles. If you are in a state of janâbah [post-sex impurity or had a sexual discharge], purify yourself [bathe your whole body with water]...﴾ *(Qur'an 5: 6)*

Bathing (a ritual shower) is compulsory in Islam in cases of nocturnal emission (of semen, or the corresponding fluid in women), sexual intercourse and for women, after menstruation and at the end of the period of post-childbirth bleeding. In addition, there are some cases where bathing is recommended in the Sunnah, like the shower on the two Eid days and every Friday, before the congregational prayers that mark those days. Prophet Muhammad (ﷺ) said:

«Allah has a right on every Muslim that he takes a shower (at least once) in every seven days and if he has perfume to wear some of it.»[60]

There is a very important physical reason for the wisdom behind these Islamic requirements. Bacteria and viruses — especially the common cold — collect on the hands, in between fingers and under fingernails; feet and toes, too, get dirty quickly. The mouth, nose, and ears are also places that germs tend to collect, and the eyes are very susceptible to infection. The Islamic ritual ablution ensures that all these parts of the body are rinsed free of surface germs before the prayer.

The wisdom of the Islamic requirements of ablution and bathing before prayers is of particular significance for the communal prayers. That is, men are required to pray communally at the mosque five times each day. The requirements of Muslim prayer mean that prayer participants must stand shoulder-to-shoulder with each other, their hands often touching others, and their faces (noses, eyes, mouth, ears) close to each other. In addition, when they prostrate, their faces touch the floor surface where others' faces may have touched only minutes before, and the feet of those praying in the row ahead are only centimetres from the faces of those behind. By performing ablution (*wuḍoo'*) before each prayer, the chances of infection are lowered. (Interestingly, the hand-washing instructions given to medical practitioners in hospitals and clinics all over the world are strikingly similar to the process of ablution, for such personnel are instructed to wash in between the fingers and under the fingernails.)

Moreover, the gatherings for the Jumu'ah (Friday) and Eid prayers, and especially for hajj, are much larger than the regular five daily prayer gatherings. For these larger gatherings, Muslims are expected to take a full shower (*ghusl*), to further guard against the spread of disease among large groups of people in close contact.[61]

The Prophet (ﷺ) ordered Muslims to take care of their hair and keep it clean; he himself used to oil his hair and comb it. In addition, one should keep his or her ears clean from dirt, and remove dirt and excess mucus from the nostrils by inhaling and exhaling water via the nostrils during ablution. According to a well known hadith, it is also part of the *fiṭrah* (the natural inclination) to trim and clean the fingernails and toenails, and to remove the pubic hair from armpits and private parts.

In the Sunnah, we also learn that perfumes were among the substances dearest to the heart of our Prophet (ﷺ). He said: «Whoever is offered some perfume should not refuse it.»[62] Ibn al-Qayyim said that pleasant scents and perfumes are 'food for the soul'.[63]

Oral Hygiene

Good dental care plays a great role in overall physical health, not to mention its role in increasing one's self-confidence through a pleasant smile and a fresh-smelling breath. Dental caries (cavities) start when bacteria in the mouth react with the carbohydrates (sugars and starches) from food to produce acids. These acids erode or 'eat away' tooth enamel (the hard outer covering of the teeth), causing tooth decay. The damage caused by oral bacteria continues for twenty to forty minutes after eating. The risk factors are basically the frequency of eating starchy and sugary food and how long this food stays in your mouth.[64] The faster the food dissolves and leaves the mouth, the less chance there is of cavity production.

Prophet Muhammad (ﷺ) taught us that the mouth is the pathway of the Qur'an; therefore, we should keep it clean. He always commenced his ablution with the use of a tooth-cleansing-stick (siwâk). He said:

«"Had it not been difficult for my followers, I would have ordered them to use the siwâk before each prayer."[65] He also said: "The use of the siwâk purifies the mouth and pleases Allah."»[66]

Siwâk is the Arabic name for *Salvadore persica*, a plant native to the Arabian Peninsula. The best type of siwâk is said to come from the 'Arak' tree. It acts as an effective tool in the removal of soft oral deposits, thus preventing plaque formation. Scientific research has proved that the effectiveness of siwâk in oral hygiene is due to many reasons:[67]

> It contains antibacterial agents that clean the mouth and kill germs. These are natural disinfectants that also prevent gum disease.

> The chloride and silica content of siwâk help to cleanse and whiten the teeth.

> Siwâk contains also vitamin C and *sitosterols*, which help to strengthen the gum and oral blood vessels; in addition to the role of vitamin C in reducing inflammation.

> The alkaline nature of siwâk helps neutralize the effect of damaging acids formed by oral bacteria due to its content of *trimethyl amine*.

In addition to these advantages, siwâk has an agreeable scent that gives the breath a naturally fresh smell; the sulphur in it helps to disinfect the mouth and its fluoride content is essential in hardening tooth enamel and preventing decay. The constituents in siwâk also increase saliva production, which is a natural cleansing system for the mouth. Siwâk is also an ideal natural toothbrush, with a gentle abrasive action that is suitable for cleaning between the teeth, removing plaque and food debris without damaging the gums or the enamel.

Note that siwâk should be regularly renewed by cutting off the used tip of the twig to expose new fibres, as it loses the effective antibacterial action over time. You can feel its effectiveness as long as it still has a slightly sharp, mustard-like flavour and mild aromatic fragrance. The use of siwâk is most effective when the deposits on the teeth are still soft. If the plaque hardens, the efficiency of siwâk will be reduced (as will be the efficiency of any toothpaste), and that is why it is crucial to use it regularly as we were taught by our beloved Prophet (ﷺ).

Prophet Muhammad (ﷺ) also used to rinse his mouth with water after drinking milk, saying: «It has fat.»[68] Now we know that the fats in milk are the main cause of dental caries in young children; recent scientific recommendations advise parents not to bottle-feed or give milk to children in bed, as they would go to sleep without rinsing their mouths thoroughly afterwards. (This is not the case with breast milk, which does not cause cavities.) Of course, milk is not bad for teeth. Some nutrients — such as calcium, phosphorus and vitamin D — present in milk and dairy products make teeth stronger and tend to prevent tooth decay. These nutrients also help to build a strong jawbone which keeps the teeth in place.

Saliva produced in the mouth helps protect the teeth by rapid clearing of food debris. To insure proper saliva production, drink enough fluids. Water is the best choice, as it does not contain the carbohydrates that cause the problem in the first place. The French usually end their meals with a piece of cheese; this helps increase the flow of saliva and neutralize the acids produced — and of course it is a good source of calcium and phosphorus. So do not forget your piece of cheese!

Health of Different
Body Systems

Respiratory System

$\mathcal{B}$reathing or respiration is a natural and indispensable function common to all living creatures. It constitutes the vital force or energy that flows through your body. We are all born knowing how to breathe, but do we breathe properly?

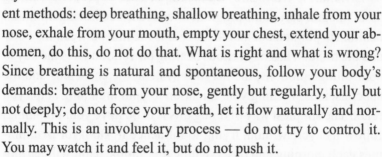

We are bombarded with lots of myths and theories that advise different methods: deep breathing, shallow breathing, inhale from your nose, exhale from your mouth, empty your chest, extend your abdomen, do this, do not do that. What is right and what is wrong? Since breathing is natural and spontaneous, follow your body's demands: breathe from your nose, gently but regularly, fully but not deeply; do not force your breath, let it flow naturally and normally. This is an involuntary process — do not try to control it. You may watch it and feel it, but do not push it.

We may live for days without food and for hours without water, but we cannot tolerate more than about four minutes without breathing — the brain begins to suffer irreparable damage after this point. Breathing provides our body with the oxygen essential for cellular function and metabolism.

Prophet Muhammad (ﷺ) said: «No human fills a vessel worse than his own abdomen; a few bites are enough for man to keep his body upright, but if it is indispensable, then a third for his food, a third for his drink and a third for his breath.»[69]

In this hadith, the Prophet (ﷺ) was emphasizing the importance of proper breathing by pointing out that it is as essential as food and drink.

Proper breathing enhances concentration and performance as it increases the oxygen supply to the brain. It calms you down, improves your mood and controls your emotions. This technique has proved especially efficient for hyperactive children and individuals with consistently high stress levels. Breathing enhances stamina, physical coordination and immunity. It also balances the metabolism and harmonizes the hormonal system.

Dr. Andrew Weil[70] stressed the importance of proper breathing as an integral part of his program intended for achieving optimum health. He pointed out that the breath is the link between the body and the mind: it has marvellous healing powers, and it is the key to controlling emotions, the nervous system, the conscious and the subconscious. Turning your attention to your breathing helps you relax. The simplest way of doing this is to observe your breathing; follow its cycle without trying to influence it. Do it for five minutes each morning and observe how this simple habit will harmonize your body, mind and soul.

If we breathe deeply as advised by many books and yoga teachers, it is true that we inhale more oxygen, but we also lose more carbon dioxide. According to Dr. Teresa Hale,[71] the author of the valuable book *Breathing Free*, when the level of carbon dioxide is reduced in our blood, the body cells will not be able to fully use the inhaled oxygen. The aim should be to balance the level of both gases in the blood, as they are both essential for our health. Carbon dioxide is not a villain that we have to get rid of, as we used to think in the past. On the contrary, Dr. Hale points out that it is essential for the proper use of oxygen by the body's cells; it is also essential for the functioning of the cardiovascular and respiratory systems. Carbon dioxide is a natural *bronchodilator* (that is, it keeps the passageways in the lungs free from blockage) and it also regulates the body's acid-base (pH) balance, which in turn is essential for the proper function of the immune system.

The best way I know to regulate your breathing is to recite the Qur'an. Recite it as it was recited by our beloved Prophet Muhammad (ﷺ). Dhahabi said:

> Each organ has its own suitable exercise, and the exercise of the chest is Qur'an recitation. Start with a whispering voice, than gradually increase the tone.[72]

It is amazing how you feel afterwards; even the recitation of few verses is a great breathing exercise. The Qur'an is of Divine origin: no other book exists or will ever exist which contains in its passages this degree of perfection and balance. It is of surpassing beauty, melody and rhythm. Try it: learn proper Qur'an recitation (*tajweed*) to master your breath, create equilibrium and harmony for your body, mind and soul.

﴿ وَنُنَزِّلُ مِنَ ٱلْقُرْءَانِ مَا هُوَ شِفَآءٌ وَرَحْمَةٌ لِّلْمُؤْمِنِينَ ... ﴾ (سورة الإسراء: ٨٢)

﴿And We send down from the Qur'an that which is a healing and a mercy to those who believe [in Islamic monotheism and act on it]...﴾
(Qur'an 17: 82)

Cardiovascular system

When we mention the cardiovascular system, the first thing that comes to mind is the heart. Prophet Muhammad (ﷺ) said:

«In the body there is an organ which if healthy, causes the health of the whole body; and if it sickens, it causes the sickness of the whole body; this organ is the heart.»[73]

This hadith can be interpreted with both the physical and spiritual meanings of the word 'heart'.

As a physical organ, the heart consists of four chambers: two atria and two ventricles. The collected blood flows into the atria then passes to the ventricles which are chambers whose job is to propel the blood out into circulation. The amount of work that the heart does is incredible. At rest, a normal heart performs 75 beats per minute, pumping out around 5.25 litres of blood; thus circulating the entire blood supply throughout the body once every minute.[74] So as we can see — and as our Prophet (ﷺ) told us — on this small muscle depends the life of all the cells in the body. To appreciate its incredible role, it is enough to note that the brain cells could be irreversibly destroyed if they were deprived of the supply of oxygenated blood for only five minutes.

Islam makes important recommendations to keep our hearts and circulatory systems healthy, the first of which is physical activity. Ibn al-Qayyim showed that any organ that is used regularly in a type of physical activity will grow stronger and healthier, while a saying sometimes attributed to Prophet Muhammad (ﷺ) and otherwise attributed to 'Umar (ﷺ) stressed the importance of performing different sports and teaching them to our children:

"Teach your children javelin throwing, swimming and horse riding."

The Messenger of Allah (ﷺ) also prohibited laziness and sluggishness.[75] According to the American Heart Association (AHA), one of the most important recommendations to enjoy a healthy heart is to keep physically active. They recommend making aerobic exercises a part of your daily routine. Even 30 minutes of daily physical activity will benefit the heart; this reduces the risk of heart disease by improving blood circulation, keeping weight under control, boosting energy and releasing tension. Physical exercise also reduces blood cholesterol levels and controls hypertension; moreover, it strengthens different body muscles — including the heart.

In addition to other forms of exercise that you do, the act of stretching the muscles during prayer (ṣalât) enhances blood circulation through gently massaging the blood vessels involved. This is especially obvious in prostration which has been found to alleviate the pain of varicose veins and reduce the risk of thrombosis (formation of blood clots) in the legs. The whole circulatory system is also stimulated by both bowing and prostrating through the synchronized action of respiration and diaphragm movement, which leads to more efficient pumping of blood by the heart. The movements of the neck during and at the end of prayer further vitalize the blood vessels that deliver blood to the brain. So, taking five to seven minutes from your work routine to perform prayer not only revives your spirit, but also energizes your body and mind.

In addition to exercise, Islamic medicine makes certain dietary recommendations for a healthy heart and circulation:

➤ Do not overeat

➤ Eat a variety of fruits and vegetables

> Eat whole grain products
> Reduce red meat intake
> Eat more fish
> Use ginger, garlic, onions and olive oil in your food
> Drink red grape and pomegranate juice regularly

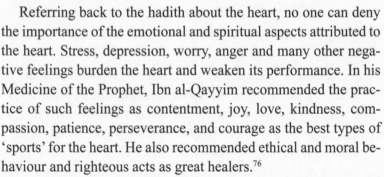

Each will be discussed in detail in the biochemical section of this book (Chapter Two).

Referring back to the hadith about the heart, no one can deny the importance of the emotional and spiritual aspects attributed to the heart. Stress, depression, worry, anger and many other negative feelings burden the heart and weaken its performance. In his Medicine of the Prophet, Ibn al-Qayyim recommended the practice of such feelings as contentment, joy, love, kindness, compassion, patience, perseverance, and courage as the best types of 'sports' for the heart. He also recommended ethical and moral behaviour and righteous acts as great healers.[76]

The Prophets have taught us these remedies for the spiritual diseases of the heart. These Prophetic remedies, when practiced to the degree that they reside firmly in one's heart, strengthen the heart and increase faith and reliance on Allah. Moreover, whenever one's heart becomes spiritually stronger, s/he will be able to defeat physical illness. Allah says in His Holy Book:

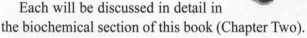

(سورة يونس: ٥٧)

❨O people! There has come to you good advice from Allah [the Qur'an, ordering all that is good and forbidding all that is evil], and a healing for that [disease of ignorance, doubt, hypocrisy and differences] in your breasts, a guidance and a mercy [explaining lawful and unlawful things] for the believers.⟩   *(Qur'an 10: 57)*

Skin

You can look at your skin as a protective shield; if you had none, you would easily fall prey to microbes and lose water and heat from your body. The skin performs many vital functions; the most important one is to protect your tissues from bacterial invasions, ultra-violet (UV) radiation from sunlight, heat, cold and physical injury. The skin aids in controlling body temperature; it also acts as an excretory organ to rid the body of waste and toxins through the sweat glands. Vitamin D, a fat-soluble vitamin important for bone integrity, is synthesized through the action of sunlight on the skin. The skin synthesizes several proteins important for immunity. It holds the body's water and other essential fluids and prevents external water and foreign substances from invading your system — imagine if all the water, soap and shampoo you use was absorbed into your body each time you take a shower![77]

The skin is composed of an outer layer (the epidermis) and the underlying dermis made from dense connective tissue. Under the dermis the hypodermis, formed mainly of adipose tissue (the fat storage area) anchors the skin to the underlying organs and forms an insulating cushion.[78]

The epidermis is avascular[79] and most of its cells are keratinocytes, which means they produce and store keratin, a fibrous protein that gives the outer skin its strength and firmness. The deeper

cells of the epidermis receive their nourishment from the underlying dermis, and are constantly dividing: producing millions of
new cells daily that push each other upwards away from the nutrient supply. By getting closer to the skin's surface, the cells eventually die; then, they rub and flake off gradually but continuously
and are replaced by new cells from the deeper layers. It is interesting to imagine that, when you look at someone, almost everything we see is literally dead! Our outer skin layer is completely
replaced every 25 to 45 days[80]. If these dead keratinized cells accumulate on the skin's surface (even if invisible to the naked eye),
they can clog sweat pores and isolate the skin, preventing it from
performing its vital functions.

Protecting your skin

1. Ablution

We mentioned in the section on cleanliness the following verse
from the Qur'an:

$$﴿يَٰٓأَيُّهَا ٱلَّذِينَ ءَامَنُوٓاْ إِذَا قُمۡتُمۡ إِلَى ٱلصَّلَوٰةِ فَٱغۡسِلُواْ وُجُوهَكُمۡ وَأَيۡدِيَكُمۡ إِلَى ٱلۡمَرَافِقِ وَٱمۡسَحُواْ بِرُءُوسِكُمۡ وَأَرۡجُلَكُمۡ إِلَى ٱلۡكَعۡبَيۡنِۚ وَإِن كُنتُمۡ جُنُبًا فَٱطَّهَّرُواْ ... ﴾﴿٦﴾$$

(سورة المائدة: ٦)

﴿O you who believe! When you intend to offer ṣalât [the prayer],
wash your faces and your hands [and forearms] up to the elbows,
rub [by passing wet hands over] your heads, and [wash] your feet
up to the ankles. If you are in a state of janâbah [post-sex impurity or had a sexual discharge], purify yourself [bathe your whole
body with water]...﴾

(Qur'an 5: 6)

Knowing the functions of the skin, we can now understand the
physical importance of ablution. In addition to clearing the skin's
pores and removing debris, ablution regularly cleans all exposed

parts of the body: skin, nails and natural body 'ports', such as the eyes, mouth, nose and ears. This simple act protects the body from any harmful chemicals or micro-organisms which land on it as well as from any harmful toxins that the body is trying to excrete.

2. Sun protection

The Prophet (ﷺ) said: «If one of you was in the shade and then the shade receded and exposed a part of his body to the sun, let him move from that place.»[81]

The most common cause of skin cancer is excessive exposure to the damaging effects of UV radiation from the sun. There are two types of UV radiation: UVA, which has a long wave length, and UVB radiation, which has a shorter, more damaging wavelength and which is mainly responsible for skin lesions. For your safety, you should avoid direct exposure to sunlight during the hours of the day when (in your part of the world) the sun's rays are most harmful. That is why Allah (ﷻ) specified shade as one of His great blessings:

﴿ وَٱللَّهُ جَعَلَ لَكُم مِّمَّا خَلَقَ ظِلَـٰلًا وَجَعَلَ لَكُم مِّنَ ٱلْجِبَالِ أَكْنَـٰنًا وَجَعَلَ لَكُمْ سَرَٰبِيلَ تَقِيكُمُ ٱلْحَرَّ ... ۝ ﴾   (سورة النحل: ٨١)

{And Allah has made for you that from which He has created shade, and has made for you places of refuge in the mountains, and has made for you garments to protect you from the heat...}

(Qur'an 16: 81)

3. Oiling the skin

Prophet Muhammad (ﷺ) said: «Eat (olive) oil and use it as ointment, as it comes from a blessed tree.»[82] It has been scientifically proven that applying olive oil locally after (not during — it is not a sunscreen) exposure to sunlight reduces the risk of skin cancer.[83] Olive oil is a very effective skin emollient and hair treatment. Imam Shâfi'i recommended oiling the skin with olive oil on alternate days.

Olive oil is a main ingredient of many easy-to-make home recipes for healthy skin, nails and hair. Just rubbing warm oil on rough skin areas is a very helpful emollient, as is massaging your nails and fingertips with the oil. This is especially important after exposure to chemicals and detergents — after washing the dishes, for instance — to help protect your nails and strengthen them. For the hair, an easy home recipe prepared by blending the pulp of 1 avocado with ½ a cup of olive oil, applying to the hair for 10-15 minutes after shampooing then rinsing works very well, especially with dry or brittle hair.[84]

4. Aloe Vera

Aloe vera was known and used at the time of the Prophet (ﷺ) as a skin moisturiser and was even beneficial as a beauty treatment when applied to the face, according to Ibn al-Qayyim.[85]

Aloe vera is a potent skin hydrator and immediate soothing agent in case of burns. It has an emollient and moisturizing effect on dry skin and is also effective on minor wounds to prevent scarring as well as a treatment for fungal infections and insect bites. Ibn al-Qayyim recommended blending it with rose water for use as an ointment. Aloe Vera gel can be used as hair gel instead of the commercial synthetic gels. It does not share their damaging effect on the hair; instead, it gives strength and reduces brittleness. Beautician Janice Cox also suggests some useful preparations that use Aloe Vera in her book Natural Beauty at Home.[86]

The immune system

In Islam, great care is taken to develop a healthy immune system starting from infancy, for Allah ordered parents to ensure that their children are breastfed for a full two years after birth:

﴿ ۞ وَٱلۡوَٰلِدَٰتُ يُرۡضِعۡنَ أَوۡلَٰدَهُنَّ حَوۡلَيۡنِ كَامِلَيۡنِ ... ﴾   (سورة البقرة: ٢٣٣)

❨Mothers shall breastfeed their children for two whole years...❩
(Qur'an 2: 233)

Elsewhere in the Qur'an, Allah reemphasizes that the weaning of the child should be after it reaches its second year:

﴿ وَوَصَّيۡنَا ٱلۡإِنسَٰنَ بِوَٰلِدَيۡهِ حَمَلَتۡهُ أُمُّهُۥ وَهۡنًا عَلَىٰ وَهۡنٍ وَفِصَٰلُهُۥ فِي عَامَيۡنِ أَنِ
ٱشۡكُرۡ لِي وَلِوَٰلِدَيۡكَ إِلَيَّ ٱلۡمَصِيرُ ﴾   (سورة لقمان: ١٤)

❨And We have enjoined on a person [to be dutiful and good] to his parents. His mother bore him in weakness and hardship upon weakness and hardship, and his weaning is in two years; give thanks to Me and to your parents, unto Me is the final destination.❩
(Qur'an 31: 14)

Research has proved that breast-fed babies are better protected from allergies and common illnesses and are less likely to develop intolerance to certain foods than are bottle-fed babies. Human milk has been found to contain at least one hundred ingredients that infant formula does not have. Colostrum[87] is rich in vitamin A, proteins and antibodies (thus acting as the baby's first immunization). According to the American Dietetic Association (ADA), breast-fed children are less likely to develop certain chronic diseases later on in their lives, such as diabetes, some cancers and certain stomach and intestinal diseases[88]. In addition, two fatty acids found naturally in breast milk — DHA (docosahexaenoic acid) and ARA (arachidonic acid) — are important components of cell membranes forming the human brain and the retina of the eye.

Another valuable piece of advice concerning immunity was given by Ibn al-Qayyim to doctors stating that if a disease had already progressed, the doctor should not resort to drugs for treatment. Ibn al-Qayyim reasoned that if medication is given, the body will be busy dealing with it when it should instead be concentrating on fighting the disease. Thus, according to Ibn al-Qayyim, at that stage the doctor should be concerned primarily with strengthening the body's defences.[89]

To understand how this advice can increase the effectiveness of the immune system's capacities, we have to learn how this system works: When a foreign substance enters the human body, its marker protein (called an antigen) binds to the surface of specified immune system cells called B-lymphocytes, which are then activated and multiply rapidly to form an 'army' of cells which differentiate into what are called plasma cells, the antibody-producing 'factories'. Plasma cells produce a highly specific antibody at a surprisingly high rate (about 2000 antibodies per second), then the plasma cells die within four to five days, leaving a high level of antibodies in the blood whose role is to deactivate and destroy the invading antigen. After that, another type of lymphocyte called suppressor T-cells release chemicals that suppress the activity of the immune response to wind it down and finally stop it after the invaders have been successfully destroyed. All the involved immune cells then die away except some specialized lymphocytes called memory cells which remain to provide a memory for the encountered antigen in case of any subsequent invasion. This enables the body to deal with future attacks much faster and more efficiently with minimal symptoms of discomfort, because all the preparation for the defence has been already made.[90]

The role of antibiotic drugs is to attack the bacteria directly, bypassing all the natural stages of defence by the body. Sometimes the use of antibiotics is a must, and can be life saving as in cases of compromised immunity or in epidemics, but when they are taken regularly, they suppress the immune system, in addition to their harmful effect on the body's natural flora,[91] leading to the overgrowth of yeasts and Candida in the intestine.

Sometimes people resort to anti-inflammatory drugs to reduce the unpleasant symptoms of infections, forgetting that the inflammation is a natural part of the healing process and a crucial alarm system for natural immuni-ty to perform its job. These anti-inflammatory drugs — especially the steroidal anti-inflammatory drugs like cortisol, hydrocortisone and prednisone — suppress the body's immunity, causing a rapid reduction in the number of lymphocytes. So as we can see, it is definitely better to give the body the chance to fight its own war against disease, so that it becomes stronger and healthier over time. This fight may take some more time to show its effects compared to the antibiotic 'Miracle Cure', it may even cause some temporary unpleasant symptoms, and you may need more rest, but when it is over, you will definitely end up with a strong and courageous 'army' within your own body ready to defend against any future attacks.

Ibn al-Qayyim stated in his book Medicine of the Prophet that the physician should choose the simplest type of medicine for the treatment and should not prescribe medication until s/he investigates the options of food and diet. He believed that treatment with food instead of medicine was a true sign of the physician's professional skills.[92]

We cannot talk about the immune system without mentioning the lymph. This is a clear, colourless fluid that contains white blood cells drained from tissues in the body. The lymphatic system is an important body system that is often ignored. It is composed of lymphatic vessels transporting fluids that have escaped from the blood vessels along with lymphocytes (immune cells), enzymes, fats and hormones. The system also comprises the lymphatic organs[93] which house phagocytic cells (capable of absorbing foreign matter) and lymphocytes essential for the body's defence and fighting disease. The lymph nourishes cells, eliminates waste, defends the body and helps in tissue regeneration.

Unlike the circulatory system (the blood vessels), the lymphatic system has no 'pump': the lymph is transported by the action of the skeletal muscles, movement of the bowels and the pressure changes in the thorax during breathing.[94] To effectively perform its mission, the lymph has to circulate properly throughout the body. Islamic teaching surely enhances this by advising regular physical activity and proper breathing, as mentioned above. Still another Islamic practice plays an important role in stimulating lymphatic drainage, and that is ablution (wuḍoo') and the full body wash or shower (ghusl). The gentle steady massaging applied along the path of the lymph-collecting vessels has been found to help lymphatic circulation and increase the activity of lymph glands (the 'forts' of immune cells) via the manual stimulation of the whole system.

Imam Ahmed reported that the Prophet (ﷺ) described the actions performed in ablution as a form of massage. According to the opinion of Imam Mâlik, rubbing or massaging the parts of the body that are washed during ablution is an obligatory act, in addition to being from the Sunnah. Massaging should be performed also in ghusl (ritual bathing), where we are taught to massage the whole body starting with the head, then the right side followed by the left side of the body. The water should reach every part of the skin and hair as there are authentic hadiths that state that this is how Prophet Muhammad (ﷺ) used to perform ghusl.

The lymphatic vessels (lymphatics) form one-way channels in which lymph flows only towards the heart, where it is collected in the veins through two large lymphatic ducts:[95]

The right lymphatic duct, which drains the lymph from the right arm and the right side of the head and thorax (the part of the body between the neck and the abdomen).

The thoracic duct, which receives lymph from the rest of the body.

Can this explain the wisdom behind the requirement that we always start with the right side of the body? Allah knows.

Musculo-skeletal system

Most of us nowadays live a sedentary lifestyle. Many of us work sitting at a desk, use machines to perform many household activities, take the elevator instead of climbing the stairs, and ride comfortably in a car instead of walking. Our bodies are not designed to sit around all day: low activity levels compromise our health and lead to different degenerative diseases as arteriosclerosis,[96] osteoporosis, muscle weakness and even diabetes.

The early Muslims did not lead the kind of sedentary life we do; they walked or rode horses and camels for their transportation; they worked hard farming their lands or as commercial dealers — even the women worked hard in the house and the fields, cleaning, cooking, washing and tending the crops.

No one is asking you to change your job, sell your car, or throw away your dishwasher and washing machine. Still, you can include some activities in your daily routine without compromising your comfort. For instance, park the car some distance away from your destination and enjoy a walk, then climb the stairs instead of taking the elevator; visit your friend instead of calling him or her on the phone, go to the supermarket yourself instead of asking for delivery.

In the Qur'an, Allah orders humankind to walk on the earth and eat from its fine produce:

﴿هُوَٱلَّذِى جَعَلَ لَكُمُ ٱلْأَرْضَ ذَلُولًا فَٱمْشُوا۟ فِى مَنَاكِبِهَا وَكُلُوا۟ مِن رِّزْقِهِۦ... ﴾ (١٥)

(سورة المُلك: ١٥)

◆He it is, Who has made the earth subservient to you [easy for you to walk, to live and to do agriculture on it], so walk in the path thereof and eat of His provision,...◆ *(Qur'an 67: 15)*

Many of our Islamic practices require us to exert a certain amount of physical effort, ranging from the highly demanding physical activity of the pilgrimage (Hajj) with all its rites and obligations, or simple daily requirements like helping other people achieve their needs, visiting the sick, following funerals, walking to the mosque to perform congregational prayers and Friday (jumu'ah) prayers.

Exercise is essential for building a healthy body and spirit. Physical activity in general enhances the performance of the heart, circulatory and respiratory systems, and increases strength, suppleness and endurance.[97] It stimulates the flow of the lymphatic system helping in the elimination of body waste, boosting natural immunity and regenerating body cells and tissues. In addition, exercise enhances the production of natural endorphins, which are hormone-like substances in the brain responsible for the feeling of satisfaction and wellbeing and relieving stress. Exercise also improves sexual performance by boosting energy and increasing libido.[98]

Remember that Muslims are urged to teach their children different sports: "Teach your children javelin throwing, swimming and horse riding." This helps them build a healthy body and thus a healthy mind.

Ibn al-Qayyim, in Medicine of the Prophet, summarized the importance of exercise in a way that modern science is beginning to prove correct. He said that the body cannot get rid of all the remains of food and drink consumed, and this unexcreted waste accumulates in the body, clogging different vessels. Physical activity, he taught, was the best way to prevent the accumulation of that morbid matter, as moving heats the organs, aiding them to get rid of any unexcreted 'leftovers'. By exercising regularly, the body would be able to optimize its food intake and the joints, muscles and ligaments would become stronger and firmer. According to Ibn al-Qayyim, moderate physical activity — which we now call aerobic exercise — improved immunity, nourished the organs, and lifted the mood. He further stressed the importance of choosing the right type of exercise, which should be performed under the proper conditions.[99]

Exercise can be classified into three main types: aerobic exercises, muscle building or strength exercises and stretching exercises:

1. Aerobic exercises

Aerobic exercises are gentle exercises that you can perform at your own pace without the need to gasp for breath. They are essential for everyone at any age. Prophet Muhammad (ﷺ) used to take his wife 'Â'ishah (may Allah be pleased with her) for walks; they even sometimes raced on foot and she won the race once.[100] Dhahabi advises in his book Medicine of the Prophet:

> «Walking after dinner is useful, or instead you can perform prayer (ṣalât) to let the food settle in the stomach which improves digestion.»[101]

Aerobic exercises include walking, hiking, jogging, swimming, bicycling, friendly football or basketball games, gymnastics and many similar activities. These exercises improve blood flow to the brain, which in turn improves memory and general cognitive functions — especially important for the elderly. They also help to improve lung capacity, heart rate, and blood circulation and — if performed regularly — they help to tone muscles and lower blood pressure. When Prophet Job (Ayyoob) was suffering from illness, Allah commanded him to walk or stamp with his feet and to treat the disease with cool water:

(٤٢ :سورة ص)   ﴿أَرْكُضْ بِرِجْلِكَ هَٰذَا مُغْتَسَلٌ بَارِدٌ وَشَرَابٌ ۝﴾

❨Strike the ground with your foot: This is a spring of water to wash in, cool and a [refreshing] drink.❩   *(Qur'an 38: 42)*

Aerobic exercises raise your basal metabolic rate (BMR),[102] which contributes an important benefit for dieters. During dieting, the body tends to reduce its BMR as a natural defence mechanism to preserve energy, because it treats the sudden reduction in calorie intake as a case of starvation.

These types of exercises are also thought to be the best way to burn body fats and adjust body composition to result in a higher muscle-to-fat ratio. The sources of energy to fuel any activity are body carbohydrates, fats or proteins which are only used when carbohydrates and fats are not available. These fuels should be broken down to give adenosine triphosphate, commonly known as ATP, the body's fuel supply. How efficiently ATP is produced depends on the availability of oxygen to the body. Carbohydrates can be used to supply energy either with or without oxygen; while fats can only be used to supply energy (ATP) in the presence of oxygen[103] where the triglycerides in fat stores are burnt for energy supply. At rest, blood can deliver enough oxygen to the cells for aerobic metabolism, so most of the energy is produced from the breakdown of fats. During exercise, the muscles need more oxygen, so if the exercises are not very intense, fats as well as carbohydrates can be used for fuel, which is why these are called aerobic exercises. Conversely, if the exercises are strenuous and of high intensity, oxygen cannot be delivered fast enough to the cells so they are forced to rely on anaerobic metabolism, meaning that they burn only carbohydrates for fuel.[104]

Oxygen is transported from the lungs and delivered to the cells via the red blood corpuscles (RBCs). The ability to deliver oxygen is determined by the amount of RBCs in the blood and the efficiency of the heart's pumping action. That is why with a healthy diet and regular aerobic exercise, you will find yourself capable of spending more time in energy-consuming activities. You need to exercise aerobically for at least 20 to 30 minutes per day, three days a week, to get all the physical and cardiovascular benefits from aerobic activity.[105]

2. Muscle building or strength exercises

These are strenuous exercises aimed at increasing the bulk and/or tone of the muscles. Muscle-building or weight-bearing exercise firms up the body, improves stamina and pumps calcium into the bones, which aids in maintaining their density and strength. Ibn al-Qayyim observed in Medicine of the Prophet that the regular involvement of different organs in a suitable type of physical activity strengthens them.[106]

Strength exercises are also called anaerobic exercises, as the heart in this case cannot pump oxygen fast enough to support the energy needs for these intense training sessions, so the body has to rely solely on the breakdown of carbohydrates. Under anaerobic conditions, the carbohydrates are still not fully broken down; this yields lactic acid as an end product, which causes cramps and fatigue when it accumulates in the muscles. That is why after high intensity muscle training, it is useful to have a mild cool-down like a gentle walk, stretches or easy movements to allow enough blood flow to the muscles. This will deliver oxygen to remove the built-up acid, thus relieving the cramps.[107]

Anaerobic exercises include running, jumping, high intensity gymnastics, weight-lifting or any activities involving high levels of effort sustained over a short period of time. Women especially are advised to perform some type of anaerobic or strength exercise at least once a week to help reduce the risk of osteoporosis[108] and other post-menopausal symptoms.

3. Stretching exercises

These are very important in developing flexibility and suppleness of the muscles and joints. They are performed slowly and gently: you simply sink into and feel the right posture, then r lease your muscles or return gradually to the original position.[109] This type of exercise is beneficial to your physical posture; in addition, it can be an aid in meditation techniques, leading to more mental clarity and emotional tranquillity.

If you have a pet, you probably know that animals also practice stretching. Humans are said to be the only mammals who forget to stretch upon waking up — this has a negative effect on our posture and our general muscular flexibility. Stretching is especially important for sedentary people: it permits the realignment of all body axes, the redressing of the vertebral column (spine), and contributes to toning the muscles and a more flexible pelvis. Stretching releases tension, adjusts the respiratory rhythm and brings about a total equilibrium of the body and mind. Stretching the muscles is like squeezing the blood out of them, then pumping it through again. This helps to cleanse the muscles from cellular waste and improve blood circulation.[110]

The most important thing here is to relax, calm down, relieve tension and breathe normally. The more you practice stretching, the easier it will be and the more flexibly your muscles will move. But remember, do not push yourself too hard: continue as long as you feel comfortable.

Ṣalât (prayer) can be regarded as a type of stretching exercise; the physical acts performed during ṣalât are gentle, simple exercises suitable for all ages and conditions. During ṣalât, we perform continuous gentle muscle contraction and relaxation with perfect harmony and balance, inducing flexibility without overexhaustion. Almost all body muscles, bones and joints are involved in the performance of ṣalât:

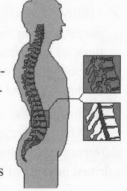

➤ By raising our hands in the beginning of the prayer for takbeer, we stretch the fingers, shoulder and all anterior arm muscles, and cause the elbows to flex.

➤ Upon standing, body weight is evenly distributed so that the back does not take all the strain, and the neck and shoulders are relaxed.

> Upon bowing (rukooʻ), we stretch the trunk, back, pelvis, hip, thighs and leg muscles, in addition to shoulders, arms and neck muscles. Prophet Muhammad (ﷺ) said: «Then, bow till you feel secure in your position, then redress yourself till you are standing upright.»[111] The action of bowing followed by redressing is a very useful exercise for the weak back by regularly, yet very gently, stretching the back muscles. These muscles are called erector spinae; they span the entire length of the vertebral column, providing resistance that helps control the action of bending over at the waist. If not properly exercised, these muscles go into spasms, causing back pain.

> Prophet Muhammad (ﷺ) stressed that we should properly straighten up after bowing and prostrating: «One's ṣalât is not complete unless he straightens his back after bowing and prostrating.»[112]

> Prostrating (sajdah) also exercises the same muscles that bowing does, with more stress on the neck, toes and legs. We are ordered to prostrate twice with a gentle sitting posture in between. The Prophet (ﷺ) said: «Then, prostrate till you feel secure in your position, then sit till you feel secure in your pose, then prostrate again till you feel secure in your position.»[113]

> Finally, as we say the final salutation (tasleem) at the end of the prayer, turning the head to the right and left massages the neck muscles and increases their flexibility. This is especially useful for people in sedentary jobs who sit in front of their monitors all day long, and then complain from neck strain.

So imagine the physical benefits you gain from performing your five daily prayers. Perform this daily routine and enjoy the difference. Of course, we should always keep in mind that the spiritual benefits of ṣalât are more important, and thus we should always keep our intention in performing the prayer purely for the worship of Allah.

Reproductive system

Sexual desire is a built-in instinct in all humans and animals, Allah created it for the preservation of the species and the continuation of life. Human beings use this sacred instinct not only for reproduction, but also for physical and emotional satisfaction. This is a gift from Allah, if used properly and lawfully within a legal marriage.

﴿ وَمِنْ ءَايَـٰتِهِۦٓ أَنْ خَلَقَ لَكُم مِّنْ أَنفُسِكُمْ أَزْوَٰجًا لِّتَسْكُنُوٓا۟ إِلَيْهَا وَجَعَلَ بَيْنَكُم مَّوَدَّةً وَرَحْمَةً ۚ إِنَّ فِى ذَٰلِكَ لَءَايَـٰتٍ لِّقَوْمٍ يَتَفَكَّرُونَ ۝ ﴾   (سورة الروم: ٢١)

﴿And among His Signs is this, that He created for you spouses from among yourselves, that you may find repose in them, and He has put between you affection and mercy. Verily, in that are indeed signs for a people who reflect.﴾   *(Qur'an 30: 21)*

Sexual passion, if enjoyed within its religious and ethical limits, fulfils an emotional and physical need in addition to the ultimate purpose of its creation, which is the preservation of humankind. On the other hand, if this divine gift is misused by engaging in illegitimate relationships, the harmonious social system will be consequently disrupted, destroying family ties and transgressing others' rights.[114]

Allah (ﷻ) says in the Qur'an:

﴿ وَلَا تَقْرَبُوا۟ ٱلزِّنَىٰٓ ۖ إِنَّهُۥ كَانَ فَـٰحِشَةً وَسَآءَ سَبِيلًا ۝ ﴾   (سورة الإسراء: ٣٢)

﴿And do not come near to unlawful sexual intercourse. Verily, it is a great sin, and an evil way [that leads one to Hell unless Allah forgives him].﴾   *(Qur'an 17: 32)*

Prophet Muhammad (ﷺ) said: «Whoever can guarantee the chastity of whatever is between his two jaw-bones (the tongue, meaning refraining from sinful speech) and what is between his two legs (the private parts — meaning refraining from illegal sexual acts), I guarantee him Paradise.»[115] Islam teaches that sexual passion is stronger than any other human desire; it can control one's mind and lead to shameful crimes. Most people refrain from it owing to fear, shame or even illness; but the true believer is the one who can control it under any and all circumstances. Allah reminds us of the story of Prophet Yoosuf (Joseph) who refrained from submitting to the beautiful wife of Egypt's minister:

$$\text{﴿وَرَٰوَدَتْهُ ٱلَّتِي هُوَ فِي بَيْتِهَا عَن نَّفْسِهِۦ وَغَلَّقَتِ ٱلْأَبْوَٰبَ وَقَالَتْ هَيْتَ لَكَ ۚ قَالَ مَعَاذَ ٱللَّهِ ۖ إِنَّهُۥ رَبِّيٓ أَحْسَنَ مَثْوَايَ ۖ إِنَّهُۥ لَا يُفْلِحُ ٱلظَّٰلِمُونَ ۝﴾}$$

(سورة يوسف: ٢٣)

❨And she, in whose house he was, sought to seduce him [to do an evil act], she closed the doors and said: Come on, you. He said: I seek refuge in Allah [or Allah forbid]! Truly, he [your husband] is my master! He made my stay agreeable! [So I will never betray him]. Verily, the oppressors and evil-doers will never be successful.❩   *(Qur'an 12: 23)*

Prophet Muhammad (ﷺ) taught us: «Allah will give shade to seven persons under His Throne on the Day of Judgment, a day on which there will be no shade except His shade. One of them will be he who refrains from satisfying the sexual desire of a beautiful woman who comes from a respectable family when she calls him, and he says: I fear Allah, the Master of the universe.»[116]

Islam takes a strong stand against this social crime, showing all believers the abominable results of this act in this worldly life as

well as in the afterlife. Islam considers as sinful any act that may
lead to adultery, for example, it considers the sin of the fornication of the eye as the greatest among the minor sins; Allah says in
the Qur'an:

قُل لِّلْمُؤْمِنِينَ يَغُضُّوا مِنْ أَبْصَرِهِمْ وَيَحْفَظُوا فُرُوجَهُمْ ذَلِكَ أَزْكَىٰ لَهُمْ إِنَّ اللَّهَ
خَبِيرٌ بِمَا يَصْنَعُونَ ۝ وَقُل لِّلْمُؤْمِنَتِ يَغْضُضْنَ مِنْ أَبْصَرِهِنَّ وَيَحْفَظْنَ فُرُوجَهُنَّ
وَلَا يُبْدِينَ زِينَتَهُنَّ إِلَّا مَاظَهَرَ مِنْهَا ... ۝ ﴾   (سورة النور: ٣٠-٣١)

《Tell the believing men to lower their gaze [from looking at forbidden things], and protect their private parts [from illegal sexual
acts]. That is purer for them. Verily, Allah is All-Aware of what
they do. And tell the believing women to lower their gaze [from
looking at forbidden things], and protect their private parts [from
illegal sexual acts] and not to show off their adornment except
only that which is apparent...》   *(Qur'an 24: 30-31)*

It was narrated that Jesus Christ said, "Take care of your eye as
it sows the seed of sexual passion in the heart and that is sufficient
for the creation of danger." Similarly, when Prophet John (Yaḥya)
was once asked, "What is the source of fornication?" he replied,
"Eyesight and greed."[117]

According to Ghazâli (the Elder) in his Ihyâ' 'Uloom ad-Deen,
Prophet Muhammad (ﷺ) said:

«The eyesight is a poisonous arrow from the arrows of the
devil; Allah awards the man who gives it up for fear of Allah
(the kind of) faith which grants satisfaction to his heart.»[118]

The gaze in fact is scientifically believed to trigger a hormonal stimulation that prepares the body and sexual organs for intercourse. These hormones affect every organ in the body. When
these hormones are unnecessarily stimulated, they remain unused
in the blood circulation causing severe tissue damage, ranging

from skin acne, excessive sweat secretion and migraine head-aches, to osteoporosis, atherosclerosis[119] and hypertension.[120]

Islam warns against provoking these sexual desires unneces-sarily, and gives us advice on how to prevent the problem: women should not reveal their adornment and beauty in the presence of men unrelated to them, and neither men nor women should look or gaze at, nor should they sit in close or private contact with, members of the opposite sex who are not part of their immediate family. Another solution is to get young people to marry as soon as they can afford it, and if they cannot, let them fast to learn to control their passions. Prophet Muhammad (ﷺ) said:

«O young men, take recourse to marriage if you can afford it; he who is unable to do it, let him fast, as fasting curbs his sexual desire.»[121]

All these measures are essential for establishing the welfare of society; by preventing the disintegration of family bonds, the prevalence of unwanted children and the spread of sexually trans-mitted diseases (STDs) such as syphilis, gonorrhoea and herpes; all of which are dangerous, difficult to treat and generally incur-able. The latest sexually-transmitted epidemic is a world disaster: AIDS (acquired immune deficiency syndrome) is a disease that was first identified in the USA in the early 1400s H/1980s CE among young homosexual men.

The AIDS virus can be briefly explained in this way: The body's immune system depends on two main types of lympho-cytes: T — and B-lymphocytes. The T-type act as detectors of any invading microbes in the blood, and thus urge the B-lymphocytes to produce the suitable antibodies. The AIDS virus attacks and de-stroys the T-lymphocytes, resulting in the breakdown of the whole immune system, leaving the body defenceless against diseases that it would otherwise be able to fight.

Prophet Mohammed (ﷺ) taught:

«Indecency never appears in people and they declare it unless the pestilence and torments that were not known by their ancestors have spread among them.»[122]

Looking at the hadith, we can understand the reason for the prevalence of this dangerous and incurable disease, which would be easy to avoid just by leading a virtuous life. Prophet Muhammad (ﷺ) said:

«Obscenity and bawdiness are not part of Islam.»[123]

Allah (ﷻ) says in His Holy Book:

﴿ قُلْ إِنَّمَا حَرَّمَ رَبِّيَ ٱلْفَوَٰحِشَ مَا ظَهَرَ مِنْهَا وَمَا بَطَنَ ... ﴿٣٣﴾ ﴾ (سورة الأعراف: ٣٣)

﴿Say [O Muhammad]: [But] the things that Allah has indeed forbidden are great sins [including every kind of unlawful sexual act] whether committed openly or secretly...﴾   *(Qur'an 7: 33)*

Among these obscenities is homosexuality. Homosexuality is a major sin in Islam; it was mentioned to have happened during the time of Prophet Looṭ (Lot). Allah clearly prohibits homosexuality in the Qur'an:

﴿أَتَأْتُونَ ٱلذُّكْرَانَ مِنَ ٱلْعَٰلَمِينَ ﴿١٦٥﴾ وَتَذَرُونَ مَا خَلَقَ لَكُمْ رَبُّكُم مِّنْ أَزْوَٰجِكُم بَلْ أَنتُمْ قَوْمٌ عَادُونَ ﴿١٦٦﴾ ﴾ (سورة الشعراء: ١٦٥-١٦٦)

﴿Do you go in unto the males of the human species, and leave those whom Allah has created for you to be your wives? Indeed, you are a trespassing people!﴾   *(Qur'an 26: 165-166)*

﴿ وَلُوطًا إِذْ قَالَ لِقَوْمِهِۦٓ أَتَأْتُونَ ٱلْفَٰحِشَةَ وَأَنتُمْ تُبْصِرُونَ ﴿٥٤﴾ أَئِنَّكُمْ لَتَأْتُونَ ٱلرِّجَالَ شَهْوَةً مِّن دُونِ ٱلنِّسَآءِ بَلْ أَنتُمْ قَوْمٌ تَجْهَلُونَ ﴿٥٥﴾ ﴾

(سورة النمل: ٥٤-٥٥)

❨And [remember] Looṭ [Lot], when he said to his people: Do you commit evil [great sin, including every kind of unlawful sexual intercourse and sodomy] while you see [one another doing evil without any screen]? Do you approach men in your lusts rather than women? Indeed, you are a people who behave senselessly.❩

(Qur'an 27: 54-55)

Allah prescribes severe punishments for anyone who commits this sin, reflecting the danger it poses to the health of individuals and society:

﴿وَٱلَّٰتِي يَأْتِينَ ٱلْفَٰحِشَةَ مِن نِّسَآئِكُمْ فَٱسْتَشْهِدُواْ عَلَيْهِنَّ أَرْبَعَةً مِّنكُمْ فَإِن شَهِدُواْ فَأَمْسِكُوهُنَّ فِى ٱلْبُيُوتِ حَتَّىٰ يَتَوَفَّىٰهُنَّ ٱلْمَوْتُ أَوْ يَجْعَلَ ٱللَّهُ لَهُنَّ سَبِيلًا ۝ وَٱلَّذَانِ يَأْتِيَٰنِهَا مِنكُمْ فَـَٔاذُوهُمَا فَإِن تَابَا وَأَصْلَحَا فَأَعْرِضُواْ عَنْهُمَآ إِنَّ ٱللَّهَ كَانَ تَوَّابًا رَّحِيمًا ۝﴾   (سورة النساء: ١٥-١٦)

❨If any of your women are guilty of lewdness, take the evidence of four [reliable] witnesses from amongst you against them; and if they testify, confine them to houses until death does claim them, or Allah ordain for them some [other] way. If two persons among you are guilty of lewdness, punish them both. If they repent and amend, leave them alone; for Allah is Oft-Returning, Most Merciful.❩   *(Qur'an 4: 15-16)*

Islamic laws are aimed at establishing the welfare of the community; they are clear proof of Allah's kindness, mercy and provision for humanity. The Qur'an and the Sunnah teach believers chastity, faithfulness and abstinence. Nevertheless, scholars believe that the main responsibility for implementing Islamic rules and preventing sexual crimes lies with the leaders of a nation, who should take necessary measures to make marriage affordable and prevent the prevalence of indecency in the society.

The punishment for adultery according to Islamic law is very harsh:

﴿ الزَّانِيَةُ وَالزَّانِي فَاجْلِدُوا كُلَّ وَاحِدٍ مِّنْهُمَا مِائَةَ جَلْدَةٍ وَلَا تَأْخُذْكُم بِهِمَا رَأْفَةٌ فِي دِينِ اللَّهِ ... ﴿٢﴾ ﴾

(سورة النور: ٢)

﴿The woman and the man guilty of illegal sexual intercourse, flog each of them with a hundred lashes. Do not let pity withhold you in their case, in a punishment prescribed by Allah.﴾ *(Qur'an 24: 2)*

However, the sentence cannot be executed unless there are four impartial witnesses, who swear an oath that they saw the crime happen before their own eyes, or else:

﴿ وَالَّذِينَ يَرْمُونَ الْمُحْصَنَاتِ ثُمَّ لَمْ يَأْتُوا بِأَرْبَعَةِ شُهَدَاءَ فَاجْلِدُوهُمْ ثَمَانِينَ جَلْدَةً وَلَا تَقْبَلُوا لَهُمْ شَهَادَةً أَبَدًا وَأُولَٰئِكَ هُمُ الْفَاسِقُونَ ﴿٤﴾ ﴾

(سورة النور: ٤)

﴿And those who accuse chaste women, and do not produce four witnesses, flog them with eighty lashes, and reject their testimony forever; they indeed are [rebellious liars] disobedient to Allah.﴾
(Qur'an 24: 4)

This condition is almost impossible to fulfil. These provisions are aimed primarily at those who are so devoid of self-respect that they would commit sexual acts in public. Laws and punishments alone cannot be responsible for building a righteous society. Virtuous societies and strong, honest nations are the result of true faith that leads to good manners and pure souls.[124]

Another Islamic instruction concerning the reproductive system is to abstain from intercourse during a woman's menstrual period, as Allah (ﷻ) says:

﴿وَيَسْـَٔلُونَكَ عَنِ ٱلْمَحِيضِ قُلْ هُوَ أَذًى فَٱعْتَزِلُوا۟ ٱلنِّسَآءَ فِى ٱلْمَحِيضِ وَلَا
تَقْرَبُوهُنَّ حَتَّىٰ يَطْهُرْنَ فَإِذَا تَطَهَّرْنَ فَأْتُوهُنَّ مِنْ حَيْثُ أَمَرَكُمُ ٱللَّهُ إِنَّ ٱللَّهَ يُحِبُّ ٱلتَّوَّٰبِينَ
وَيُحِبُّ ٱلْمُتَطَهِّرِينَ ۞ ﴾   (سورة البقرة: ٢٢٢)

❝They ask you concerning menstruation. Say: that is a harmful thing [for a husband to have a sexual intercourse with his wife while she is having her menses], therefore keep away from women during menses and do not go into them till they have become pure [from menses and have taken a bath]. And when they have purified themselves, then go in unto them as Allah has ordained for you. Truly, Allah loves those who turn unto Him in repentance and loves those who purify themselves [by taking a bath and cleaning and washing thoroughly their private parts and bodies, for their prayers, etc.].❞   *(Qur'an 2: 222)*

The normal bacterial flora in a woman's vagina creates an acidic environment which constitutes a primary defence line against invading harmful micro-organisms. These helpful bacteria feed on the sugar stored in the cells lining the vaginal tract converting it into lactic acid for protection. During menses, the sugar storage depletes and so do the beneficial bacteria, shifting the vaginal environment towards the alkaline side, so the micro-organisms flourish in the vagina during that time of the month. The only protection against these harmful organisms from reaching the inside of the reproductive organs is the normal shedding of the uterine lining, including the blood. So if intercourse is performed during this time, there is an increased risk of infection of the reproductive system for both the male and the female.[125]

Note that the condition stated in the Qur'anic verse for resuming the sexual life between couple is not only the end of the menstrual period, but the cleansing and purification of the vaginal area (and of course the whole body) to ensure a safe environment.[126]

It was related that 'Â'ishah said:

«A woman asked the Prophet (ﷺ) concerning the bath which is taken after the cessation of menstruation. The Prophet (ﷺ) instructed her to perform the ritual shower or ghusl, and then he said: 'Purify yourself with a piece of cloth scented with musk.' The woman asked: 'How should I purify myself with it?' He said: 'Glory be to Allah! Purify yourself with it!' I pulled her over to myself — said 'Â'ishah — and told her: 'Use it to follow the path soiled with blood'.»[127]

Islamic laws and manners do not forbid the husband from being kind and loving to his wife during this time of the month. Actually, if he were following the Prophet's teachings and behaviour with his wives during their menstruation, he should be more loving and caring, in the realization that women are emotionally vulnerable during this time, due to hormonal changes. This is completely contrary to the ancient beliefs that women are 'toxic' during this time of the month and that men should avoid them. In many belief systems (including orthodox Judaism), menstruating women are considered impure, and told to keep entirely away from their husbands during this period. The Messenger of Allah (ﷺ) showed us otherwise.

In a well-known hadith, Umm Salamah, may Allah be pleased with her, reported:

«While I was lying with the Messenger of Allah (ﷺ) in a bed cover I menstruated, so I slipped away and I took up the clothes (which I wore) in menses. Upon this Allah's Messenger (ﷺ) asked: Did you start your menses? I said: Yes.

He called me and I lay down with him in the bed cover.
(And she further) said that she and Allah's Messenger (ﷺ)
used to take a bath from the same vessel after major impurity (sexual intercourse).»[128]

'Â'ishah, may Allah be pleased with her, reported:

«When anyone among us (among the wives of the Holy
Prophet) menstruated, Allah's Messenger (ﷺ) asked her
to tie a waist-wrapper over her (body) and then embraced
her.»[129]

These two hadiths demonstrate that there is nothing wrong
with a husband and wife being close and intimate with each other
during her menses. The only prohibition is that the man should not
come in contact with her private parts, and she should keep them
covered for this reason.

CHAPTER 2

BIOCHEMICAL BODY

$\mathcal{A}$s described at the beginning of this book, the biochemical body includes your food and nutrition habits as well as the environmental conditions around you. Let us start with the nutritional habits.

As I mentioned earlier, the Arabs at that time had an elaborate system of healthy nutritional practices and were well acquainted with proper food choices.[1] Of course, not all foods and herbs are mentioned by name in the Islamic sources. The Prophet's (ﷺ) tradition (Sunnah) in general, encourages healthy eating habits and a healthy lifestyle; but, where a reliable hadith is known about a particular treatment or prevention, it will be noted in this chapter.

Nutrition

I do not believe in diets that tell you how and what to eat. They may lead to an initial weight loss, but you will end up feeling frustrated and deprived, leading finally to overeating and weight regain. If you want to become healthy and fit — and stay that way, you have to change your whole lifestyle, including your eating habits. I will start by recalling these holy words:

﴿ ... وَكُلُوا۟ وَٱشْرَبُوا۟ وَلَا تُسْرِفُوٓا۟ إِنَّهُۥ لَا يُحِبُّ ٱلْمُسْرِفِينَ ۝ ﴾

(سورة الأعراف: ٣١)

❨...And eat and drink but do not waste by extravagance, certainly He [Allah] does not like those who waste by extravagance❩
(Qur'an 7: 31)

The words are so clear and simple: eat what you want but do not overdo it. This is further explained by the hadith of Prophet Muhammad (ﷺ) that I introduced in the first chapter:

«No human fills a vessel worse than his own abdomen; a few bites are enough for man to keep his body upright, but if it is indispensable, then a third for his food, a third for his drink and a third for his breath.»[2] He (ﷺ) also said: «The food for two is enough for three, and the food for three is enough for four.»[3]

Do not fill your stomach with food; leave equal space for water and for breath, and just eat what is enough to keep you going. Patrick Holford, in his best-selling book Optimum Nutrition Bible, recorded that many studies found that when animals were given a highly nutritious but low calorie diet, they lived healthier and longer lives. Such studies are very difficult to con-

duct on human beings, as it is hard to control and monitor their food consumption accurately over a long period of time, but, according to Holford, it makes sense according to what is known about nutrition in humans that a diet that gives the body just what it needs and no more will definitely improve health and may increase longevity.[4]

A well-known saying[5] in Arabic goes: "We are a people that do not eat unless we are hungry, and when we eat we do not reach satiety."

I have to stop and marvel at this wise comment. First, it explains that you should not eat unless you are hungry, so no in-between-meal snacks or junk food. Second, when you actually sit to eat, do not continue until you are completely full. Recent scientific experiments have proved that the message sent from the stomach to the brain that gives you the actual feeling of satiety, takes about twenty minutes to 'arrive'. This means that if you keep on eating until you feel full, you actually should have stopped eating twenty minutes earlier.

Ibn Sina advised: "Do not eat before digesting your food." Ibn al-Qayyim explained in his book Medicine of the Prophet that many digestive problems stem from the fact that we tend to eat before the body finishes digesting the previous meal. We also consume more than our body needs and we have poor food choices — especially with our contemporary fast-paced lifestyles — that are based on low nutrients, difficult to digest and complex or fatty foods.[6]

'Umar ibn al-Khaṭṭâb (ﷺ) said: "Beware of overeating; it ruins the body and causes sickness and laziness in performing prayers. Seek moderation; it is more healthful for the body and more distant from waste."[7] 'Â'ishah narrated: «The family of the Messenger of Allah (ﷺ) never ate their fill of barley bread two days running till he died.»[8]

Another precious piece of advice concerning food can be found in the Qur'an:

(سورة البقرة: ١٦٨)   ﴾يَٰٓأَيُّهَا ٱلنَّاسُ كُلُوا۟ مِمَّا فِى ٱلۡأَرۡضِ حَلَٰلٗا ... ﴿١٦٨﴾﴾

﴾O people! Eat of that which is lawful and good on the earth...﴿
(Qur'an 2: 168)

Two terms need to be explained: What is 'lawful' food and what is 'good' food in this context?

What is lawful (halal) food?

There are two conditions for the food to be halal according to Islamic law;

First, the money you bought it with, or the source you obtained it from has to be purely lawful and legally earned. There is a hadith related by Abu Hurayrah (ﷺ), in which the Messenger of Allah (ﷺ) said:

«Allah the Almighty is Good and accepts only that which
is good. And verily Allah has commanded the Believers to
do that which He has commanded the Messengers. So the
Almighty says:

﴿ يَٰٓأَيُّهَا ٱلرُّسُلُ كُلُوا۟ مِنَ ٱلطَّيِّبَٰتِ وَٱعْمَلُوا۟ صَٰلِحًا إِنِّى بِمَا تَعْمَلُونَ عَلِيمٌ

(سورة المؤمنون: ٥١)   ﴿٥١﴾

◀O you Messengers! Eat of the good foods which Allah
has made legal [meat of slaughtered eatable animals, milk
products, fats, vegetables, fruits, etc.], and do righteous
deeds.▶   *(Qur'an 23: 51)*

Allah (ﷻ) also says:

﴿ يَٰٓأَيُّهَا ٱلَّذِينَ ءَامَنُوا۟ كُلُوا۟ مِن طَيِّبَٰتِ مَا رَزَقْنَٰكُمْ ... ﴿١٧٢﴾ ﴾

(سورة البقرة: ١٧٢)

◀O you who believe [in the Oneness of Allah]! Eat of the
lawful things with which We have provided you...▶
                                                (Qur'an 2: 172)

Then he (ﷺ) mentioned (the case) of a man who, having
journeyed far, is dishevelled and dusty, and who spreads out
his hands to the sky saying "O Allah! O Allah!", while his
food is harâm (unlawful), his drink is harâm, his clothing
is harâm, and he has been nourished with what is harâm, so
how can (his supplication) be answered?»[9]

Second, it should not include any of the food stated in the
Qur'an to be forbidden, or clarified and demonstrated by Prophet
Muhammad (ﷺ) to be forbidden. We have to be confident that
any forbidden food must be harmful, because remember that
Allah (ﷻ) says:

$$\{\ ...\ وَيُحِلُّ لَهُمُ الطَّيِّبَاتِ وَيُحَرِّمُ عَلَيْهِمُ الْخَبَائِثَ\ ...\ ﴿١٥٧﴾\ \}$$

(سورة الأعراف: ١٥٧)

❴...He allows for them as lawful all good things, and prohibits for them as unlawful all evil things]...❵   *(Qur'an 7: 157)*

Allah (ﷻ) also tells us:

$$\{\ حُرِّمَتْ عَلَيْكُمُ الْمَيْتَةُ وَالدَّمُ وَلَحْمُ الْخِنزِيرِ وَمَا أُهِلَّ لِغَيْرِ اللَّهِ بِهِ وَالْمُنْخَنِقَةُ$$
$$وَالْمَوْقُوذَةُ وَالْمُتَرَدِّيَةُ وَالنَّطِيحَةُ وَمَا أَكَلَ السَّبُعُ إِلَّا مَا ذَكَّيْتُمْ وَمَا ذُبِحَ عَلَى النُّصُبِ$$
$$وَأَن تَسْتَقْسِمُوا بِالْأَزْلَامِ ذَلِكُمْ فِسْقٌ\ ...\ ﴿٣﴾\ \}$$ (سورة المائدة: ٣)

❴Forbidden to you [for food] are: dead animals [that were not ritually slaughtered], blood, the flesh of swine [pork], and the meat of that which has been slaughtered as a sacrifice to anyone other than Allah, [or that has been slaughtered for idols, or on which Allah's Name has not been mentioned while slaughtering], and that which has been killed by strangling, or by a violent blow, or by a headlong fall, or by the goring of horns, and that which has been [partly] eaten by a wild animal — unless you are able to slaughter it [before its death] — and that which is sacrificed [slaughtered] on stone altars. [It is] also [forbidden] to use arrows seeking luck or decision, [all] that is abomination [disobedience of Allah and sin]...❵   *(Qur'an 5: 3)*

Dead meat means an animal that has not been properly slaughtered. As soon as the animal dies, all sorts of bacteria find a perfect medium for their growth. The presence of blood in the animal's corpse speeds the rate of putrefaction (spoiling) and tissue degradation. We are forbidden to eat all dead meat except fish and locust as the Prophet (ﷺ) said.[10] However, a wise saying from Islamic teachings specifies: "Whatever is cast out by the sea or appears from the ebb tide, you can eat; but what dies in it and floats, do not eat it." When dead fish are left unpreserved, their bodies also start to putrefy and become suitable media for different sorts of infectious diseases.

In 1406 H/1986 CE, the wisdom behind the prohibition of dead meat was further understood and reinforced when 'mad cow disease' appeared in the United Kingdom. Mad cow disease is the commonly used name for Bovine Spongiform Encephalopathy (BSE), a rapidly progressive, degenerative, and fatal disease affecting the central nervous system of cattle. Some in the cattle industry were recycling the leftovers from dead cows and sheep and drying them to add to the meal fed to the livestock. The disease appeared first in the animals that were fed on this meal, and it soon spread from them to the human beings who had eaten the meat from these cows. The definitive nature of the BSE agent is not completely known. The agent is thought to be a modified form of a protein, called a prion, which becomes infectious and accumulates in neural (brain) tissues causing a fatal neurological disease. These prions are resistant to common food disinfection treatments — even cooking does not destroy them. In 1417 H/1997 CE, USA and Canada prohibited, with some exceptions, the use of protein derived from mammalian tissues in animal feed intended for cows and other ruminants. However, blood is still exempted from the Canadian and the U.S. feed bans. In many farm factories, the milk given to young calves is enriched with cow serum to improve its protein quality and the weaned calves' food is sometimes even sprayed with cow's blood.[11]

Here we have to remember the hadith of Prophet Muhammad (ﷺ) recorded by Tirmidhi that prohibits the consumption of the meat or the milk of an animal that has been fed on impurities and filth[12] — like, for example, other animals' remains or slaughterhouse waste. It was related that he (ﷺ) advised quarantining these animals and feeding them on proper vegetarian food for a suitable period of time until their bodies were detoxified.[13]

One scientist wrote a shocking report stating that in the United States slaughterhouses, cattle are usually hit on the head to lose consciousness before being slaughtered. Scientific studies showed that these animals show fragments of brain tissue in their bloodstream as well as in other body organs which is likely to cause the spread of the prion protein — the cause of mad cow disease — all through the cow's body instead of being localized in the brain and neural tissues.[14] This is clear proof of the great importance of sticking to our Islamic (halal) slaughter method.

What does Islam say about blood?

Allah (ﷻ) says in His Holy Book:

﴿ قُل لَّآ أَجِدُ فِي مَآ أُوحِيَ إِلَيَّ مُحَرَّمًا عَلَىٰ طَاعِمٍ يَطْعَمُهُۥٓ إِلَّآ أَن يَكُونَ مَيْتَةً أَوْ دَمًا مَّسْفُوحًا أَوْ لَحْمَ خِنزِيرٍ فَإِنَّهُۥ رِجْسٌ أَوْ فِسْقًا أُهِلَّ لِغَيْرِ ٱللَّهِ بِهِۦ فَمَنِ ٱضْطُرَّ غَيْرَ بَاغٍ وَلَا عَادٍ فَإِنَّ رَبَّكَ غَفُورٌ رَّحِيمٌ ﴾ ۝

(سورة الأنعام:١٤٥)

﴿Say [O Muhammad]: I find not in that which has been inspired to me anything forbidden to be eaten by one who wishes to eat it, unless it be a dead animal or blood poured forth [by slaughtering or the like], or the flesh of swine [pork] for that surely is impure, or impious [unlawful] meat [of an animal] which is slaughtered as a sacrifice to someone other than Allah [or on which Allah's Name has not been mentioned while slaughtering]. But whosoever is forced by necessity without wilful disobedience, nor transgressing due limits, [for that person] certainly, Allah is Oft Forgiving, Most Merciful.﴾   *(Qur'an 6: 145)*

In early 1426 H/February 2005 CE, a young man from northern Vietnam returned home after work bringing with him a fresh duck to celebrate with his mother the traditional Lunar New Year. After slaughtering the duck, they used its blood to prepare a traditional Vietnamese soup. The man had the soup and five days later he fell ill and was carried to the hospital to be diagnosed with 'bird flu', or the H5N1 virus. By then, the virus had already spread through his lungs. Faced with such a highly threatening virus, the body's immune system initiates a strong defensive mechanism, causing a major inflammatory response so that the lungs are flooded with fluids and dead cells. Some bacteria such as pneumoccoci can take advantage of the situation, making it worse, and the person can finally drown in his own body fluids.[15]

When an animal gets infected, the invading microbes multiply in its blood, which also carries different body toxins. Once the animal dies, the microbes in the blood have an immediate chance to multiply and grow without the defence that the living body would have put up; so even if the animal showed no symptoms while it was alive, its blood can still carry a considerable amount of toxins that are not destroyed by cooking processes.

Still, according to a hadith, we are "allowed to eat two bloods: liver and spleen."[16] Why? These two organs contain specific cells called the reticuloendothelial cells. Their role is to engulf the microbes circulating in the blood and destroy them. In addition, the liver is the main detoxifying organ of the body which treats toxins found in the blood through different metabolic processes, turning them into simpler compounds that the body can get rid of. That is why the blood of the liver and spleen are the purest form of blood in the body.[17]

Flesh of swine

Pork is known to be very rich in
saturated fats, the fats that raise blood
cholesterol levels and increase the cardiovascular and circulatory risks. Moreover, science has proven that the pig's body is
an incubating vessel for a number of highly dangerous microbes.
This is not surprising, knowing the filthy living and feeding habits
of these animals.

There is a wide range of diseases carried by pigs; the most
common examples are Trichinella spiralis and Taenia solium
worms, both causing painful and sometimes deadly diseases in
humans. These parasites find their way through the intestines of
the infected person to the whole body — including the muscles,
the heart and even the brain.[18] Pigs are also a source of many bacterial and viral infections, even if they do not carry the symptoms
of the disease themselves. Dr. Carleton Gajdusek, awarded the
Nobel Prize in Medicine for his work on a neurological disorder
similar to mad cow disease,[19] has been quoted as saying that he
believed that pigs, like cattle, can carry this fatal disease.[20] Nevertheless, the severity of the human infection with mad cow disease
is less obvious in the case of pigs, which are usually slaughtered
before showing the first signs of the disease. On the other hand,
cows are usually slaughtered at the age of two years or they are
raised for milk production, which is why the disease symptoms
are clearly manifested.

In the spring of 1423 H/2003 CE, an unusually severe pneumonia virus emerged in China. Dr. Malik Peiris, a renowned Sri Lan-
kan virologist, started the investigation which led to the discovery
of the new genetic make-up of a virus now known as SARS (Se-

vere Acute Respiratory Syndrome).[21] Although SARS is a deadly virus, it is not easily spread among human beings; and this is why the world's human population escaped (thanks only to Allah for this) a lethal epidemic. Nevertheless, it is still highly possible for the SARS virus or other bird viruses, like H5N1, to mutate into a form capable of spreading quickly among people like the common flu. According to Professor Peiris, pig farms can cause this deadly mutation. Since pigs already carry another human flu virus and they live next to poultry on many of these farms, this is an available setting for viral crossover, in which pigs will become the crossing link between bird and human viruses[22].[23]

What is good food?

Many people have difficulty understanding what good food is, because nowadays it is pretty difficult to actually find 'good' food. Good food is whole food that has retained its original constituents. Fresh fruits for example, are good food, but jams and fruit preserves are not; they are processed to create a 'better' look and texture, they have been loaded with additives to improve their colour, odour and flavour or prolong their shelf life. Similarly, flour made from pure ground wheat or barley grains is good, whole food; while flour prepared by removing the bran and germ, and then bleaching the final product with chlorine to become white flour (yes, the same chlorine that you use in your laundry room), is not a whole food — even after it is enriched with artificial vitamins and minerals.

Good foods, whether they are grains, vegetables, fruits, or derived from animals (like meat and milk products) contain all the nutrients that we need. The more we process them, changing them from their original state, the less benefit we get out of them. With new vitamins, minerals and phytonutrients[24] constantly being discovered, it is increasingly obvious that our knowledge is extremely limited, and we are therefore not qualified to attempt to change Allah's perfect creation through our naïve and ignorant efforts.

 In my opinion, the only way we can guarantee that we are getting all the nutrients we need for our healthy growth and development is to get them from whole food. It does not make sense to eat synthetic, over-processed and nutrient-depleted food, and then to spend time and money on vitamins and supplements to try to recover all the nutrients that were taken out of our food. In fact, processed and empty-calorie food actually has the ability to withdraw nutrients from our own bodies. For any food to be assimilated in the body, it first needs to be metabolized through various biochemical reactions, and these in turn need to be catalyzed by different enzymes and vitamins. Processed food is usually lacking the vitamins and minerals necessary to undertake these reactions, and thus it actually needs to withdraw the required nutrients from the body.[25]

The Food Guide Pyramid

$\mathcal{B}$ookshops and the mass media carry a huge array of popular theories and self-help advice concerning healthy eating habits. The one I find most compatible with our Islamic teachings is the United States Department of Agriculture (USDA) Food Guide Pyramid. (Shown below) The USDA is responsible for food and nutrition guidelines in the US. This pyramid aims at spreading good nutrition practice by planning diets that meet nutrient requirements, promote health and prevent diseases.

The pyramid divides the food categories into six groups, and places them in a pyramid-shaped chart, with the group that should be comsumed in the greatest quantity at the base, and the group that should be consumed in the smallest quantitiy at the top of the pyramid. The pyramid shape thus helps demonstrate the relative contribution each group should make to the diet. At the base of the pyramid is the bread and cereals group: carbohydrate-rich food

Food Guide Pyramid

which should be the foundation of the diet, and from which it is recommended to eat around six to eleven servings per day. If you are watching your weight, stick to the lower number of servings.

Above the cereals group are the two groups of plant-derived food: vegetables and fruits, of which the recommended numbers of servings are three to five of vegetables and two to four of fruits. Dieters are usually advised to increase their consumption from these two groups at the expense of the cereals group, as these — especially the vegetables — have fewer calories per serving unit due to their high fibre content.

On the third level from the bottom are the protein and dairy groups: the recommended daily intake here is two to three servings per day from each. Finally come the fats and sweets at the narrow tip of the pyramid, which makes them the least recommended. The minimum intake of this food category is advisable.[26]

The main advantage of the food guide pyramid system is that it is flexible enough to suit the needs and preferences of different people with various cultures, habits and beliefs, and this conforms exactly with the teachings of our Prophet (ﷺ), as he would never forbid a food unless it was harâm. He (ﷺ) ate what he liked, and never complained about any type of food presented to him: if he did not like it, he simply would not eat it. He emphasized that people should eat what they like, but in moderation.

Most of the plants described here are available in supermarkets and produce markets around the world. If there is a plant listed here that you have not found in your area, you can substitute a plant with similar properties. For example, if chard is not available, you might find beetroot leaves (silq, in Arabic) or spinach instead. This list is not meant to be exclusive, but rather a starting point for your journey to better health.

Let us take a closer look at each of these groups.

Bread and Cereals

For thousands of years, cereals have been the staple food

essential for human life. The type of grain used differed from one region to another according to the climate.

Grains, wheat and sprouts are mentioned many times in the Qur'an.

In most of these instances, Allah describes His gifts of food to humankind; grains are listed first, which probably emphasizes their importance over other food categories. Allah states in His Holy Book:

﴿وَأَنزَلْنَا مِنَ ٱلْمُعْصِرَٰتِ مَآءً ثَجَّاجًا ۝ لِّنُخْرِجَ بِهِۦ حَبًّا وَنَبَاتًا ۝ وَجَنَّٰتٍ أَلْفَافًا ۝﴾

(سورة النبأ:١٤-١٦)

{And have sent down from the rain-laden clouds abundant water, that We may produce therewith corn[27] and vegetation, and gardens of thick growth.} *(Qur'an 78: 14-16)*

﴿فَلْيَنظُرِ ٱلْإِنسَٰنُ إِلَىٰ طَعَامِهِۦٓ ۝ أَنَّا صَبَبْنَا ٱلْمَآءَ صَبًّا ۝ ثُمَّ شَقَقْنَا ٱلْأَرْضَ شَقًّا ۝ فَأَنۢبَتْنَا فِيهَا حَبًّا ۝ وَعِنَبًا وَقَضْبًا ۝ وَزَيْتُونًا وَنَخْلًا ۝ وَحَدَآئِقَ غُلْبًا ۝ وَفَٰكِهَةً وَأَبًّا ۝ مَّتَٰعًا لَّكُمْ وَلِأَنْعَٰمِكُمْ ۝﴾

(سورة عبس:٢٤-٣٢)

{Then let human beings look at their food, that We pour forth water in abundance, and We split the earth in clefts, and We cause therein the grain to grow, and grapes and clover plants [green fodder for the cattle], and olives and date-palms, and gardens, dense with many trees, and fruits and herbage [greens], [to be] a provision and benefit for you and your cattle.} *(Qur'an 80: 24-32)*

According to the USDA Food Guide Pyramid, the base of our food should consist mainly of bread, cereals and grains. The recommended servings provide vitamin B, fibre, iron, magnesium and zinc, in addition to a multitude of enzymes, antioxidants[28] and phy-

Serving Size of Grains /Breads
• 1 slice toast
• ¼ pita bread
• ½ cup cooked rice or pasta
• 1 cup cereal
• 1 small pancake or tortilla
• 5-6 low fat crackers
• 3 cups popped corn

tonutrients.[29] Whole grain bread and cereals, brown r ice and whole wheat pasta should be chosen over more processed forms of grain.

The whole grain consists of

1) an outer husk called the bran, which is rich in fibre, B vitamins and minerals;

2) a starchy filling called the endosperm, consisting mainly of carbohydrates and proteins; and

3) a nutritious inner seed called the germ, which is rich in vitamins E and B and other minerals, and contains some protein. The whole grain thus provides many needed nutrients. However, the refined forms — available in the market as white flour, white rice and pasta — have had the germ and the bran removed, and so are deprived of those beneficial nutrients.

The grains known in the Arabian Peninsula during the Prophet's life were mainly wheat and barley. The people at that time did not process the grains as we do today; the whole grains — including their bran and germ — were used, thus these good foods were fully nutritious and beneficial. In the Qur'an, Allah lists the grains with their husk among His many gifts to us:

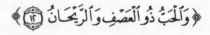

(سورة الرحمن:١٢)   ﴿ وَٱلْحَبُّ ذُو ٱلْعَصْفِ وَٱلرَّيْحَانُ ۝ ﴾

❲And also grain, with [its] husks, leaves and stalk for fodder, and sweet-scented plants.❳   *(Qur'an 55: 12)*

During Prophet Muhammad's time, flour was prepared by grinding the whole grains and people ate bread made from unrefined flour. "Sahl said he was asked: During the Prophet's lifetime did you have white flour? Sahl answered: No; then he was asked: Did you sift barley flour? He replied: No, but we used to blow on it (to remove the chaff)."[30]

Hundreds of years ago, societies in Asia began to remove the outer layer of the rice grain to produce polished white rice. This fateful intervention caused the spread of a disease called beriberi characterized by depression and weakness, poor coordination and nervous tingling in the arms and legs. It was not until the late nineteenth century that a surgeon in the Japanese navy discovered that the effects of beriberi could be reversed by the addition of whole grains to the diet.[31]

Nutritious benefits of grains
• Carbohydrates
• B vitamins
• Fibres
• Iron
• Magnesium
• Zinc

Whole grains are now known to be good sources of thiamine (vitamin B_1). In addition to this essential B vitamin, scientific studies have proved that whole grains are also rich in:[32]

➢ Antioxidants like vitamin E and selenium

➢ Other B vitamins

➢ Essential minerals such as iron, magnesium and zinc

➢ Lignan, a phytonutrient that blocks estrogen action, thus reducing the risk of breast, ovarian, colon, prostate and other cancers

> Lignin, an insoluble fibre which helps to prevent colon cancer
> Phytic acid, which binds to minerals preventing the formation of free radicals, thus reducing cancer risk

Barley شعير

Barley was once the main cereal in the Arabian Peninsula. Barley has a specifically low glycemic index, which means that it causes a slow rise in the blood sugar level after consumption; this in turn slows down the release of insulin, thus stabilizing blood levels of the hormone, controlling hunger, and reducing the risk of obesity and diabetes. In addition, barley grains are rich in chromium, a mineral that helps insulin in its role of controlling blood sugar level.

In comparison with other grains, barley is particularly rich in niacin (vitamin B_3); it is also a good source of vitamin B_6, folate, zinc, copper and iron. Barley germ is rich in essential fatty acids (linoleic and linolenic acids) which cannot be synthesized by the body. Among other functions, these acids perform a crucial role in the synthesis of hemoglobin, prostaglandin,[33] and cell walls, in addition to their role in energy production, cell division, and maintaining the proper function of heart muscle.

Bread made from barley flour was the preferred bread in the Prophet's house; he also liked barley porridge.[34]

"It was reported that Hassan ibn 'Ali, Ibn 'Abbâs and Ibn Jâ'far went to Umm Salamah and asked her to prepare for them a dish that the Prophet (ﷺ) had liked to eat. She replied: We do not crave it nowadays. They said: Yes, but we do; prepare it for us. So she ground some barley, put it in a pot, poured some oil over it and cooked it with some pepper and spices. She presented it to them and said: The Prophet (ﷺ) liked this and ate well from it."[35]

'Â'ishah, the wife of the Prophet (ﷺ) said: "When a member of the family of the Messenger of Allah (ﷺ) would fall sick, he (ﷺ) would order barley soup and the invalid would be urged to have some of it. The Prophet (ﷺ) used to say: It strengthens the heart of the sad person and relieves the heart of illness, just as one of you would wash dirt off her face with water."[36]

Barley soup is prepared by boiling one portion of whole barley grains in five portions of water over moderate heat until the water is reduced to two-fifths of its volume.

Recent studies have shown that barley grains are rich in fibre, in particular a soluble fibre (called Beta-glucan) which has the ability to bind fatty substances, bile acids and cholesterol in the gut, excreting them as waste, thus reducing blood cholesterol. Based on this discovery, since 2006, manufacturers of whole barley products (such as barley meal, flour, flakes, and grits) have been authorized by the Food and Drug Administration (FDA) to make the health claim that the grain reduces the risk of coronary heart disease. This soluble fibre also helps control the rise of blood sugar levels after meals — probably by making the stomach contents more viscous, thus prolonging the gastric emptying time, so that carbohydrates would be absorbed more slowly.

Another preparation made from barley is talbeenah.[37] 'Â'ishah said that when a relative of hers died, she would order that talbeenah be prepared. Then, thareed (a traditional Arabic dish made from meat and bread) would be made, and she would pour the talbeenah on it. 'Â'ishah would then ask the women to eat saying, "I heard the Messenger of Allah (ﷺ) saying: Talbeenah brings relief to the heart of the sick and takes away some of the anguish."[38]

Studies show that barley grains are rich in amino acids,[39] some of which are used by the body to synthesize neurotransmitters (chemical substances essential for the proper function of the brain and the nervous system, and which also contribute to mood elevation).[40]

'Â'ishah also reported that when the Messenger of Allah (ﷺ) was told that someone was in pain and would not approach any food, he would say: «Make him some talbeenah; by the One Whom my soul is in His Hands, it washes one's stomach just as one of you would wash the dirt off her face.»[41]

The high fibre content of barley grain acts as a laxative and a carminative (relieves flatulence) thus minimising stomach ache. It promotes regular bowel movements, prevents constipation and reduces the intestinal transit time.[42]

There are many forms of barley available in supermarkets and health food stores:[43]

➢ Whole grain barley (also called pot barley) is the most nutritious form, but it needs several hours of cooking, so it is better to toast it first, or soak it overnight.

➢ Polished barley, also known as pearl barley: it has lost most of the bran and germ and thus most of its vitamins, minerals and fibre contents.

➢ Barley flakes are made by flattening the grains to speed up the cooking process. These make delicious porridges with milk and sweetened with honey or date syrup.

➢ Barley flour is used to make bread, adding sweetness to the taste, but since barley is low in gluten content;[44] it is better mixed with wheat flour. Needless to say, whole barley flour is much more nutritious than the refined flour.

> Barley water is a drink made by boiling the grains in water, then flavouring it with honey, orange or lemon.

> Barley syrup or malt extract used as natural sweetener in many desserts.

Wheat قمح

Wheat is the most universally grown and most important food grain used today. It is available in a number of forms, of which the whole grain is the most nutritious, for the bran and germ with their fibre, mineral and vitamin content have been retained. Wheat grains are very high in gluten, which is the protein responsible for holding the gas bubbles when bread rises thus assisting the yeast fermentation process. This makes it the most suitable grain for the preparation of leavened bread. Wheat whole grain is very rich in enzymes, phytonutrients, vitamins, minerals, protein and fatty acids.

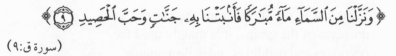

When Allah describes His many blessings to us, He specifies wheat grains:

﴿ وَنَزَّلْنَا مِنَ ٱلسَّمَآءِ مَآءً مُّبَٰرَكًا فَأَنۢبَتۡنَا بِهِۦ جَنَّٰتٖ وَحَبَّ ٱلۡحَصِيدِ ﴾ ٩

(سورة ق:٩)

❲And We send down blessed water [rain] from the sky, then We produce therewith gardens and grains[45] [every kind of harvest] that are reaped.❳   *(Qur'an 50: 9)*

Wheat grain — especially the bran — is very rich in fibre. The fibre found in wheat differs from that found in barley as it is mostly insoluble. Insoluble fibre has the ability to hold water in the intestines. This means it helps to add bulk and soften the stool, which promotes regular bowel movements and speeds transit time, which in turn reduces the contact between harmful waste products and the intestinal lining and limits the reabsorption of harmful substances. The promotion of regular bowel movements helps to prevent constipation and reduces the risk of haemorrhoids[46] and diverticulosis.[47]

The increased bulk of the stool dilutes the concentration of potential carcinogens, leading to a reduced risk of colon cancer; this benefit is increased by the fact that this fibre helps to control the intestinal pH balance (the level of acidity), reducing the ability of intestinal microbes to produce potential carcinogens.

Wheat comes in many forms:[48]

➤ Wheat flour is widely used in cakes and breads. It can be made from either the whole grain (whole meal flour) or from the polished, less nutritious form.

➤ Bulgar (or burghul) is formed of roasted or steamed cracked wheat grains. It needs no or very little cooking. It is widely used in traditional Mediterranean salads and Middle Eastern pilaffs, or mixed with meat to prepare Lebanese meatballs (kibbah).

➤ Semolina is produced from the starchy endosperm of the grains; it is mainly used for porridges and puddings and in the manufacture of pasta.

➤ Couscous is made of semolina coated with flour. It also requires very little cooking time and can accompany meat and vegetable stews (like the traditional Moroccan dish) or is eaten with sugar, nuts and cream (a popular Egyptian dessert).

➤ Pasta is another product of wheat flour that has been kneaded with water or eggs.

Other grains

Various grains are used as the staple food around the world. The difference is probably due to the climatic conditions which determine which cereal can be cultivated in a particular region.[49]

Rice

Rice is the second most important cereal in the human diet. There are many types of rice, and their nutritional value depends mainly on the degree of milling and refining:[50] We will mention a few of the most common varieties:

Brown rice: This is the least refined form, from which only the husk is removed leaving the bran attached to the grain, thus it is higher in fibre than white rice and retains its B vitamins and minerals. It needs a longer cooking time and more cooking water or stock.

Parboiled rice: Compared to white rice, this is more nutritious due to its higher content of B vitamins which diffuses into the grains when subjected to steam before milling.

Basmati rice: This is long-grain aromatic rice with a distinctive flavour. It has a lower glycemic index compared to ordinary white rice; that means it causes a slower rise in the blood sugar level and thus a slower insulin surge.

Wild rice: It looks like rice, but it is not actually rice; though it is still a member of the grass family. It is higher in protein, vitamin B$_2$ and zinc than ordinary brown rice and it is lower in carbohydrate content. It has a special nutty flavour which goes well in salads, soups and stir-fries.

Corn

Corn is a rich source of carbohydrates, fibre and minerals such as potassium, magnesium and phosphorus. Although corn grains are a rich source of the B vitamin niacin (B$_3$), it is present in a form that is not readily available for absorption.[51]

➤ Sweet corn can be eaten boiled, roasted or grilled; it is also a nutritious addition to salads, Sbreakfast — especially when eaten with fresh milk.

➤ Popcorn is also a nutritious snack for kids — and adults — but avoid adding too much salt and butter.

➤ Cornmeal is used to make corn muffins, cakes and breads.

➤ Corn is also an important source of cholesterol-free cooking oil.

Oats

Oats with the hull removed are called groats. Groats are used for the preparation of variety of products: rolled oats, oat flour and oat bran (which is one of the richest sources of soluble fibre). Oatmeal is finely milled oats steamed before they are ground; it supplies a considerable amount of vitamin E, essential fatty acids and iron, though it is best mixed with a vitamin C-rich food to enhance iron absorption. Oats are excellent as sweet or salty porridges, and constitute a very healthy addition to soups and stews.[52] Oats are well known for their cholesterol-lowering effect, and they are a suitable carbohydrate source for diabetics due to their low glycemic index.

Rye

Rye is lower in gluten than wheat, so it is less allergenic, and must be mixed with wheat for baking leavened bread. Rye is rich in B vitamins and minerals such as magnesium, copper, zinc and iron; it is also a good source of fibre. Rye also contains *rutin*[53], a phytonutrient that helps relieve circulatory problems. Pumpernickel bread is a very popular rye bread prepared from the whole grains.

Millet

Millet is a rich source of iron and B vitamins. It is also less allergenic than wheat due to its low gluten content. It is well tolerated by sensitive digestive systems and has the advantage of being easy and quick to cook.[54] It can be cooked like ordinary rice, added to soups and stews, or used to prepare puddings.

Quinoa

One of the best sources of protein in the plant kingdom, quinoa is a very good choice for vegetarians.[55] It cooks faster than other grains. It is also low in gluten and rich in vitamins B and E, in addition to calcium, phosphorus and iron.

Buckwheat

Buckwheat is not a true cereal, but a seed of an herbaceous plant[56]. It is rich in B vitamins, iron and other minerals, fibre and rutin. Buckwheat seeds are better roasted before cooking. Porridge made from buckwheat (known as kasha) is very popular in Russia. The crushed grain can also be added to soups and casseroles.[57]

Sprouting

﴿مَّثَلُ ٱلَّذِينَ يُنفِقُونَ أَمْوَٰلَهُمْ فِى سَبِيلِ ٱللَّهِ كَمَثَلِ حَبَّةٍ أَنۢبَتَتْ سَبْعَ سَنَابِلَ فِى كُلِّ سُنۢبُلَةٍ مِّائَةُ حَبَّةٍ وَٱللَّهُ يُضَٰعِفُ لِمَن يَشَآءُ وَٱللَّهُ وَٰسِعٌ عَلِيمٌ ۝﴾

(سورة البقرة:٢٦١)

﴿The likeness of those who spend their wealth in the Way of Allah is as the likeness of a grain [of corn]; it grows seven ears, and each ear has a hundred grains. Allah gives manifold increase to whom He pleases. And Allah is All-Sufficient for His creatures' needs, All-Knower.﴾   *(Qur'an 2: 261)*

Seeds, beans and grains are sometimes referred to as 'live food' as they carry the plant embryo ready to germinate when subjected to the proper conditions, producing healthy, nutritious sprouts. Some wheat grains were found in the tombs of ancient Egyptian pharaohs, and they were still able to germinate after being dormant for more than five thousand years. Sprouts constitute a beneficial, natural, compact source of concentrated nutrition that is easily digested and readily assimilated by the body.

Sprouting seeds produce a wide and abundant array of concentrated vitamins (like pro-vitamin A, vitamin B-complex, vitamins C and E), and minerals like calcium, iron, magnesium, potassium, selenium and zinc. Sprouts also contain chlorophyll; enzymes[58] and antioxidants.[59] Sprouts can help a body that is consistently exposed to toxic chemicals and is immune suppressed.[60]

The consumption of sprouted cereals has been a part of the traditional diet of many cultures for centuries, and it is becoming popular in various parts of the world. Sprouting grains causes increased activities of *hydrolytic* [61] enzymes, breaking down starches into simpler sugars, proteins into amino acids and fats into fatty acids; thus improving their digestibility. There is also an improvement in the contents of certain essential amino acids, total sugars, and B-group vitamins — some sprouts have even been found to contain the B_{12} vitamin, otherwise only available from animal food sources. [62]

Do it yourself fresh sprouts [63]

By the time sprouts make it to the supermarket shelves, they are often old and wilted, no longer fresh. Sprouts are easily grown at home. You can try growing your own sprouts with any available grains.

1. Choose seeds or beans, such as wheat, barley, rye, oats, lentils, fava beans, fenugreek, sesame seeds, chickpeas or mung beans. Make sure first that you use whole grains, still carrying the germ part which contains the growing embryo.

2. Put the grains or seeds in a jar and soak in some water overnight.

3. In the morning, pour off the water (if your grains are dry, this means they still need more soaking water).

4. Rinse and drain your grains, then cover the jar with muslin. Each morning rinse the grains with more fresh water and drain well by leaving the jar tilted in a dish rack; if water is left inside, the grains may rot.

5. Your sprouts will be ready in about 3 to 7 days. You can toss them into salads or add them to stir-fries. The sprouts can be stored in plastic or glass containers in the fridge for 5 to 10 days.

Wheat and barley grass

Wheatgrass and barley grass are very rich in *chlorophyll*.[64] Research shows that chlorophyll plays an important role in the prevention of certain cancers, probably by inhibiting the ability of certain DNA-damaging chemicals to cause cell mutations (cellular genetic changes).[65] Wheat and barley grass are highly alkaline, and thus are ideal in counteracting an unhealthy acidic modern diet. The acid/alkaline balance of the body is critical for your energy level. To maintain good health it is important to store an alkaline reserve in your system; any excess acid wastes[66] are deposited in body tissues, stressing and intoxicating different organs.[67] Wheat and barley grass contain beta-carotenes, vitamins B (including B_{12}), C, E and K and, they also contain iron and potassium. They provide most of the known amino acids including the eight essential ones.[68] These grasses help detoxify the liver, repair tissue, improve blood sugar levels, strengthen immunity, boost vitality and clean the lymphatic system. They also restore stamina and improve skin texture.[69]

Wheat and barley grass are easy to grow at home, just like their sprouts. In only seven days, they will be ready and can be cut and juiced using a blender, juicer or food processor into a deep green, highly nutritious juice. To be effective, the juice has to be drunk immediately after juicing.

Vegetables

According to the food guide pyramid, we need to eat at least three to five servings of vegetables per day; these supply loads of vitamins, minerals, phytonutrients and fibre: in particular, vitamin C, folate (a B vitamin), beta-carotenes, magnesium and iron.

Nutritious Benefits
• Carotenes (vitamin A precursors)
• Vitamin C
• Folate
• Iron and Magnesium
• Fibres
• Phytonutrients

The best way to ensure the intake of a variety of vitamins is to eat different colours of vegetables. Allah says:

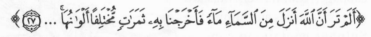

﴿أَلَمْ تَرَ أَنَّ ٱللَّهَ أَنزَلَ مِنَ ٱلسَّمَآءِ مَآءً فَأَخْرَجْنَا بِهِۦ ثَمَرَٰتٍ مُّخْتَلِفًا أَلْوَٰنُهَا ...﴾ ٢٧

(سورة فاطر:٢٧)

﴾Do you not see that Allah sends down water [rain] from the sky, and We produce therewith fruits[70] of varying colours...﴿

(Qur'an 35: 27)

Allah created vegetables in beautiful colours, and each colour represents certain group of vitamins, minerals or phytonutrients. For example, dark green leafy vegetables like spinach, beetroot leaves, and chard are good sources of folate, vitamin C and iron. They also contain particularly large amounts of chlorophyll, a detoxifier[71] and possibly an anticancer agent.[72]

Orange and yellow vegetables, like carrots, pumpkins, and sweet potatoes, are rich in beta-carotene which is an antioxidant, anti-cancerous and a precursor of vitamin A in the body. Red vegetables like tomatoes supply *lycopene,* a powerful antioxidant believed to have anti-cancerous action. The *anthocyanidins* are complex flavonoids that produce blue, purple or red colours. They can be found in beets, blackberries, blueberries, cherries, purple and red grapes, and purple cabbage. Anthocyanidins are essential for healthy connective tissue, are powerful antioxidants, possess a potential cancer-fighting ability and a significant anti-inflammatory effect. They also reduce blood cholesterol and strengthen and protect blood capillaries.[73]

Sulphur compounds are also present in a variety of colourful food including garlic, onion, pineapple and the crucifer family (which includes broccoli, Brussels sprouts, cabbage, cauliflower, mustard greens, radishes and turnips). Sulphur-containing compounds in plants are well known for their detoxification and cancer-protective actions.[74]

Few vegetables were common in the Arabian peninsula at the time of the Prophet (ﷺ), and this is obviously due to the desert nature of the land. Still, valuable vegetables and herbs used in the Prophet's time were mentioned by Ibn al-Qayyim and Adh-Dhahabi in their books on the 'Medicine of the Prophet (ﷺ)'.

Cucumber

Cucumbers are very healthy vegetables; they belong to the same family as pumpkin, zucchini, watermelon and other types of squash.

Prophet Muhammad (ﷺ) combined cucumbers with ripe dates saying: "The heat of the latter is reduced by the coolness of the former."[75]

About 95% of the cucumber 's weight is water, which makes it a natural hydrating agent for healthy skin. Cucumbers also contain ascorbic acid (vitamin C) and caffeic acid, both of which help soothe skin irritation and reduce water retention; that is why cucumbers are common ingredients of facial masks and are often used as eye pads to reduce under-eye darkening and swelling; they are also helpful topically on sunburn and dermatitis.

The cucumber's green skin is rich in fibre and contains a variety of beneficial minerals, including silica, potassium, magnesium and molybdenum. Silica is an essential component of healthy connective tissue found in muscles, tendons, ligaments, cartilage, and bone. That is why cucumber juice is often recommended to improve the complexion and health of the skin. The presence of potassium and magnesium, in addition to the high fibre content of cucumbers, makes them a perfect snack for hypertensive people. Cucumbers also contain powerful antioxidant bioflavonoids believed to possess an anticancerous action; these phytonutrients act in synergy with the vitamin C content of the cucumbers.[76]

Cucumbers are either eaten fresh in green salads and yogurt dishes, pickled or added to soups.

Carrots

Carrots were also among the available vegetables at the time of the Prophet (ﷺ), and he was reported to have liked them. He is

said to have eaten them with parsley as part of a light, healthy
dinner followed by a cup of
buttermilk to help digestion.[77]

Carrots are rich in *carotenes*
(antioxidant pigments among which are the beta-carotene s),
which are used by the body to synthesize vitamin A, the essential vitamin for protection against night blindness and cataract.
Their high beta carotene content makes them a good detoxifier
and antioxidant food.[78] They are great immune boosters[79] due to
their high content of phytonutrients including lycopene, which
also provides good protection against prostate cancer.[80] Carrots
are very rich in fibre, which makes them excellent bowel regulators[81] and their high content of both fibre and potassium makes
them heart-healthy vegetables and a valuable aid in cholesterol
reduction. Carrot juice is a known diuretic and is used as a treatment for hyperacidity and heartburn.[82]

Carrots can be stored unwashed in the refrigerator; they keep
well provided they do not come in close contact with ethylene-
producing fruits like apples, pears and bananas.[83] Carrots are an
excellent addition to salads; they are also very nutritious when cut
in thin strips, then stir-fried in olive oil. The heat of cooking breaks
down the tough cell walls of the fibre, causing the easier release
and assimilation of the carotene and other phytonutrient content.

Capers

Capers are small green flower buds or fruits said to be native
to the Mediterranean countries. They are usually pickled in vinegar or brine solution and used as stomachic or condiment.[84] Capers are closely related to the cabbage family, especially its spicy

herbs like cress, black and white mustard, wasabi and horserad-ish. All of these contain mustard oil glycosides, thus they all share the sharp, slightly pungent flavour similar to that of mustard and black pepper.[85]

Among the caper's flavonoids, the antioxidant bioflavonoid rutin is the most important — its white crystals can be seen on the surface of the pickled capers.[86]

Adh-Dhahabi noted the beneficial effects of capers for the function of the spleen; he also noted an interesting saying of olden times: "Heaven laughed and it produced truffles, and the earth laughed and produced capers."[87]

Capers are known to reduce flatulence and rheumatic discomfort. In *ayurvedeic* medicine (traditional therapy from India) capers are recommended for improving liver function. Capers have reported uses for *arteriosclerosis* and as a diuretic, kidney disinfectant, vermifuge (expelling intestinal worms) and a tonic (restoring vigour).

In the kitchen, capers are widely used in Italian and Mediterranean dishes such as pasta sauces, pizza, fish, meat dishes and raw and cooked salads.

Truffles and mushrooms

Prophet Muhammad (ﷺ) said: «The truffle is among the *Mann* (Allah's favours) and its water cures the eye.»[88]

It was said that among the Manna sent down by Allah to the Children of Israel were several plants that grow in the wild without effort. Some scholars consider truffles to be a kind of Manna, although the word Manna in the Qur'an refers to the sweet dew that descended from the trees.[89] The hadith already mentioned is relevant here, too: "Heaven laughed and it produced truffles, and the earth laughed and produced capers."

Truffles grow wild underground, and the Arabic name *kama'ah* indicates this meaning. They are a type of fungi sometimes regarded as a mushroom. Truffles have a strong flavour and fragrance; they possess an unappealing irregular and somewhat round shape, with a thick, rough, wrinkled skin that varies in colour from very dark grey to off-white.

Truffles have been admired by gourmets for centuries and were credited by the ancient Greeks and Romans with both therapeutic and aphrodisiac powers, although these powers have not been scientifically proven. Ancient Egyptian hieroglyphics reveal that mushrooms were thought to bring immortality and valued them as both food and medicine. Many studies suggest that some types of mushrooms or their extracts have strong anticancer potential, boost immunity and reduce the risk of coronary heart disease.[90]

Researchers are still investigating this issue, especially since there is a large number of various mushroom species available in nature.

Edible mushrooms in general have a high protein content; they can be an important dietary source of essential amino acid s for vegetarians. Mushroom protein is of intermediate quality between meat and vegetable proteins. Mushrooms are also an excellent source of fibre, vitamins, and some minerals like selenium. Mushrooms are low in fat, and like vegetables, they are cholesterol-free. Their low energy value and low fat content enable them to be used in low-calorie diets. The body of a mushroom is an excellent source of B-complex vitamins including B_{12}. Mushrooms are unique in that they contain Vitamin B_{12}, something that vegetables cannot usually produce at all. This is an added benefit to vegetarians.

Truffles and mushrooms can be stored well packaged in a cool, damp place for up to one week. They do not freeze well.[91] They can be eaten either raw or cooked although personally, I do not recommend eating them raw: some studies associate eating raw mushrooms with digestive discomforts and other health concerns, though the evidence is not very conclusive.[92]

Lemon grass

Lemon grass is a long, thick grass with a solid white root end and green slender leaves at the top. It has a fresh, citrus-like aroma and flavour with a hint of ginger taste.

Lemon grass has diuretic, tonic and stimulant effects. It is good for digestion, and its preparation with pepper has been traditionally used for the treatment of menstrual pain and nausea. Its infusion is used in cases of fever to induce perspiration.[93] The essential oil of lemon grass is widely used as a mild insect repellent (citronella),[94] in soap manufacture and in cosmetics to clean oily skin, and in aromatherapy as a mild relaxant.

In a well-known hadith, "...it was narrated that the Prophet (ﷺ) said (about Makkah when the Muslims were about to enter the city after they had reclaimed it in battle against the pagans): 'Do not cut its plants', to which 'Abbâs pleaded, 'Except for the lemon grass (الإذخر) O Messenger of Allah, for the people of Makkah use it and they also use it in their houses'. So the Prophet (ﷺ) said: 'Except for the lemongrass'."⁹⁵

Ibn al-Qayyim reported that lemon grass dilates the veins or arteries; he said that it increases urine and menstruation flow, calms nausea and dissolves stones and hard tumours of the stomach, liver and kidneys.⁹⁶

Lemongrass is a common ingredient in Indian and Chinese recipes. It is a pleasant addition to meat, poultry, seafood, vegetable dishes and curries, and its stems are used to add flavour to different teas and pickles.⁹⁷

Chard

Chard is a dark green, leafy vegetable with white, yellow or red leaf stalks. It is closely related in its flavour, nutritional values and cooking methods to other leafy plants such as spinach, kale, collards, beetroot leaves and mustard greens.

«It was reported that Prophet Muhammad (ﷺ) and 'Ali (ﵠ) went to Umm Mundhir one day while 'Ali was still in convalescence. She had some hanging clusters of dates, so the Messenger of Allah (ﷺ) started eating from them and 'Ali joined him. Prophet Muhammad (ﷺ) then told 'Ali: Stop, 'Ali! You are still recuperating. 'Ali stopped eating, and Umm Munthir prepared some barley with chard and brought it to them. The Prophet (ﷺ) said: O 'Ali, eat from this; it is more beneficial for you.»⁹⁸

Chard contains huge amounts of minerals and vitamins, especially beta-carotene s, calcium, phosphorus, iron and potassium. It is naturally high in sodium and also contains vitamin C and the B-complex vitamins thiamine, riboflavin and niacin. Chard and dark leafy greens in general, are major sources of folic acid, a B vitamin that regulates protein metabolism and offers great protection against atherosclerosis and coronary heart disease. In addition, chard has high levels of protein, chlorophyll and fibres.

In your supermarket, you can find chard either in the form of young tender leaves which can be cooked as such; or you will find it as larger mature leaves with tough stems that are better removed before cooking. Chard and most green leaves are quickly perishable and should be stored in the refrigerator for a minimum period of time.[99]

Young, tender chard leaves can be eaten raw, adding a slightly pungent, mustard -like flavour to salads and sandwiches; in this form they are an excellent source of C and B vitamins — especially the folates, which are easily destroyed by heat. Chard can also be used to replace spinach in any recipe,[100] the mineral, phytonutrient and fibre contents are more readily available in the cooked form, and the addition of lemon or lime juice will convert the iron in these vegetables into a form that is better absorbed by the body.

Garlic

The medicinal benefits of garlic have been well known since ancient times. Garlic has antifungal, antiviral properties, and is highly effective against *salmonella* (the bacteria that causes food poisoning). There is also evidence that diets rich in garlic lead to lower rates of cancer development. Garlic is also rich in minerals, including potassium, zinc, iron and selenium.[101]

Eating garlic reduces blood pressure and blood cholesterol due to the active phytonutrient *allicin*; it also reduces the formation of blood clots due to its content of *ajone,* another volatile phytonutrient.[102] These healthful effects are only activated upon crushing or cutting the garlic cloves, as this releases the enzyme *allinase,* which converts compounds in the garlic into the beneficial active nutrients.

Due to its distinctive smell which is sometimes offensive to others, "The Prophet (ﷺ) forbade eating garlic unless it was cooked," as reported by 'Ali ibn Abi Ṭâlib.[103] This is an indication that — contrary to what is commonly believed — cooking garlic does not reduce its valuable benefits.

The Prophet (ﷺ) himself did not eat garlic at all. "Abu Ayyoob Ansâri narrated that food was being presented to the Prophet (ﷺ) while he was staying at his house and he used to eat and send some to him. One day, the Prophet sent him some food from which he did not eat as it contained garlic. Abu Ayyoob asked the Prophet: Is it harâm ? The Prophet (ﷺ) replied: No, but I dislike it because of its smell. So Abu Ayyoob said: I dislike what you dislike!"[104]

"Anas (ﷺ) was asked about garlic; he stated that the Messenger of Allah (ﷺ) had said: He who eats of this plant should neither approach us nor pray along with us."[105] So, when you plan to eat garlic, try not to do so when the time for the prayer is approaching — and cook it thoroughly first to reduce the strong odour. It may be useful to chew some fresh parsley or mint or some anise seeds and honey afterwards to reduce the smell of garlic.

Onions

The onion family includes chives, shallots and leeks. Like garlic, their medicinal properties have been recognized for thousands of years. Traditionally, onions were used to treat coughs and bronchitis and as general tonics:[106] the ancient pharaohs used to feed onions to the workers who were building the pyramids to give them strength.

Studies show a strong antioxidant action with onion due to its content of the phytonutrient *quercetin*. This aids in clearing the body of harmful free radicals which can contribute to heart disease, atherosclerosis and cancer[107]. In addition, onion is a strong antimicrobial agent; it also reduces blood sugar levels, an additional benefit for diabetics.

Like garlic, onions also have an offensive odour: As a sign of respect to Allah's houses, the Prophet (ﷺ) forbade anyone who had just eaten onions or leeks from entering the mosque, explaining that the angels are offended by anything that offends humans: "Whoever eats from this offensive plant let him stay away from our mosque, for the angels are harmed by the same things that harm people."[108] So, as with garlic, we are advised to cook onions thoroughly, and not to approach the mosques with 'onion breath'. The Prophet (ﷺ) advised us to "cook it thoroughly" for it to lose its strong odour.[109]

Squashes and pumpkins

This group of vegetables belongs to the genus Curcurbita,

which includes soft-skinned vegetables such as courgettes, marrows and cucumbers as well as hard-skinned vegetables like pumpkins and squashes.[110]

The pumpkin (or a similar vegetable) is also mentioned in the Qur'an, in the story of Prophet Yoonus (Jonah):

(سورة الصافات:١٤٦)   ﴿ وَأَنۢبَتۡنَا عَلَيۡهِ شَجَرَةٗ مِّن يَقۡطِينٖ ۝ ﴾

❨And We caused a plant of gourd to grow over him.❩

(Qur'an 37: 146)

Prophet Muhammad (ﷺ) was thought to have loved squash; he was reported to have once asked his wife, 'Â'ishah: "O 'Â'ishah! If you prepare a casserole, increase the squash in it, as it strengthens the grieving heart."[111]

«Anas ibn Mâlik said: The Prophet loved gourd. A tailor once invited the Prophet over some food he had made. Anas went with the Prophet and the tailor brought him some bread made from barley and some soup with gourd and dried meat in it. Anas said: I saw the Messenger of Allah follow the traces of the gourd all around the edge of the pot (with a piece of bread), which made me love gourd ever since.»[112]

It is not exactly known which type of squash was meant by the Prophet's advice, but we know that nearly all the vegetables in this group contain beta- and alpha-carotenes, and vitamins E and C, in addition to potassium and fibre. Due to their high antioxidant content, pumpkins, gourds and squashes are beneficial in heart disease, as they reduce the damage to the artery wall caused by free radicals. In addition, pumpkin is believed to strengthen the immune system and protect against cancer, cataract and the common cold.[113]

The hard-skinned gourds can be cooked by boiling or baking, and can be added to casseroles and roasts. Pumpkins can also be made into delicious desserts like pumpkin pie, or puddings with sugar and milk. Courgettes and marrows can be cooked whole, or cut and stir-fried, steamed, or added to stews. Stuffed zucchini (courgettes) is a Middle Eastern favourite.

Pumpkin seeds

Seeds in general are good sources of protein, unsaturated fats, minerals and vitamins. They actually belong with the protein group of the food guide pyramid. Pumpkin seeds are rich in zinc, selenium and iron. Both zinc and selenium are crucial for the health of the prostate gland and for male fertility. Iron, as is well known, is a vital part of your blood in the haemoglobin molecule.[114]

The seeds are also good source of essential *omega-3* fatty acids, which reduce the risk of blood clotting, reduce cholesterol and improve the health of the cardiovascular system. In addition, the seeds supply essential *omega-6* fatty acids, which are used by the body to synthesize prostaglandins. Pumpkin seeds are beneficial for a healthy skin, giving it softness and alleviating inflammatory conditions such as psoriasis.[115]

The seeds should be dried well and stored in air-tight dark glass containers, away from heat and direct sunlight to prevent the oil from becoming rancid and thus losing its beneficial actions.

They make a healthy snack, and can be added to salads, cereals, stir-fries or even cakes and breads. However, be aware that their benefits are much reduced when roasted or heated.

Herbs

Ginger زنجبيل

Ginger root has been used as medicinal herb in Asia for thousands of years. Ginger is mentioned in the Qur'an as a drink for the pious ones in paradise:

(سورة الإنسان: ١٧)   ﴿وَيُسْقَوْنَ فِيهَا كَأْسًا كَانَ مِزَاجُهَا زَنجَبِيلًا ۝﴾

《And there they will be given to drink a cup [of wine] mixed with Zanjabeel [ginger].》   *(Qur'an 76: 17)*

It was reported that the king of Rome sent a jar of ginger as a present to the Prophet Muhammad (ﷺ) who fed every one of his Companions a piece.[116]

In his book, *The Medicine of the Prophet*, Ibn al-Qayyim introduced ginger as a very useful digestive agent, *antiflatulent* (prevents or relieves intestinal gas), *expectorant* and *mucolytic* (loosening and expelling excess mucus); he also noted that it was said to be good for the eyesight and the liver and even as an aphrodisiac.[117]

Today, fresh ginger root is used as expectorant and an antiseptic for throat infections, and as a respiratory and circulatory stimulant. Ginger has proved an efficient treatment for nausea, motion sickness and severe morning sickness during pregnancy[118]. Ginger is believed to warm the body especially in cases of the common cold.[119] It also acts as a general cleansing, detoxifying agent and immune system stimulant. When consumed with food, ginger powder helps digestion by enhancing the activities of different digestive enzymes. In addition, it brings about a pronounced stimulation of bile flow, thus activating liver function and helping to digest fat.[120]

Ginger contains many active principles; only some of them are known to us, while many more are still under study. Scientific experiments have revealed about fifty antioxidant compounds in ginger root, the most powerful of which is *gingerole*.[121] Gingerole was found to interrupt a pathway responsible for the activation of a factor involved in many disorders, like cancer, atherosclerosis, heart attack, diabetes, allergy, asthma, arthritis, multiple sclerosis, Alzheimer's disease, osteoporosis, psoriasis, and even AIDS.[122]

Moreover, certain constituents of ginger were found to possess powerful analgesic and anti-inflammatory properties that help against rheumatoid arthritis by interfering with the synthesis of prostaglandins.[123] The mechanism of their action resembles that of aspirin and other non-steroidal anti-inflammatory (NSAI) drugs. In comparisons between these elements and NSAIs, the components naturally present in ginger were found to be even more effective in preventing blood clotting, and this of course without the unpleasant stomach irritation and other side effects of the NSAI drugs.[124] Gingerole — the most studied active constituent of ginger root — was found to be also effective against *Helicobacter pylori* bacteria, the primary cause of dyspepsia, peptic ulcer disease and the development of gastric and colon cancer.[125]

Some ginger preparations are common as home remedies, such as its infusion with cinnamon and honey used to treat cold chills and menstrual cramps. Ginger infusion with milk and honey is a very effective respiratory stimulant and expectorant in bronchitis and chest infection. It is also useful with honey in cases of flatulence, nausea, abdominal disorders, as an appetite stimulant and as a general intestinal tonic and cleanser.

As a spice, ginger is the main ingredient in Chinese dishes and many Indian dishes. It can also be added to stews and sauces. Powdered ginger is a wonderful spice in gingerbreads, cakes and cookies.

Basil ريحان

Basil is mentioned in the Qur'an as a gift for humankind:

(سورة الرحمن: ١٢)   ﴿ وَٱلْحَبُّ ذُو ٱلْعَصْفِ وَٱلرَّيْحَانُ ۝ ﴾

﴾Also grain, with [its] leaves and stalk for fodder and sweet-smelling plants.﴿[126]   *(Qur'an 55: 12)*

Basil was also recommended by the Prophet (ﷺ) in his hadith:

«Whoever is offered basil let him not refuse it, as it is from heaven.»[127]

Basil has long been considered as an important tonic. It is believed to have antidepressant, antiseptic, carminative and expectorant actions. Studies show that it reduces blood sugar levels and lowers blood pressure. Fresh basil leaves reduce itching and inflammation when rubbed on insect bites,[128] and as an infusion it boosts the immune system and has strong antioxidative effects. The phenolic compounds of the plant — especially an acid known as rosmarinic acid — are assumed to be responsible for its antioxidative power;[129] this acid showed a *synergistic*[130] action when combined with vitamin E (which is found mainly in vegetable oils, seeds and nuts). Furthermore, recent studies have shown a detoxification power associated with basil leaves; while basil essential oil has been found to exhibit an antimicrobial activity against a wide range of bacteria, fungi, yeast, and mould.

In a hadith of the Prophet (ﷺ), he recommended basil for its sweet smell, for he said: «Whoever is offered basil let him not refuse it, as it is light to carry and nice to smell.»[131] A recent study performed on humans inhaling the fragrance of the essential oil of basil found that its smell produced a favourable impression, especially when mental work was undertaken.[132]

Basil is widely used in Italian dishes; it is wonderful in pasta sauces and salad dressings.

Marjoram مردقوش

Marjoram was mentioned in Ibn al-Qayyim's *Medicine of the Prophet*, where he noted its use as an inhalation in cases of colds, phlegm and headaches. Its infusion has been used as a home remedy for colds, headaches, cough and irritability.[133] Recent studies proved an antioxidative and protective activity of marjoram against the DNA damage induced by oxidative stress.[134] Experiments have also demonstrated the strong antimicrobial power of the essential oil of the herb against numerous types of bacteria, fungi, yeast and even some viruses.[135]

Marjoram, like oregano, is widely used in Mediterranean cooking, especially in salad dressing, sauces and marinades for meat and poultry dishes. It is a wonderful addition to pizza and roast beef.

Thyme زعتر

Thyme was widely used in the time of the Prophet (ﷺ), probably due to its availability in the unique ecological conditions of the desert. Its infusion was a popular drink with carminative, digestive and diuretic actions, and it was also believed to have an aphrodisiac effect.[136]

Studies show the powerful antimicrobial activity of thyme against Salmonella and E. coli strains of bacteria that cause food poisoning; this activity has been attributed to the phenolic content of the herb. Thyme infusion is useful in treating chest and throat infections, indigestion and irritable bowel syndrome. The herb also has reported antiseptic, expectorant and antispasmodic actions. It has shown an antibacterial effect against Helicobacter pylori, the bacteria that cause gastric ulcers.[137]

In aromatherapy, thyme oil is used for its stimulating and uplifting nature. The volatile oil of thyme, along with lavender oil, when dissolved in almond or sunflower oil, can be used locally in massages for rheumatic pains as a *rubefacient* (that is, it increases blood flow to the desired area).[138] At the time of the Prophet (ﷺ) it was the practice to burn incense in the home with frankincense and thyme.[139]

Finally, as a common herb in the kitchen, thyme constitutes a delicious addition to poultry, fish, pasta dishes and pizza.

Rosemary حصالبان

Rosemary was used in ancient times as a symbol for good memory faculties. In folk medicine, it is used as a tonic, general stimulant and to induce vitality.[140] Adh-Dhahabi noted a hadith in which 'Ali (ﷺ) reported that a man complained to him of forgetfulness, he said: «Resort to rosemary, it encourages the heart and treats forgetfulness.» The same advice was also given by Ibn 'Abbâs and Anas on other occasions.

Scientifically speaking, rosemary has good digestive, carminative and diuretic properties; in addition to its tonic effects on the heart, circulatory and nervous systems, it also promotes sweating and bile flow.[141] Recent studies have demonstrated that the herb has significant antioxidative effects and stimulates the immune system.[142] In aromatherapy, the essential oil of rosemary has been proven to uplift the mood and to enhance cognitive functions — including memory performance.[143] Rosemary infusions have long been used to treat colds, influenza, rheumatism, and indigestion, and as a general stimulant. They can also be used as hair rinse for dandruff control.[144]

In your kitchen, rosemary is an aromatic addition to fish, lamb and poultry dishes; it also gives a great aroma to stir-fries and vegetable stews.

Eucalyptus كافور

Eucalyptus has traditionally been used as an inhalation or as a topical rub for colds and bronchitis. According to one interpretation, the 'camphor' mentioned in the Qur'an as drink for the righteous in paradise is eucalyptus:

$$ ﴿إِنَّ ٱلۡأَبۡرَارَ يَشۡرَبُونَ مِن كَأۡسٍ كَانَ مِزَاجُهَا كَافُورًا ۝﴾ $$

(سورة الإنسان: ٥)

﴿As to the Righteous, they shall drink of a Cup [of Wine] mixed with Kâfoor [eucalyptus].﴾   *(Qur'an 76: 5)*

Eucalyptus inhalations have stimulant, antiseptic, antispasmodic and expectorant actions. The oil or fresh leaves are used in hot water for steam inhalation to treat chest infections, and when dissolved in almond oil, it can be used in chest rubs for easing pulmonary disorders. It can also be used for massage in rheumatism and arthritis.[145] Its infusion, especially with added lemon and honey, is a very effective gargle for sore throat.[146]

Aloe vera الصبر

Ancient Egyptians called Aloe vera the plant of immortality. According to both Ibn al-Qayyim and Adh-Dhahabi, at the time of the Prophet (ﷺ) Aloe vera and cress were known as 'the two bitters' and were used for their healing properties. Bitter herbs (known as bitters) are generally used in the treatment of liver mal-functions. They stimulate bile flow and help the body to get rid of excess cholesterol and oestrogens.[147]

Ibn al-Qayyim recommended the use of two spoons of Aloe vera mixed with water to relieve the body from bilious mixtures and accumulated phlegm.[148] Aloe vera relaxes the bowels and treats *hyperacidity* (excess acid). It is also a powerful laxative, a stomach tonic and efficient at healing ulcers. It promotes bile flow, reduces blood sugar and cholesterol levels. Research suggests that it might be active against breast and liver cancers and HIV infections. This suggestion came from studies done on a compound in Aloe called *acemannan.* Acemannan is currently used in the treatment of feline leukaemia which, according to some opinions, is resultant from a viral infection related to HIV.[149]

John Gray, in his book *Mars and Venus Diet and Exercise Solutions,* recommended the use of Aloe Vera juice daily to reduce internal tissue oedema[150] and strengthen the immune system.[151] Studies show that regular consumption helps to maintain a normal, healthy stomach lining and good digestion. Research also shows that it works as a general body tonic, immune booster, anti-viral and antiseptic. It helps tissue regeneration and stimulates healthy cell growth; this may explain why there is reduced scarring and sometimes no scar left after a wound or burn is treated with its gel. The juice, according to Dr. Gray, detoxifies the bowels, relieves stomach acidity, treats chronic constipation and heals ulcers. It also regulates blood sugar levels, reduces tissue inflammation and swelling, rids the body of toxins and reduces overgrowth of Candida yeast in the gut, restoring the normal bowel flora. Make sure the gel you are getting is cold pressed, and has undergone minimum processing. Alternatively, you can easily grow your own plant in a sunny balcony and directly squeeze the leaves for their juice.[152]

Watercress الحُرف أو الثُفَاء

Water and garden cress belong to the family Brassicaceae (the cabbage family). It has a spicy, peppery fragrance and a refreshing, slightly pungent flavour. Adh-Dhahabi reported that it has the same effects as mustard.

Like many other members of the cabbage family (black and white mustard, horseradish, wasabi, rocket), all cresses contain nutrients that are volatile and easily lost by heat and broken down by moisture; so cress leaves should be used fresh, as the phytonutrients in these leaves cannot withstand any method of cooking or drying.[153] Eating watercress regularly will increase your antioxidant potential.

Cress leaves, like rocket, can be used for sandwich spreads (as with butter, cream cheese, pesto, olive spreads or crème fresh) and salads. Cress leaves can also be added to cooked recipes, like vegetable soups and casseroles, pasta sauces or scrambled eggs,[154] and they can also be added to stir-fried vegetables at the end of the cooking process to maintain their nutritional value.

Mustard الخردل

As mentioned earlier, *thufâ'* ثُفاء was identified as cress or mustard. Mustard seeds were widely used in Greece and ancient Egypt as both flavour and medicine. The Romans also knew mustard and commonly used it in their diet.[155] Mustard is very easily grown, and matures quickly; you can try growing your own herbs in a plant pot on your window sill.

Mustard seeds contain many phenolic and flavonoid antioxidants. Research has shown that when regularly used as part of a well balanced diet, they can help to prevent cancer, and enhance the body's antioxidant defence system.[156] In some folk medicine, the powdered seeds are used to make a poultice (warm paste) to relieve the pain and inflammation caused by rheumatism and arthritis;[157] this works by warming up the painful joint and increasing blood flow to the surrounding area.

There are different varieties of mustard ranging from the most pungent, black mustard seeds to the mild white mustard. Turmeric is usually added to the later to give the desired brownish yellow colour, and this adds to the antioxidant potential of the resulting paste.

Dill الشبت

Prophet Muhammad (ﷺ) said: «Use senna (a known laxative herb) and *sanoot*, as they cure every disease except death.»[158]

There is a question about what is meant by 'sanoot'; some opinions suggest that it refers to cumin seeds, fennel or dill. The three are umbelliferous fruits which belong to the same family (*Apiacea*), along with coriander, caraway, parsley, celery, lovage and anise. All umbelliferous fruits are rich in aromatic volatile oils that act as stimulants and carminatives, and aid in digestion. Their oil is especially useful in the treatment of colic and flatulence in babies and infants; they reduce the spasms with no reported side effects. In folk medicine, they are often used to stimulate the flow of milk during breast feeding.[159] Recent studies have also demonstrated their antibacterial action and their considerable antioxidant activity, superior even to the known antioxidant *ascorbic acid* (vitamin C) when used on a regular basis to spice food.[160]

There is good "reasoning for seasoning", was the conclusion drawn during a recent study on some commonly used food spices. The research involved a factor called kappa B, whose activation has been linked with a variety of inflammatory diseases (see the section on ginger, above). The extensive studies showed that the pathway that activates this factor can be interrupted by phytochemicals derived from spices such as turmeric, red pepper, cloves, ginger, cumin, anise, fennel, basil, rosemary, garlic and pomegranate.[161]

Dill seeds — as well as the dried and fresh leaves — are often used as a condiment in cooking; they are combined with pickled vegetables and used in salads, fish sauces and soups.

Fennel الشمر

Fennel oil and water are widely used as remedies in both folk and conventional medicine. Fennel water is official in the British Pharmacopoeia as a remedy for flatulence, and as a sweet, tasty additive to other medicines to prevent indigestion.

Studies have shown that the oral administration of fennel extract minimized the effects of inflammatory diseases and some allergic reactions; they also revealed that the herb acts as a central analgesic (pain reliever) and bronchodilatory relaxant. Moreover, fennel extract was found to significantly increase the activity of a potent internal antioxidant and raise the level of high density lipoprotein (HDL) cholesterol ('good' cholesterol).[162] The essential oil of fennel was found to protect against some liver toxic chemicals.

An herbal tea mixture consisting of liquorice root, fennel and thyme was found very useful for clearing mucus from the throat. This mixture works by regulating of bronchial mucus secretion, in addition to its antispasmodic and antimicrobial actions.[163]

Fennel shares the characteristic aroma and flavour of aniseed. The herb is used in salads, roasts and stews, while the highly fragrant seeds are used as flavouring for fish, bread, cookies and many Mediterranean dishes.

Cumin الكمون

This seed is, like coriander, a common Mediterranean spice. Cumin shares the same medicinal action of other umbelliferous fruits; it is antiflatulant, mildly stimulant, stomachic, aromatic, and antispasmodic. It is, however, less commonly used due to the strong and sometimes unpleasant odour and taste of its infusion. It is actually advised by some paediatricians to wean the child off the feeding bottles. In cases of infant colic, cumin can be replaced by caraway, another equally effective umbelliferous fruit that has a much more palatable flavour.

Cumin seeds are rich in essential oils, which have been found to possess potent antibacterial and antimicrobial properties, making the herb suitable as a natural food preservative, disinfectant and antiseptic.[164] The plant extract has also proved effective against Helicobacter pylori bacteria.[165]

Mixtures of cumin with some other commonly used spices like coriander, turmeric, red chilli, black pepper and ginger were found to enhance digestion by increasing the activities of digestive enzymes and stimulating bile flow.[166] Cumin is also rich in flavonoids that possess powerful antioxidant properties — they protect body cells from the damaging effects of free radicals — and the seed is currently being evaluated for possible anticancer effects.

In the kitchen, cumin goes well with beans, cabbage and cauliflower as it eases their digestion and reduces their flatulent effect. It is also a common addition to Arabic spice mixes in meat and vegetable casseroles.

Nigella (Black seed) حبة البركة أو الحبة السوداء

Prophet Muhammad (ﷺ) said: «Use this black seed, as it cures every disease, except death.»[167]

Nigella is a black seed also called black cumin or Indian cumin. It is commonly used in folk medicine all over the world for the treatment and prevention of a number of diseases and conditions that include asthma and diarrhoea. Black cumin has been known as an herbal treatment for thousands of years; a bottle of black cumin oil was even discovered in the tomb of the Egyptian pharaoh Tutankhamen.

The seed contains both essential and fatty oils. *Thymoquinone* and *nigellone* are the main active constituents of the essential oil. Nigellone has bronchodilating, anti-histaminic and antispasmodic effects; thus making it useful in treating asthma and allergies. Thymoquinone, on the other hand, is responsible for the anti-inflammatory and analgesic effects of the seed. It is also a powerful antioxidant and a stimulant of bile production and this is what gives the seed its very effective detoxifying quality.[168]

The fatty oil constitutes the major part of the seed. It is mainly formed of polyunsaturated fats which are essential to human health; they aid in the regulation of general body metabolism and hormonal production, and are essential in the maintenance of a healthy cell membrane and the development of a functional nervous system. In addition, the oil contains two important active ingredients: a *saponin* (*melathin*) and a bitter principle (*nigellin*). Both constituents have digestant, appetite stimulant and mild intestinal cleansing effects. They also promote the function of the liver, gall bladder and kidneys, and help reestablish the body's pH balance. Saponins have mucolytic and expectorant effects (they help to break up and remove mucus from the bronchial passages). The oil also contains a sterol phytochemical demonstrated to lower blood cholesterol levels[169].

The unrefined extracts of the seeds offer protection against toxicity of the kidneys and liver. Both the seeds and the oil also have potent anti-inflammatory, antiallergic, antioxidant, analgesic, antipyretic, antimicrobial and antitumor activities. Black seed oil decreases blood pressure, improves respiration and shows beneficial effects in thrombosis[170], with an effect similar to that of aspirin without the unpleasant side effects.[171] Furthermore, the seeds were shown to inhibit the growth of bacteria and yeast. Nigella sativa is also one of the plants commonly used in folk medicine for the treatment of diabetes. Studies show that the seeds do possess an anti-diabetic activity which may be — at least in part — brought about by stimulated insulin release.[172]

Black cumin has long been used externally for skin and hair treatment. No large scientific studies have been done in this area; but some studies showed a potential contact dermatitis action of the oil when applied topically in susceptible individuals (the seed actually causes dermatitis in some individuals).[173]

The extraordinary therapeutic effects of black seed cannot be fully explained on the basis of the components that have been so far discovered in the seed's oils. This fact suggests a highly synergistic effect between the various components of the essential and fatty oils of the seed, and perhaps between other components yet to be discovered.[174]

Fenugreek الحلبة

Ibn al-Qayyim noted a hadith in which the Prophet (ﷺ) was reported to have visited Sa'd ibn Abi Waqqâs once when he was ill while in Makkah, and he called for a doctor to see him. Al-Hârith ibn Qaladah came to examine Sa'd, and he said: "There is nothing wrong with him, just cook some fenugreek with dates and let him eat them." It was reported that Sa'd did that and was then healed.[175]

Fenugreek belongs to the family leguminosae. Ancient Egyptians valued fenugreek as food, and in healing and embalming. Fenugreek sprouts are still a popular Egyptian snack. The Romans, Greeks and Indians also used the herb as both food and medicine.[176] During the time of the Prophet (ﷺ) some physicians were reported to have said: "If people knew about the benefits of fenugreek, they would buy it with its weight worth of gold."[177]

The seed contains a high amount of *mucilage*[178] which was the reason for its traditional use to stimulate digestion, ease flatulence, diarrhoea and cough. The herb also contains a hormone-like substance, *diosgenin*, which is used in the synthesis of oral contraceptives and sex hormone treatments. Fenugreek is rich in antioxidant flavonoids and it has demonstrated a potential protective effect against breast cancer.[179]

Traditionally, fenugreek has been used for hundreds of years by lactating women to increase breast milk production as well as to return the mother to a healthy state after delivery, decrease the risk of placental retention (as it acts as a uterine cleansing agent) and restore energy and strength lost during the delivery. New studies have found that the use of fenugreek after childbirth increased the quantity of breast milk, yet the milk retained its quality (in regard to macro- and micronutrient composition).[180]

Research on fenugreek also led to the discovery that it has a *hypoglycemic* effect (it reduces blood sugar level), which makes it useful for diabetic patients.[181] It has also been found that fenugreek seed extract is useful in reducing the weight gain induced by a high-fat diet, as it significantly reduces plasma triglyceride[182] and serum cholesterol levels.[183]

Purslane الرجلة

Adh-Dhahabi says in his *Medicine of the Prophet* that purslane is useful with vinegar both as food and as a dressing for sores and ulcers. Purslane (*Portulaca oleracea*) is a good edible herb native to the Middle East and India. Purslane leaves are relatively rich in protein and omega-3 fatty acids compared to other leafy vegetable plants.[184] Omega-3s aid the body in regulating blood pressure and clotting, and in controlling inflammation. They are also a factor in lowering 'bad' cholesterol (LDL, or low-density lipoproteins), preventing certain cancers, boosting the immune system and strengthening the cardiovascular system. In addition, recent studies suggest that omega-3s may have positive effects on some central nervous system (CNS) conditions like depression, Alzheimer's disease and hyperactivity.[185]

The purslane plant is a general tonic and possesses antibacterial, vermifuge and diuretic effects. Research increasingly suggests the valuable role of purslane in the reduction of tumour cell growth; in addition, purslane extracts combat oxygen free radicals, and it may have a role in the treatment of diabetes mellitus (type II).[186]

Recent studies have shown that the leaves are useful in a poultice when applied to burns, and both the leaves and the plant juice are particularly effective in the treatment of skin diseases and insect bites and stings.[187]

Purslane can be eaten raw in salads and sandwiches or cooked in soups and stews. Unlike cress, the leaves keep their beneficial actions when dried.[188]

Frankincense اللبان

Frankincense (*lubân* in Arabic) is the resin or sap of a tree (genus Boswellia) native to the southern Arabian Peninsula. The Prophet (ﷺ) recommended burning it indoors as incense:

«Burn incense in your houses with frankincense and thyme.»[189]

In his *Medicine of the Prophet*, Ibn al-Qayyim advocated chewing lubân alone or with thyme to expel phlegm, relax the tongue muscle and improve mental functions. As incense, lubân — according to Ibn al-Qayyim — purifies and freshens the air and alleviates some ailments.[190]

Recent studies have discovered a powerful anti-inflammatory agent in frankincense known as Boswellic acid. It proved effective against painful conditions such as arthritis.[191] Usage of NSAI (non-steroidal anti-inflammatory) drugs declined in patients suffering from rheumatoid arthritis when they were given Boswellia (frankincense) daily. Studies have also shown that frankincense is effective in other types of allergy and inflammation, such as chronic *colitis* (inflammation of the lining of the colon) and bronchial asthma. In Arab traditional medicine, frankincense is used — after soaking the resin in water overnight and then drinking the solution — as an efficient expectorant and anti-arthritic remedy.

Frankincense is sometimes used in traditional Arabic cuisine as flavouring for soups and casseroles.

Fruits

Fruits stand with vegetables on the second step of the food guide pyramid. You need to eat two to four servings of fruit per day. Fruits are packed with vitamins, minerals, phytonutrients and fibre. Although they are very nutritious, do not exceed the recommended number of servings, especially if you are diabetic or watching your weight, as fruit is high in simple sugars and carbohydrates.

Personally, I prefer fresh fruits over juices, since juicing removes a good portion of the beneficial fibres.

Nutritional value of fruits
• Vitamins A & C
• Potassium
• Fibres
• Phytonutrients & antioxidants

Fruity tips

➤ To maximize their nutrient content, try not to peel your fruits. Of course I mean by that fruits with an edible skin, like apples, apricots and figs,... Also, try to eat some of the white pith of oranges and other citrus fruits as it is the best source of flavonoids. You can also use the zest (grated rind) of oranges and lemons in cakes and meat dishes, or even to flavour drinking water.

➤ Dried fruits constitute a very healthy snack for school kids and teens. They are packed with vitamins and antioxidants, and they provide energy and lots of fibre. Use figs, apricots, prunes and dates; you can even stuff them with nuts for extra boost of energy, proteins and healthy oils.

➤ Try to make your own fruit juices at home. If you do not have time, buy those made from 100% pure fresh fruit and containing no added sugars, colours or preservatives.

➤ On hot summer days you can freeze fruit juice to make your own ice-lollies (popsicles): sweet, healthy treats for kids.

Fruits are mentioned many times in the Qur'an as a gift from Allah (ﷻ), both on earth and in paradise:

What counts as a serving?
• 1 medium apple or pear
• ½ cup chopped fruits
• ¾ cup fruit juice
• ¼ cup dried fruits

﴿إِنَّ ٱلۡمُتَّقِينَ فِي ظِلَٰلٍ وَعُيُونٍ ۝ وَفَوَٰكِهَ مِمَّا يَشۡتَهُونَ ۝ كُلُوا۟ وَٱشۡرَبُوا۟ هَنِيٓـًٔا بِمَا كُنتُمۡ تَعۡمَلُونَ ۝﴾ (سورة المرسلات:٤١: ٤٣)

﴾Verily, the pious shall be amidst shades and springs, and fruits, such as they desire. [It will be said to them,] Eat and drink comfortably for that which you used to do.﴿   *(Qur'an 77: 41-43)*

﴿فَلۡيَنظُرِ ٱلۡإِنسَٰنُ إِلَىٰ طَعَامِهِۦٓ ۝ أَنَّا صَبَبۡنَا ٱلۡمَآءَ صَبًّا ۝ ثُمَّ شَقَقۡنَا ٱلۡأَرۡضَ شَقًّا ۝ فَأَنۢبَتۡنَا فِيهَا حَبًّا ۝ وَعِنَبًا وَقَضۡبًا ۝ وَزَيۡتُونًا وَنَخۡلًا ۝ وَحَدَآئِقَ غُلۡبًا ۝ وَفَٰكِهَةً وَأَبًّا ۝ مَّتَٰعًا لَّكُمۡ وَلِأَنۡعَٰمِكُمۡ ۝﴾ (سورة عبس:٢٤-٣٢)

﴾Then let humankind look at their food: that We pour forth water in abundance, and We split the earth in clefts, and We cause therein the grain to grow, and grapes and clover plants [green fodder for the cattle], and olives and date-palms, and gardens, dense with many trees, and fruits and herbage [greens], [to be] a provision and benefit for you and your cattle.﴿   *(Qur'an 80: 24-32)*

Many fruits are specifically mentioned in the Qur'an and/or in the Prophet's (ﷺ) hadiths:

Dates

Dates are delicious fruits produced by palm trees very common in the Middle East and North Africa. Palm trees are the food source most commonly mentioned in the Qur'an, pointing to their tremendous benefits:

﴿وَٱلۡأَرۡضَ وَضَعَهَا لِلۡأَنَامِ ۝ فِيهَا فَٰكِهَةٌ وَٱلنَّخۡلُ ذَاتُ ٱلۡأَكۡمَامِ ۝﴾ (سورة الرحمن:١٠-١١)

﴾And the earth He has put for the creatures. Therein are fruits, date-palms producing sheathed fruit-stalks [enclosing dates].﴿
(Qur'an 55: 10-11)

$$﴿ وَجَعَلْنَا فِيهَا جَنَّاتٍ مِّن نَّخِيلٍ وَأَعْنَابٍ وَفَجَّرْنَا فِيهَا مِنَ ٱلْعُيُونِ ۝ ﴾$$

(سورة يس:٣٤)

﴿And We have made therein gardens of date-palms and grapes, and We have caused springs of water to gush forth therein.﴾

(Qur'an 36: 34)

Prophet Muhammad (ﷺ) once told his wife, 'Â'ishah:

«A house with no dates — its people are hungry."[192] Many other hadiths show the benefits of dates: "The *'ajwah*[193] is from heaven and it is a healing against poison."[194] "There is healing in the ripe dates from 'Âliyah."[195] Each morning, Prophet Muhammad (ﷺ) used to soak seven dates in milk before eating them. He is reported to have said: "Whoever begins his day with seven ripe dates ('ajwah dates) will not be harmed that day by either poison or sorcery."[196] In still another narration: "If someone eats seven dates from the vicinity of Madinah no poison will harm him until the evening.»[197]

Ibn Atheer said: "'Ajwah dates are a kind of date whose colour is blackish, and it was initially sowed by Prophet with his own hands in Madinah." Imam Qurtubi explained, "What we understand from the narrations is that it is only 'ajwah dates of Madinah that have this characteristic of protecting against poison and magic. However, some other scholars are of the view that if one does not find dates from Madinah, he can eat from any kind of dates that he has."[198]

The combination of both dates and milk form a complete meal of protein, carbohydrates, fats, vitamins, minerals and fibre. The fats present in milk reduce the rapid absorption of the simple sugars of the dates, thus preventing a sudden rise in the blood sugar level.

Prophet Muhammad (ﷺ) also liked eating dates with other foods; he ate ripe dates with cucumber, and it was reported that he said that the heat of former overcame the coolness of the latter.[199] He (ﷺ) also ate dates, with butter, with bread, with watermelons or alone.

The Messenger of Allah (ﷺ) recommended breaking the fast in Ramadan with dates whenever possible:

«If anyone of you is fasting, let him break his fast with dates. In case he does not have them, then with water. Verily water is a purifier.»[200]

Dates contain large amounts of energy-producing carbohydrates, present mainly as simple sugars that are easily and rapidly absorbed. So breaking the fast on dates after a long day gives the body — and especially the brain — a rapid boost of energy to resume its normal functions.

Dates provide significant amounts of fibre, thus preventing constipation and haemorrhoids, lowering blood cholesterol and protecting from colon cancer. Amino acids, the building blocks of proteins, are also found in dates, in addition to a number of beneficial enzymes, vitamins and minerals.

Dates are a good source of:

➢ Iron, the mineral that prevents anaemia and which is a part of the haemoglobin molecule in the blood

➢ Magnesium, which has an important role in nervous system integrity and in energy production

➢ Potassium, useful in cases of hypertension

➢ Calcium and phosphorus, essential for healthy bones

➢ Vitamin A, for healthy skin and eyesight

➢ Vitamin B_3 (Niacin), protecting from *pellagra*, a disease which is manifested as dermatitis, dementia and fatigue. Niacin also reduces triglycerides and cholesterol levels (LDL) in the blood, thus protects the heart and circulatory system

➢ Folic acid, essential for protection against atherosclerosis and heart problems, and for proteina metabolism

Another use for dates was mentioned in the chapter of the Qur'an that relates the story of Mary, mother of Jesus (peace be upon them both):

﴿وَهُزِّيٓ إِلَيْكِ بِجِذْعِ ٱلنَّخْلَةِ تُسَٰقِطْ عَلَيْكِ رُطَبًا جَنِيًّا ۝ فَكُلِي وَٱشْرَبِي وَقَرِّي عَيْنًا

... ۝﴾   (سورة مريم:٢٥-٢٦)

❨And shake the trunk of date-palm towards you; it will let fall fresh, ripe dates upon you. So eat and drink and be glad...❩

(Qur'an 19: 25-26)

According to scientific studies, ripe dates contain a compound that increases the contractions of the uterus. This compound resembles *oxytocin,* a natural body hormone secreted by the pituitary gland to encourage uterine contractions at the time of delivery. Dates also increase milk production in lactating mothers; and have traditionally been used for this purpose over the centuries.

A study carried out at the faculty of Science, Cairo University, showed that a decoction of the fruit was useful in treating bronchitis, cough and colitis, and also acted as an expectorant. In addition, it was found that dates can be used as an aphrodisiac when mixed with milk and cinnamon. The study also pointed out that regular consumption of dates increases the body's immunity and resistance to cancer. Furthermore, it demonstrated that dates are able to prevent the formation of kidney stones due to their diuretic and anti-inflammatory actions.[201]

Figs

There is a soorah (chapter) in the Qur'an called *The Fig*. The fact that Allah swears by this tree indicates the tremendous benefits and great value of its fruit:

$$ ﴿وَٱلتِّينِ وَٱلزَّيۡتُونِ ۝ وَطُورِ سِينِينَ ۝ وَهَٰذَا ٱلۡبَلَدِ ٱلۡأَمِينِ ۝﴾ $$

(سورة التين:١-٣)

❨By the fig, and the olive, by Mount Sinai, and by this city of security [Makkah].❩ *(Qur'an 95: 1-3)*

Ibn al-Qayyim recommended the use of figs as a liver and spleen tonic, to cleanse the kidneys and bladder, and as a diuretic. He also suggested eating them with almonds and walnuts for extra benefits.[202]

At the time of the Prophet (ﷺ), figs were not common in the Arabian peninsula, and thus they were not mentioned in the Sunnah except in a hadith with uncertain origin noted by Qurṭubi as reported by Abu Dardâ', saying that when the Prophet (ﷺ) was offered a plate of figs, he ate and asked his companions to eat, and said:

«If a fruit ever descended from Paradise, I would say that this is it, as heaven's fruits contain no pips. Eat from it as it relieves haemorrhoids and treats gout.»[203]

Figs are sweet and a good source of dietary fibre. Many studies show that fibre-rich foods reduce risks of some types of cancer. Fibre also helps lower serum cholesterol levels, particularly the undesirable LDL cholesterol. In addition, they accelerate the rate at which food moves through the digestive system; that is why figs are recommended in the treatment of haemorrhoids, diverticulosis and chronic constipation, as they safely promote regular bowel habits.[204]

Since figs are alkaline in nature, they help to balance the acidic condition that occurs due to excess consumption of meat and junk food.[205] This, in addition to their reported diuretic effect, may be the reasons for their use in the treatment of gout as recommended by the Prophet (ﷺ). This possibility needs to be studied further.

Figs are rich in simple sugars which are readily assimilated and used by the body, providing a quick energy boost. Their high content of digestive enzymes makes them effective in the treatment of intestinal disorders; and they have a soothing and gentle cleansing effect on the lining of the gastrointestinal tract, so they are used in treating and protecting against peptic and duodenal ulcers. Figs are also used by lactating mothers to induce breast milk secretion. Figs contain many minerals and vitamins, such as potassium, iron, calcium and phosphorus (these build bones), vitamins A, C and K.[206] The latter plays an essential role in blood clotting. In some Middle-Eastern traditional home remedies, figs were used in the treatment of heavy menstruation and postpartum bleeding.

Grapes

Many scholars consider grapes along with ripe dates and figs to be the kings of all fruits, the great gift from Allah to humankind. Grapes are mentioned many times in the Qur'an in connection with Paradise (and the rewards of the hereafter) and with the countless blessings of Allah to His creatures on earth:

﴿ فَلْيَنظُرِ ٱلْإِنسَٰنُ إِلَىٰ طَعَامِهِۦٓ ۝ أَنَّا صَبَبْنَا ٱلْمَآءَ صَبًّا ۝ ثُمَّ شَقَقْنَا ٱلْأَرْضَ شَقًّا ۝ فَأَنۢبَتْنَا فِيهَا حَبًّا ۝ وَعِنَبًا وَقَضْبًا ۝ ﴾ (سورة عبس:٢٤-٢٨)

❨Then let humans look at their food, that We pour forth water in abundance, and We split the earth in clefts, and We cause therein the grain to grow, and grapes and clover plants [green fodder for the cattle].﴾ *(Qur'an 80: 24-28)*

﴿ يُنۢبِتُ لَكُم بِهِ ٱلزَّرْعَ وَٱلزَّيْتُونَ وَٱلنَّخِيلَ وَٱلْأَعْنَٰبَ وَمِن كُلِّ ٱلثَّمَرَٰتِ إِنَّ فِي ذَٰلِكَ لَءَايَةً لِّقَوْمٍ يَتَفَكَّرُونَ ۝ ﴾ (سورة النحل: ١١)

﴾With it He causes to grow for you the crops, the olives, the date-palms, the grapes, and every kind of fruit. Verily, in this is indeed an evident proof and a manifest sign for people who give thought.﴿ *(Qur'an 16: 11)*

﴿ أَيَوَدُّ أَحَدُكُمْ أَن تَكُونَ لَهُۥ جَنَّةٌ مِّن نَّخِيلٍ وَأَعْنَابٍ ... ۝ ﴾ (سورة البقرة: ٢٦٦)

﴾Would any of you wish to have a garden with date-palms and grapevines?...﴿ *(Qur'an 2: 266)*

﴿إِنَّ لِلْمُتَّقِينَ مَفَازًا ۝ حَدَآئِقَ وَأَعْنَٰبًا ۝ ﴾ (سورة النبأ: ٣١-٣٢)

﴾Verily, for those who are pious [ever conscious of Allah], there will be success [Paradise]; gardens and grapevines.﴿

(Qur'an 78: 31-32)

Prophet Muhammad (ﷺ) loved grapes. It was reported by Adh-Dhahabi that Prophet Muhammad (ﷺ) liked eating soaked raisins, though he forbade soaking both raisins and dates in the same bowl[207] (research is still missing on the reason behind this precious piece of advice). Adh-Dhahabi also reported in his book that at the time of the Prophet (ﷺ) it used to be said,

«What an excellent food raisins are; they relieve fatigue, cool away rage, strengthen the nerves, ameliorate the flavour, treat phlegm and clear the skin colour.»[208]

This saying contains information that is now known to be scientifically true.

Zuhri said: "Whoever would like to memorize the Hadith, let him eat raisins," and it was believed that if one ate raisins, pistachio and rosemary everyday, first thing in the morning, one's mind would become sharper.[209] Raisins were used in Islamic medicine as a digestive and a tonic for the stomach, liver and spleen. They were also used in cases of throat, respiratory tract and lung disorders, as well as in kidney and urinary (bladder) malfunctions.[210] Ibn al-Qayyim noted another interesting saying: "Whoever eats twenty-one red raisins every day, will not find anything in his body to complain about."

Dr. Patrick Holford recommends eating ¼ cup of raisins each day to boost your antioxidant level.[211] The latest studies show that raisins — along with prunes, berries, kale, spinach and plums — are among the most powerful natural antioxidants[212].[213]

Grapes contain a phytonutrient known as *ellagic* acid, and the skin of red grapes contains a compound known as *resveratrol*; both of these have the ability to fight off many carcinogens in the human body.

Despite their high sugar content, grapes have a relatively low *glycemic index* (they do not cause a sudden rise in the blood sugar level), which makes them perfect energy boosting snacks. Grapes are rich in potassium, a mineral known for its benefits in lowering high blood pressure and relieving mental confusion and depression.[214] Potassium is also useful in reducing water retention and treating kidney disorders due to its diuretic effect. Grapes have mild expectorant and cough sedative actions, which make them very useful in relieving respiratory congestion. They also have a mild laxative effect. Grape leaves, commonly used in traditional Middle Eastern cookery, are a very good source of calcium and vitamin A.

The red wine myth

﴿يَٰٓأَيُّهَا ٱلَّذِينَ ءَامَنُوٓاْ إِنَّمَا ٱلۡخَمۡرُ وَٱلۡمَيۡسِرُ وَٱلۡأَنصَابُ وَٱلۡأَزۡلَٰمُ رِجۡسٞ مِّنۡ عَمَلِ ٱلشَّيۡطَٰنِ فَٱجۡتَنِبُوهُ لَعَلَّكُمۡ تُفۡلِحُونَ ۝ إِنَّمَا يُرِيدُ ٱلشَّيۡطَٰنُ أَن يُوقِعَ بَيۡنَكُمُ ٱلۡعَدَٰوَةَ وَٱلۡبَغۡضَآءَ فِي ٱلۡخَمۡرِ وَٱلۡمَيۡسِرِ وَيَصُدَّكُمۡ عَن ذِكۡرِ ٱللَّهِ وَعَنِ ٱلصَّلَوٰةِ فَهَلۡ أَنتُم مُّنتَهُونَ ۝﴾

(سورة المائدة: ٩٠-٩١)

﴾O you who believe! Intoxicants [all kinds of alcoholic drinks], gambling, stone altars [used for sacrificing to idols] and arrows [for seeking luck or decision] are an abomination of Satan's handiwork. So avoid [strictly all] that [abomination] in order that you may be successful. Satan wants only to excite enmity and hatred between you with intoxicants [alcoholic drinks] and gambling, and to hinder you from the remembrance of Allah and from ṣalât [the prayer]. So, will you not then abstain?﴿ *(Qur'an 5: 90-91)*

For some years, Western society was impressed by the 'French paradox': that is, it was found that the rate of heart disease in France was lower than in other Western nations, despite the fact that French recipes use lots of meat and dairy products, which have high fat and cholesterol content. Researchers suggested that this was because red wine is a common factor in the French diet, which is not the case for other countries. (Note that the study neglected the fact that the French diet is also rich in fresh fruits and vegetables, olive oil, fish, and other healthy ingredients of a typical Mediterranean diet).[215]

The latest studies demonstrate that the antioxidant flavonoids responsible for the cardiovascular benefits of red wine are original constituents of the purple grapes used to prepare the wine, and are just as effective in red and purple grape juice. The flavonoids in grape juice are powerful antioxidants that prevent the oxidation of 'bad' cholesterol (LDL) which is the main cause of the formation of plaque in artery walls (hardening of the arteries). Grapes also contain polyphenolic compounds, which act to lower the risk of atherosclerosis and blood clots that lead to heart attacks.[216] According to John Folts, a University of Wisconsin researcher, wine could only offer its 'heart-friendly' benefits if it is consumed on a regular basis and in pretty high doses; while the grape juice offer the same benefits without the intoxicating (and toxic) effects of alcohol.[217]

Subhân Allâh (Glory be to Allah), for He said in His Holy Book:

﴿ ❋ يَسْـَٔلُونَكَ عَنِ ٱلْخَمْرِ وَٱلْمَيْسِرِ قُلْ فِيهِمَآ إِثْمٌ كَبِيرٌ وَمَنَٰفِعُ لِلنَّاسِ وَإِثْمُهُمَآ أَكْبَرُ مِن نَّفْعِهِمَا ... ﴾ (سورة البقرة: ٢١٩)

{They ask you [O Muhammad] concerning alcoholic drink and gambling. Say: In them is a great sin and [some] benefit for people, but the sin of them is greater than their benefit...}

(Qur'an 2: 219)

Furthermore, alcoholic drinks do not show the same beneficial effects on the blood vessels as grape juice does, since the alcohol generates free radicals — those unstable oxygen molecules — that can actually cause damage to the blood vessels lining, thus counteracting any of the benefits that red wine's antioxidants may offer. In addition, a recent study proved that the antioxidants in grape juice — specifically, a key antioxidant called *catechin* — appear to remain effective in the body longer than do those in wine. Apparently, a large amount of the antioxidant content in wine is wasted while trying to overcome the intoxicating effects of the alcohol itself.[218]

Since the juice is prepared by crushing the whole grapes with their skin and seeds, its benefits exceed that of the grapes without the seeds.[219] Grape seeds are rich in flavonoids, in particular a recently discovered powerful compound known as *activin,* which is a more potent antioxidant than vitamins C and E and beta-carotene s. It offers significant protection against many types of cancer and cardiovascular disease. White grapes and their juice are not as potent, because they do not contain the flavonoids that purple or red grapes do.[220]

So, drink lots of grape juice to keep your heart healthy, but choose the purple kind, which is far richer in antioxidant flavonoids than white grape juice. Note also that grape juice should be freshly squeezed, as the phenolic compounds are easily broken down by their exposure to air, thus significantly lowering the levels of heart-healthy ingredients.

Pomegranate

Pomegranate is a fruit native to the Middle East. It is mentioned many times in the Qur'an:

(سورة الرحمن: ٦٨)   ﴿فِيهِمَا فَاكِهَةٌ وَنَخْلٌ وَرُمَّانٌ ﴿٦٨﴾﴾

﴿In them [both] will be fruits, and date-palms and pomegranates.﴾   *(Qur'an 55: 68)*

Ibn al-Qayyim noted that 'Ali (﴿رضي الله عنه﴾) was reported to have said, "Eat the pomegranate with its pith, as it is tanning for the stomach."

Studies on pomegranates showed a powerful antacid action and a soothing effect on the stomach lining making them useful for people at high risk of peptic and duodenal ulcers due to the chronic use of anti-inflammatory drugs. These effects are stronger when the juice is prepared from the whole fruit including not only the seeds but the white pith as well. In traditional Islamic medicine, pomegranate was used as a stomach tonic and soothing agent, and in folk medicine the fruit rind is used as a decoction to expel intestinal worms.[221]

Pomegranates are good source of potassium, so they are recommended in cases of hypertension; they are also rich in iron, the essential mineral for haemoglobin formation. Their content of tannic acid gives them an astringent action useful in treating diarrhoea. Pomegranates contain considerable amounts of, vitamins B and C, and minerals such as calcium, phosphorus and sodium.

The juice from pomegranates is a powerful antioxidant due to its content of polyphenols. This antioxidant activity was found especially useful in combating cardiovascular diseases,[222] as it prevents oxidation of LDL cholesterol and reduces damage to the blood vessel lining. The polyphenolic content of the fruit is not restricted to the seeds but are present also in the rind which make the commercially prepared pomegranate juice more 'heart -healthy' than the home version as it is produced by the pressing of the whole fruit with its rind and pith.[223]

Bananas

In His description of Paradise, Allah says in His Holy Book:

﴿ وَطَلْحٍ مَّنضُودٍ ۝ وَظِلٍّ مَّمْدُودٍ ۝ وَمَآءٍ مَّسْكُوبٍ ۝ ﴾

(سورة الواقعة:٢٩: ٣١)

﴿Among Ṭalḥ [banana plants][224] with fruits piled one above another, in shade long-extended, by water flowing constantly.﴾

(Qur'an 56: 29-31)

Ibn al-Qayyim listed many benefits of bananas, describing their effectiveness in cough and respiratory tract disorders, their benefits for kidneys as diuretics, their aphrodisiac action and their role in increasing sperm production. He recommended eating them with honey.[225]

Bananas were called the food of the philosophers because Indian philosophers ate bananas to boost their mental performance and clarity. This is probably due to their high content of potassium, deficiency in which is connected to depression and mental confusion.[226] Also, bananas constitute a convenient low-calorie snack packed with essential vitamins and minerals.

Research has shown the efficiency of bananas in the treatment of diarrhoea, gastrointestinal disturbances, heartburn and ulcers. Bananas are a good source of fibre, which reduces blood cholesterol; they are also low in sodium and very rich in potassium, both of which aid in lowering blood pressure. This in addition to their content of folates and vitamin B_6 — essential for protection against atherosclerosis — makes them ideal for hypertensive persons, as they act to lower blood pressure and cholesterol and protect the heart and blood circulation.

Another benefit of bananas is their high content of what is called *fructo-oligosaccharides* (FOS). These compounds have the ability to sustain and enhance the presence of friendly bacteria in the gut (normal body flora); they are vital for healthy digestion and strong immunity. One study also found that eating bananas thickens the stomach lining which can be really helpful to patients on NSAI drug treatment. However, diabetics should take care, as the sugars in bananas are readily absorbed causing a sudden rise in BSL.

Watermelons

Many hadiths involving melons and watermelons were reported, but most of them are of uncertain origin except one which was reported by Tirmidhi and Abu Dâwood saying that Prophet Muhammad (ﷺ) used to eat watermelons with ripe dates commenting that the heat of one (dates) is overcome by the coolness of the other (watermelon).

Ibn al-Qayyim recommended eating watermelons before lunch to wash out the bowel and relieve its diseases.[227] Watermelons are a good source of potassium and vitamin A and also contain a considerable amount of vitamins C and B. Adh-Dhahabi noted in his *Medicine of the Prophet* that it was reported that Ibn 'Abbâs once said: "Watermelons are food, drink and nice smelling fruits; they wash out the bladder, clean the bowel, increase the water of the back, act as aphrodisiacs, cleanse the complexion and prevent colds."

The information contained in this saying is quite true. The high water and potassium content of the fruit points to their role in washing the urinary system and the gastrointestinal tract. Jane Scrivner in her book *Detox Yourself* included watermelons as a kidney tonic because this same property also helps the kidneys get rid of body toxins.[228] Further confirming that old wisdom, the vitamin A content is essential for healthy and glowing skin and the vitamin C content does fight colds. Moreover, some recent German studies pointed out the benefit of watermelon in the regeneration of cerebrospinal fluid ('water of the back'); they even advised patients undergoing cerebrospinal transplant to increase their consumption of melons and watermelons.[229]

The presence of vitamin A makes the fruit helpful in improving vision, especially night sight. In addition, vitamin A plays an important role in the maintenance of healthy epithelial tissue, the tissue that covers both the internal and external body surfaces including the skin, eye lining, intestines, lungs and bladder... This vitamin is also essential for growth, reproduction and body immunity.

Dr. Patrick Holford describes watermelons as a great anti-oxidant — high in beta carotenes and vitamin C, while the seeds are rich in vitamin E, zinc and selenium.[230] Watermelons — along with tomatoes and many other red fruits — are also a good source of the cancer-fighting nutrient lycopene. Dr. Holford recommends watermelon juice to boost the immune system; the juice, he advises, should be prepared by blending the seeds along with the flesh of the fruit to benefit from their nutritional values. No need to worry about the husk, it will sink to the bottom.

Quince
(Cydonia Oblonga) السفرجل

Quince is a golden fruit related to apples. Quince is thought to originate from Persia and is known to have also been cultivated in Greece, Turkey and Saudi Arabia.[231]

Quince is a round or pear-shaped, golden-yellow to orange fruit, with a sweet, aromatic odour. Ibn al-Qayyim noted that at the time of the Prophet (ﷺ), it was said about the quince, "It strengthens the heart, lengthens the breath and relieves chest phlegm."[232]

Quince is a good source of potassium which is needed by the heart. It also contains a considerable amount of phosphorus, calcium, iron and both vitamins A and C. It has a soothing action on the intestinal lining due to its high content of the soluble fibre pectin. As a soluble fibre, pectin has also a cholesterol-lowering effect and offers good protection against colon cancer. Quince is traditionally used as a home remedy for sore throat and intestinal irregularities.[233]

Quince is rarely eaten raw due to its slightly bitter flavour. It is usually used to prepare quince marmalade or for flavouring cakes and pies; and it is also delicious when stewed or grilled. Ibn al-Qayyim recommended eating it either grilled or slowly cooked with honey; he also suggested coring the fruit, filling it with honey and baking it. He prescribed the marmalade for strengthening the stomach, the liver and the heart.[234]

Did you know?

Quince is a practical room and cupboard deodorizer.

Citron (Citrus medica) الأترج

As their name suggests, citrons are members of the citrus family (*Rutaceae*). They are fragrant fruits, oval in shape, usually with a yellow peel. It was reported in Bukhâri that the Prophet (ﷺ) once said:

«The simile of the believer who recites the Qur'an (well, and acts upon its commandments) is like the citron. It tastes sweet and its smell is sweet.»[235]

There are many types of citrons: one of them is known as *'utruj*, and it is mainly cultivated in Palestine. It has a yellow peel and a lemon-like shape.[236]

In traditional medicine, the fruit is used as a remedy for seasickness, respiratory and gastrointestinal disorders. Nowadays, the main use of citrons is to prepare candied peel used as an ap-

petite stimulant, a tonic and an expectorant[237]. Adh-
Dhahabi[238] recommended the use of the citron
peel in the form of paste to heal the colon, stimulate appetite and as an antiflatulent.

Citrons are rich in vitamin C. Besides
the many beneficial actions of this vitamin, vitamin C has been found to be
valuable for dieters. Individuals with ad-
equate vitamin C intake burn significantly more fat when exercising than vitamin C-deficient individuals, who appear to be more
resistant to weight loss.

The outermost layer (zest) of citrons contains the essential oils
that give the fruit its superb fragrance. The inner layer of the peel
— in spite of its slightly bitter taste — holds tremendous medicinal benefits. Recent scientific studies have shown the important
benefits of citrus flavonoids as antioxidants and anticancer agents,
in addition to their role in preventing capillary fragility. *Naringenin* is a phytoestrogen present in the rind of all citrus fruits.
Along with other phytoestrogens, Naringenin reduces oestrogen-
responsive cancers and reduces the frequency and severity of
pre-menstrual syndrome (PMS) and post-menopausal symptoms.
That is why citrus peel is recommended in Chinese herbal medicine for the treatment of benign tumours as well as malignant
breast cancer.[239]

The fruit can be eaten raw or prepared as marmalades and jel-
lies. The whole fruit or the rind can also be added to flavour cakes,
puddings and candies. Citron juice tastes like lemon juice.

Bitter orange
(Citrus aurantium) النارنج

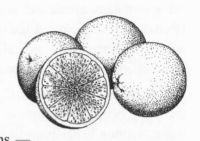

Bitter oranges also belong to the citrus family *Rutaceae*. The fruit is orange-shaped, but with a rough peel and darker in colour than oranges. As with the citrons — and most of the other members of the family — the peel contains the fragrant volatile oil and the medicinally active glycosides.[240]

Adh-Dhahabi recommended the scent of the volatile oil of the fruit for strengthening the heart. He also recommended the use of its peel in the same ways as the 'utruj or citron peels.[241] Traditional Chinese medicine recommends bitter oranges as a liver tonic and in cases of respiratory dysfunction and bronchitis. Nowadays, the fruit is used as an appetite stimulant, a digestive and a gastro-intestinal tonic. It also improves microcirculation, protects blood vessel integrity, and acts as an antioxidant due to its content of bioflavonoids. Although it is a stimulant, bitter orange has been used by dieters to suppress appetite and stimulate fat breakdown as the fruit raises the basal metabolic rate (BMR).[242] Raising one's BMR is an effective way to burn calories, thus reducing one's feeling of hunger. However, caution should be taken, for if the fruit is used in excess and over a long period of time, it can raise blood pressure, increase cardiovascular risks and over-stimulate the central nervous system.[243]

The bitter flavour of the fruit has meant that it is mainly used in jam and marmalade preparation, while its oil is used as a flavouring agent.

Christ's thorn
(Lotus Jujube or rhamnus) النبق

Jujube (or *nabq* in Arabic) is the fruit produced by the lote tree, a green spiny tree belonging to buckthorn family, *Rhamnaceae*. Prophet Muhammad (ﷺ) is known to have said: "On the night that I was taken on the Night Journey, I was shown *Sidrat al-Muntaha* (a tree in the seventh heaven) and I saw its nabq fruits which resembled the clay jugs of Hajr (a town in Arabia)."[244]

In Christian tradition, the lote tree is identified with the thorn bush, with whose branches — according to Christian belief — Jesus was crowned while he was being tortured. According to some scholars, this is the only tree considered holy by Christians, Jews and Muslims alike.[245] The tree is mentioned in the Qur'an:

﴿ وَلَقَدْ رَءَاهُ نَزْلَةً أُخْرَىٰ ۝ عِندَ سِدْرَةِ ٱلْمُنتَهَىٰ ۝ عِندَهَا جَنَّةُ ٱلْمَأْوَىٰ ۝ إِذْ يَغْشَى ٱلسِّدْرَةَ مَا يَغْشَىٰ ۝ ﴾

(سورة النجم ١٣:١٦)

❨And indeed he [Muhammad] saw him [Jibreel or Gabriel] at a second descent [another time], near Sidrat-al-Muntaha [the lote tree of the utmost boundary [beyond which none can pass], near it is the Paradise of Abode. When that covered the lote tree which did cover it!❩
(Qur'an 53: 13-16)

﴿ وَأَصْحَٰبُ ٱلْيَمِينِ مَآ أَصْحَٰبُ ٱلْيَمِينِ ۝ فِي سِدْرٍ مَّخْضُودٍ ۝ وَطَلْحٍ مَّنضُودٍ ۝ ﴾

(سورة الواقعة: ٢٧-٢٩)

❨And those on the Right Hand, who will be those on the Right Hand? [They will be] among thornless lote trees, among Talh [banana plants] with fruits piled one above another.❩

(Qur'an 56: 27-29)

The fresh and the dried fruit of the plant have a pleasant, slightly acid taste. Medicinally, they are used as an astringent, a diuretic and a tonic. Bedouins use the fruit to prepare a thick paste to be baked into bread.[246] The fruits are soothing to sore throats and are used to flavour some medicines. The fruits can be eaten fresh or dried. The dried fruits are used in Chinese traditional medicine (where they are called 'red dates') to strengthen the heart and lungs, as well as to nourish the stomach and spleen and maintain normal blood pressure.[247]

We have explored so far the first two steps of the Food Guide Pyramid; these are the most important nutrient-packed foods essential for our health. Before proceeding further, stop for a moment and reconsider your everyday food choices. Are you eating enough fibres, whole grains and fresh vegetables, fruits and herbs? Nowadays, eating healthily is a real challenge with our

lack of time, controversial nutrition information, tempting adver-
tisings, and supermarket racks packed with convenient 'empty-
calorie' foods. Still, with some time management and skill, you
can supply your family with healthy and balanced yet quick and
simple menus. The remaining sections of the Food Guide Pyramid
are the ones giving the most flavours, aromas and texture to your
plate; but remember that now we are moving up the Pyramid, so
fewer servings will be required. Still, even with small amounts of
proteins, dairy and fats you can get the best out of your food. The
keys are balance, optimum choice, variety and moderation.

Proteins

Proteins are a group of
compounds made up of
one or more strands of
amino acids.[248] The recommended daily servings
of proteins are from two
to three. Proteins are essential
nutrients in the diet as they main-
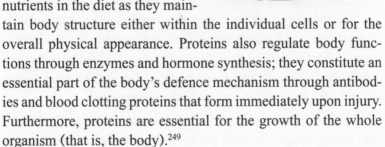
tain body structure either within the individual cells or for the
overall physical appearance. Proteins also regulate body functions through enzymes and hormone synthesis; they constitute an
essential part of the body's defence mechanism through antibodies and blood clotting proteins that form immediately upon injury.
Furthermore, proteins are essential for the growth of the whole
organism (that is, the body).[249]

When meat is mentioned in Qur'an, fruits are often mentioned
first. Allah (﷽) says:

(سورة الطور:٢٢)   ﴿وَأَمْدَدْنَٰهُم بِفَٰكِهَةٍ وَلَحْمٍ مِّمَّا يَشْتَهُونَ ۝﴾

❨And We shall provide them with fruit and meat, such as they desire.❩ *(Qur'an 52: 22)*

﴿ وَفَٰكِهَةٖ مِّمَّا يَتَخَيَّرُونَ ۝ وَلَحۡمِ طَيۡرٖ مِّمَّا يَشۡتَهُونَ ۝ ﴾   (سورة الواقعة: ٢٠-٢١)

❨And fruit; that they may choose, and the flesh of fowls that they desire.❩ *(Qur'an 56: 20-21)*

Some new research suggests that eating fruit before a meal that includes meat will provide the body with the enzymes needed to digest the meat.[250]

Protein deficiency in developed countries is uncommon; on the contrary, we suffer from protein excess, which can also be life threatening, as it causes dehydration and increases calcium loss. Protein shifts the pH balance of the blood towards the acidic side; the body then tries to counteract this change by withdrawing calcium from

What counts as a serving?
• 60-90g cooked lean meat, poultry or fish
• 1½ cup cooked beans or legumes
• 1 cup nuts (but watch out for the high fat content)

the bones, thus increasing the risk of osteoporosis. Excess protein consumption also strains the kidneys and liver, which work to eliminate the excess nitrogen produced. The excess nitrogen by-products may be deposited in the joints, causing gout. Furthermore, the excessive consumption of proteins of animal origin is usually coupled with an excess intake of fats, which causes serious risks for the cardiac and circulatory systems.[251]

Most proteins in our diet come from animal sources like meat, fish, poultry, eggs and milk products. Vegetable or plant sources also provide protein; however, most plant proteins do not provide the body with all the essential amino acids, nor are these delivered in the proper proportions required for protein synthesis in the human body. Allah reminds us about those who sought to replace the game bird meat that He sent to them from heaven with common vegetables from the earth:

﴿وَإِذْ قُلْتُمْ يَـٰمُوسَىٰ لَن نَّصْبِرَ عَلَىٰ طَعَامٍ وَٰحِدٍ فَٱدْعُ لَنَا رَبَّكَ يُخْرِجْ لَنَا مِمَّا تُنۢبِتُ ٱلْأَرْضُ مِنۢ بَقْلِهَا وَقِثَّآئِهَا وَفُومِهَا وَعَدَسِهَا وَبَصَلِهَا ۖ قَالَ أَتَسْتَبْدِلُونَ ٱلَّذِى هُوَ أَدْنَىٰ بِٱلَّذِى هُوَ خَيْرٌ ... ۝﴾ (سورة البقرة:٦١)

❴And [remember] when you said: O Moosâ [Moses]! We cannot endure one kind of food. So invoke Allah for us to bring forth for us of what the earth grows, its herbs, its cucumbers, its [wheat or garlic], its lentils and its onions. He said: Would you exchange that which is better for that which is lower?...❵ *(Qur'an 2: 61)*

Despite its incomplete proteins, a vegetarian diet can meet your body's protein needs by what we call 'protein complementa tion'. This is a technique of combining different vegetarian protein sourcepreferably in the same meal — in order to improve the quality of the diet as a whole. For example, the combination of legumes and grains or legumes and nuts or seeds pro-

vides the body with the needed essential amino acids.[252]

Common protein complementation

- Beans and rice
- Beans and corn salad
- Beans with whole grain bread
- Rice and lentils or peas
- Peanut butter and bread
- Hummus (chickpeas & sesame seeds)
- Tofu and nut stir-fries

Meat and Poultry

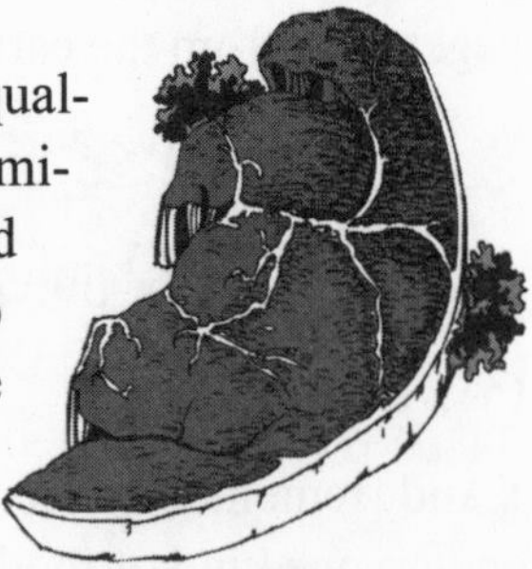

Animal proteins are considered high quality proteins: they provide the essential amino acids in a ratio closer to that needed by the human body. If we refer back to the Food Guide Pyramid, we will find the protein group in the upper section of the pyramid. This indicates that this group should constitute a relatively small proportion of the daily intake. The two to three servings recommended are more than enough to meet the body's needs. It was narrated that 'Ali ibn Abi Ṭâlib said: «If one eats meat forty days in a row his heart will become hard.»[253] This observation made so many centuries ago has now become common knowledge: too much red meat in the diet leads to heart disease.

Moreover, a hadith related by 'Â'ishah (ﷺ) states:

«We the family of Muhammad (ﷺ) used to spend (a whole month) in which we did not (need to) kindle a fire as (we had nothing to cook) we had only dates and water.»[254] In another narration, she said «We used to look at three new moons…»

In other words, between one and two months would pass in which they ate no meat.

The Prophet (ﷺ) said:

«Beware of meat, as it has ferocity like that of wine.»[255]

He (ﷺ) also said:

«Drink cow's milk as it is healing, while its meat carries disease.»[256]

Meat tends to be fatty, so we should always try to select the lean red part, and meat products such as sausages, cold cuts and

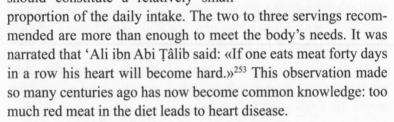

burgers should be avoided or eaten only occasionally.

On the positive side, red meat is a major source of iron. Iron is a vital constituent in two types of proteins: haemoglobin, which carries oxygen in the blood, and myoglobin, which stores oxygen in the

What does meat provide?
• Amino acids
• Niacin (B_3)
• Vitamin B_6
• Vitamin B_{12}
• Zinc and selenium
• Iron

muscles. Meat products contain the iron in a form called *haem* iron which is readily absorbed by the body; it even improves the absorption of non-haem iron from plant origin.[257] That is why red meats are recommended in the diets of anaemic people.

Meat also provides two minerals essential for the correct development of sperm: zinc and selenium. For this reason, meat was traditionally believed to improve male fertility. Zinc is involved in the development of sex organs, where it promotes cell reproduction, tissue growth and repair.[258] It is also involved in the functioning of different essential enzymes. Selenium is a strong antioxidant; it protects the sperm from free radical damage, increases the number and mobility of viable sperm,[259] aids cell growth and boosts immunity.[260]

Meat is a very good source of vitamin B_{12}, which is essential in the preservation of nerve cells. The high content of B vitamins in general means that meat helps in the maintenance of the nervous system. Ibn al-Qayyim noted that 'Ali ibn Abi Ṭâlib was reported to have said: "Eat meat, because it makes the skin colour lighter, the stomach firmer and the behaviour better. Whoever refrains from eating meat for forty days will acquire bad behaviour."[261] Again, remember that too much of anything can be harmful — more about the effect of red meat on the nervous system will be discussed in Chapter Three of this book.

According to Ibn al-Qayyim, the mutton the Prophet liked best came from the front part, which is closer to the head. In Bukhâri and Muslim, it was reported that the Prophet (ﷺ) used to like eating the mutton that comes from the shoulder.[262] One of the Prophet's (ﷺ) favourite dishes was *thareed* which is a meat and bread dish. He said:

«The virtue of 'Â'ishah as compared to other women is like the virtue of thareed as compared to all other dishes.»[263]

Furthermore Allah tells us how Prophet Ibrâheem honoured his guests with a roasted calf as a superior gesture of generosity:

(سورة هود:٦٩)   ﴿ ... فَمَا لَبِثَ أَن جَآءَ بِعِجْلٍ حَنِيذٍ ٦٩ ﴾

﴿...And he hastened to entertain them with a roasted calf.﴾

(Qur'an 11: 69)

«It was reported by Anas that they hunted a rabbit and Ṭalha sent its hip to the Prophet (ﷺ) who accepted it.»[264] Rabbit meat provides the same nutrients as red meat except that it is an even better source of selenium.

Poultry

Poultry is also an excellent source of protein and is easier to digest than red meat. In general, the meat from poultry does not contain as much iron, zinc, vitamin B_{12} and selenium. It is a good source of magnesium and vitamin B_6, but the nutritional values of poultry and game birds vary greatly. Pheasant, for example, is rich in iron, B_2, B_6 and B_{12} vitamins. Turkey meat contains much more iron in the dark meat (leg, or drumstick and thigh) than in the light meat (breast).[265] Poultry meat is usually lower in fat content than red meat;[266] this is the reason that weight-loss diets usually recommend poultry (after the removal of the skin) rather than red meat.

Quails in particular are mentioned in the Qur'an as a gift from Allah to the children of Israel:

$$\text{﴾ ... وَأَنزَلْنَا عَلَيْكُمُ ٱلْمَنَّ وَٱلسَّلْوَىٰ كُلُوا۟ مِن طَيِّبَٰتِ مَا رَزَقْنَٰكُمْ ... ۝ ﴾}$$

(سورة البقرة:٥٧)

﴾...And We sent down on you Manna and quails, [saying]: Eat of the good lawful things We have provided for you...﴿

(Qur'an 2: 57)

Quails are a rich source of protein and niacin (vitamin B_3); they are also a good source of vitamins B_1 and B_2. All poultry and game birds are a good source of the amino acid *tyrosine*, which is used by the brain to synthesize dopamine and noradrenaline. Both neurotransmitters have the ability to enhance mental concentration and alertness. Turkey is rich in the amino acid *tryptophan* which is used by the body to synthesize serotonin, a neurotransmitter that works to elevate one's mood (giving a person a feeling of well-being), and aids in appetite control.[267] So, a light lunch or a snack during break time consisting of lean turkey or chicken breast can boost your morale and mental ability for the rest of the working day.

Fish

The Prophet (ﷺ) said: «We are allowed two dead animals and two bloods: fish and locust; and liver and spleen.»[268]

When Allah mentions fish as food in Qur'an, He calls it 'tender meat':

﴿ وَهُوَ ٱلَّذِى سَخَّرَ ٱلْبَحْرَ لِتَأْكُلُوا۟ مِنْهُ لَحْمًا طَرِيًّا ... ﴿١٤﴾ ﴾   (سورة النحل:١٤)

﴿And He it is Who has subjected the sea [to you], that you eat from it fresh tender meat [fish]...﴾
(Qur'an 16: 14)

﴿ ... وَمِن كُلٍّ تَأْكُلُونَ لَحْمًا طَرِيًّا ... ﴿١٢﴾ ﴾   (سورة فاطر:١٢)

﴿...And from them both you eat fresh tender meat [fish]...﴾
(Qur'an 35: 12)

Although the many types of fish differ greatly in their nutri ent contents, in general, all fish are a good source of protein and low in saturated fats. Nutrition specialists advise eating the oily type of fish (which might be what is meant by 'tender' fish meat) like salmon, tuna, sardines, mackerel, anchovies, herrings, kippers and trout. These fish are rich in omega-3 fatty acids. These are essential fats that cannot be synthesized (produced) by the body and have to be supplied in the diet. Consumption of these fats is linked to low rates of heart disease, as they lower the risk of blood clotting and atherosclerosis. They are also needed for skin and tissue health, the healing of wounds, the regulation of inflammatory and allergic responses and for the health of the nervous system. Consuming oily fish helps to build strong healthy bones as it is one of the best sources of vitamin D,[269] which is needed for the proper absorption of calcium. In addition, canned oily fish, when eaten with their soft bones, are considered an excellent source of calcium[270].

Liver and spleen

Remember that the Prophet (ﷺ) said:

«We are allowed two dead animals and two bloods: fish and locust; and liver and spleen.»

Liver — whether of calf, ox, lamb, chicken, duck or goose — is a very rich source of iron and vitamins A, D, and B vitamins; it is also a good source of protein, zinc, copper, and selenium. Fish liver — especially cod and halibut liver — is also a very good source of both vitamin A and D. Although it is a food from animal origin, liver is a good source of vitamin C as well. This makes liver a very good choice for anaemic people and for growing children; however, it has to be consumed in moderation due to its high cholesterol content.

Liver is high in saturated fats and cholesterol and its vitamin A content is high enough to pose a possible *teratogenic*[271] hazard in pregnant women if large amounts are eaten on a regular basis. In other words, pregnant women and people with high blood cholesterol or with a history of heart problems should cut down on their liver consumption.

The organs, in general, are a very good source of *phospholipids*, which are needed for healthy brain neurons and receptor cells. In addition, some recent studies suggest that they have a positive effect on memory and brain performance. Calf spleen, for one, is a very good source of iron, vitamin B_2, niacin and vitamin C and a good source of vitamin A.

Plant-source proteins

This class of proteins comes from different plant sources:

➤ Pulses and legumes (chickpeas, peas, lentils, peanuts, and various beans)

> Whole grains (wheat, rice, quinoa, barley...)
> Nuts (walnuts, almonds, hazelnuts...)
> Seeds (flax, sesame, pumpkin, dill, anise, fennel...)

The advantages of this second sub-group of proteins are that they are lower in saturated fats and they are high in fibre. In addition, they constitute a rich source of minerals such as calcium, zinc and iron.

Beans offer a range of disease-fighting phytonutrients like the isoflavones in chickpeas and carotenes in red lentils. Soya beans, chickpeas and lentils contain phytoestrogens which provide a wide range of health benefits to the heart, breasts and prostate[272]. They also help to reduce premenstrual and menopausal symptoms such as, mood swings, water retention and hot flushes and protect from oestrogen-dependent cancers.

Seeds are rich in unsaturated fats — the essential fatty acids; they are also good sources of calcium, zinc and vitamin E. Sesame seeds and pumpkin seeds are particularly good sources of iron. Flax and pumpkin seeds supply the essential omega-3 fatty acids which protect against heart diseases and arteriosclerosis.[273] Try to avoid seeds with too much added salt, and note that their benefit is greatly reduced when roasted or cooked; they can be added to stir-fries at the last minute to preserve their nutritional value.

Nuts, a very healthy snack for kids, contain much of the same nutrients that seeds do. They are rich in iron, calcium and vitamin E. Pecans, peanuts[274] and cashew nuts are excellent sources of zinc, which make them valuable for boosting the immune system and increasing male fertility. Almonds, peanuts, walnuts, hazelnuts and cashews are also useful in fighting heart disease and in controlling high blood cholesterol.[275]

Milk and dairy products

Humans have known milk for thousands of years since they domesticated grazing animals. Milk usually comes from goats, sheep and cows, although camel milk and even mare's milk are produced com-

What does milk provide?
• Amino acids
• calcium & phosphorus
• Vitamins B_2, B_3 & B_{12}
• Vitamins A & D
• Potassium

mercially in some parts of the world. In addition to milk, there is a wide variety of dairy products sold in local supermarkets, such as the different types of cheese, yogurt, curd, buttermilk and other processed forms that are common around the globe.

Milk is the most beneficial drink for the body due to its valuable nutritional contents and closeness to the nature of the body.

It is narrated that «On the night of *Isrâ'*[276] the Messenger of Allah (ﷺ) was given two cups: one containing milk and the other wine. The Prophet looked at them, then chose the milk. Gabriel said: Thank Allah Who has led you to what is natural, if you had taken the wine, your followers would have gone astray.»[277]

Prophet Muhammad (ﷺ) taught us: «Whoever Allah gives food let him supplicate: 'O Allah! Bless it for us and grant us what is better.' And whoever Allah grants some milk let him say: 'O Allah! Bless it for us and grant us more of it,' for I do not know of a more complete food or drink than milk.»[278]

The Prophet (ﷺ) also used to eat cheese: «The Prophet brought some cheese in Tabook; he asked for a knife, said: In the Name of Allah, and cut it.»[279]

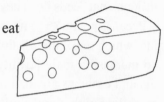

What counts as a serving?
- 1 cup of milk or yogurt
- 45g natural cheese
- 60g processed cheese
- 1 cups cottage cheese
- ½ cup ricotta cheese
- ⅓ cup milk powder

It is recommended to consume two to three servings of dairy products per day. According to the American Dietetic Association (ADA), milk, yogurt and cheese are our body's best source of calcium and riboflavin (vitamin B_2); they are also good sources of protein, phosphorus, potassium, magnesium, zinc, vitamin A and vitamin D.[280]

Milk is also mentioned in the Qur'an:

﴿ وَإِنَّ لَكُمْ فِى ٱلْأَنْعَـٰمِ لَعِبْرَةً نُّسْقِيكُم مِّمَّا فِى بُطُونِهِۦ مِنۢ بَيْنِ فَرْثٍ وَدَمٍ لَّبَنًا خَالِصًا سَآئِغًا لِّلشَّـٰرِبِينَ ۝ ﴾   (سورة النحل:٦٦)

﴿And verily, in the cattle there is a lesson for you. We give you to drink of that which is in their bellies, from between excretions and blood, pure milk; palatable to the drinkers.﴾   *(Qur'an 16: 66)*

Allah also says while describing Paradise:

﴿ مَّثَلُ ٱلْجَنَّةِ ٱلَّتِى وُعِدَ ٱلْمُتَّقُونَ ۖ فِيهَآ أَنْهَـٰرٌ مِّن مَّآءٍ غَيْرِ ءَاسِنٍ وَأَنْهَـٰرٌ مِّن لَّبَنٍ لَّمْ يَتَغَيَّرْ ... ﴾   (سورة محمد:١٥)

﴿The description of Paradise which the God-fearing [pious] have been promised is that in it are rivers of water the taste and smell of which are not changed; rivers of milk of which the taste never changes...❭   *(Qur'an 47: 15)*

In our supermarkets today we find a wide variety of dairy products, whether skimmed, fat-free or full-cream. As a general rule, dairy food with less fat usually tends to contain less cholesterol while the actual content of other nutrients — minerals, vitamins and protein — remain almost the same. Personally, I use full cream milk unless I am trying to lose weight. I always seek the more natural form of food: the fewer human-induced changes, the better it is. Our knowledge concerning nutrients is in a continuous evolution, we definitely are in no position to fool with Allah's perfect creation.

Some useful information:

➢ When buying cow's milk and other dairy products like cheese from cow's milk, try to choose certified organic milk obtained from organically fed, free-range cows. Oestrogens and antibiotics used in cattle feed and the oestrogen-like compounds resulting as by-products from pesticide use tend to concentrate in animal fat and milk products; these are linked to many health problems like premature puberty and breast, ovarian, and endometrial cancer in women as well as *gynecomastia* (abnormally large mammary glands in males) and male infertility.

➢ Some dairy products do not belong under this section of the pyramid because they have a high fat content, like butter, cream, ice cream, cream cheese and sour cream. These usually contain very small amounts of vitamins and minerals, but a lot of fat and cholesterol, so they belong to the uppermost tip of the pyramid along with the food that should be eaten sparingly.

➢ Flavoured milk delivers the same nutrients with an addition of about 60 calories per cup from sweeteners, fruit flavoured syrup or chocolate that has been added.[281]

➢ Caffeine is known to slightly increase calcium loss through urine, but the amount lost is not much, so to boost your calcium intake you can have your coffee with plenty of milk.[282]

➢ Some fad diets encourage the substitution of dairy products with calcium supplements and calcium fortified foods. Although they may fill the calcium gap (calcium is not easily available from most other sources), they do not supply all the health-promoting substances and valuable nutrients (mentioned above) found in dairy products. In addition, dairy products contain substances with potential functional benefits including *conjugated linoleic acid* (CLA), which may provide protection from some cancers and other health conditions.[283]

➢ Also, be aware that you may be getting too much calcium if you regularly consume calcium supplements and fortified foods and drinks; this 'calcium overdose' subjects your body to the risk of iron and zinc deficiency due to absorption limitation. The consumption of real milk and dairy products does not cause this calcium overload.

Buttermilk

Buttermilk is the liquid with a slightly sour taste that is left over after producing butter from full-cream milk by the churning process, hence came its name. This production method, though, is no longer used for the commercial preparation of buttermilk; the latter is produced by the action of souring agents (lactic acid bacteria) causing the fermentation which results in the characteristic sour taste of the milk. During the fermentation process, a good proportion of the lactose in the milk is turned into lactic acid. This, according to some opinions, is the reason why buttermilk is more digestible by lactose intolerant individuals.[284]

There is no butter, per se, in buttermilk; it is actually lower in fat than ordinary milk. Natural buttermilk is produced from the whey left after the butter is churned so it contains less fat than the original milk. Today, most buttermilk is made using the bacterial fermentation process starting out with fat-free or low-fat milk. A cup of buttermilk (240 ml) provides 100 calories along with 285 mg of calcium, and only 2 grams of fat and 10 mg of cholesterol. In comparison, a cup of whole milk contains 150 calories, 290 mg of calcium and 8 grams of fat, with 35 mg of cholesterol.[285]

Buttermilk and yogurt with their live bacterial culture are considered *probiotics*.[286] According to the ADA, probiotics may help keep the immune system healthy and reduce the risk of some health problems such as high cholesterol levels and some types of cancer.[287] People with digestion problems are often advised to drink buttermilk rather than milk, as it is more quickly digested. For those watching their caloric and/or fat intake, using buttermilk instead of butter or sour cream gives them both the butter flavour and the characteristic taste of sour cream with much fewer calories.

Buttermilk is excellent in baked goods, in soups and in salad dressings. It imparts a rich, hearty flavour with fewer calories than milk or cream.

Fats and sweets

Fats and sweets occur at the tip of the pyramid to indicate that they should be eaten sparingly. The food in this group supplies mostly calories and very few nutrients.

Sweets

Contrary to what is popularly believed, other than their role in tooth deterioration, studies have not linked sugars to any major health concern. Sugar itself is not a villain as claimed by many fad diets; however, we need to be aware of the different forms of sugar that we consume and how these affect our bodies. Sugars consumed daily are either naturally occurring in food, like milk, fruits, and vegetables, or are added to the food during processing. A very high proportion of sugars come from commercial food processing where they are added to almost every product to add flavour, give bulk, and improve consistency or texture. Pay close attention to the amount of hidden sugars in your diet. It is estimated that, if we rely mainly on convenience foods and packaged goods, we will be consuming about 320 calories daily from processed sugars.[288]

The closer the sugar is to its natural state, the better. Simple refined sugars tend to have a high *glycemic index*[289] (GI). Food that has a high GI means that when consumed it tends to cause a sudden increase in the BSL, thus inducing a rapid release of insulin from the pancreas. If this process is repeated frequently, the pancreas gets exhausted causing a myriad of health problems ranging from obesity and insulin resistance to diabetes.[290] Even the consumption of natural sweeteners such as honey, maple syrup, date sugar, and molasses should be moderate. Although they have many health benefits, they still have a high GI causing a rapid rise in BSL, a quick mood and energy boost, followed by a sudden drop, irritability and depression.

Try to aim for naturally occurring, whole, unrefined sugars, but remember that there is always room for variation; so if you fancy some sweets or simple sugars now and then, it is okay, but you can do yourself much good by consuming along with it some protein or fat-containing food to slow down and stabilize the rise in your BSL.[291]

General guidelines for fats & sweets:

- Use vegetable oils for cooking instead of butter or ghee
- Avoid fried food
- Avoid commercially available salad dressing. Prepare your own or use olive oil, lemon juice and herbs instead
- Go easy on processed spreads, icings and toppings
- Reduce consumption of cream cheeses, creams, butter and ghee
- Limit your intake of soft drinks, ice cream, sweets and candies
- Reduce your sugar intake — especially white processed sugars

---

Note for parents: Read the label very carefully before giving any processed food to your child. Be aware that sugars are addictive, and despite the lack of concrete data, more and more studies point to the role that processed sugars play in causing problems in behavioural and physical development in children. As mentioned earlier, sugar is not necessarily harmful, but when it comes to sweets and desserts, we usually do not follow our Islamic 'golden rule': moderation. Limit your child's access to television commercials advertising sugar cereals and junk food, which basically brainwash children into wanting that kind of food.

Health problems such as obesity, insulin-resistance and diabetes result from a complex interaction of genetic make-up, personality, emotional state and social environment, sedentary lifestyle, poor nutritional choices and excessive calorie intake. Glucose is essential to the body and brain normal functions; it is converted to fats only if we consume more calories than our body needs. Thus, the main problem with this group of food is that it supplies almost no nutrients, only empty calories.

Refined sugar was not commonly used and remained very expensive until around the 1500s when it was first mass produced using slave labour. It did not take long for this new product to replace honey and other natural sweeteners in the European diet and food industry, and from Europe it spread to the rest of the world. Honey, on the other hand, has been used as a sweetener for ages. Ancient drawings dating back to the Stone Age showed the collection and use of honey by our ancestors. Ancient Egyptian papyri and Greek manuscripts indicated the widespread use of honey as sweetener over 3000 years ago, and this remained the case in the Western world until the colonial era.[292]

It was reported by his wife 'Â'ishah that Prophet Muhammad (ﷺ) loved sweets and honey.[293]

He (ﷺ) also once prepared for his Companions a sweet dessert: «He (ﷺ) asked for a pot in which he put some flour, ghee[294] and honey; he then ordered for it to be cooked and ate with his Companions, saying: This is called 'Khabees' in Persia.»[295]

Honey holds a special place in our Islamic tradition; it is mentioned in the Qur'an as a healing for humans:

$$ ﴿ ... يَخْرُجُ مِنْ بُطُونِهَا شَرَابٌ مُّخْتَلِفٌ أَلْوَانُهُ فِيهِ شِفَاءٌ لِّلنَّاسِ إِنَّ فِي ذَلِكَ لَآيَةً $$

$$ لِّقَوْمٍ يَتَفَكَّرُونَ ۝ ﴾ $$

(سورة النحل:٦٩)

﴿...There comes forth from their bellies, a drink of varying colour wherein is healing for people. Verily, in this is indeed a sign for people who think.﴾   *(Qur'an 16: 69)*

Prophet Muhammad (ﷺ) was said to have regularly started his day with a spoonful of honey dissolved in half a cup of water.[296]

J. Scrivner, from the British School of Complementary Therapy, recommends drinking one teaspoonful of honey dissolved in a cup of warm water in the morning as kidney tonic (this mixture is to increase the detoxifying power of the kidneys).[297]

«A man came to the Prophet (ﷺ) and said: My brother is complaining about his stomach (he has diarrhoea). The Prophet said: Give him some honey to drink. The man left and came back later saying: I have given him some honey but it did not help, or in other words, 'it made his diarrhoea worse'. The Prophet (ﷺ) told him again: Give him some honey to drink. The man repeated this twice or three times and each time the Prophet (ﷺ) gave the same answer. The third or fourth time, the Prophet (ﷺ) said: Allah has spoken the truth while your brother's stomach has lied. It was reported that the man's brother was finally cured.»[298]

The use of honey in treatment of ailments dates back thousands of years. In Chinese medicine, honey is used to detoxify the liver, ease pain, and treat hypertension, stomach ulcers and sore throat.[299] Honey has also been traditionally used in the treatment of cough and various intestinal disorders and was applied locally to minor burns and skin injuries.

Until recently, many nutrition books referred to honey as an empty calorie carbohydrate. They considered it as a mere mixture of sugars; but current research indicates that this is mistaken. Here are some benefits of honey as discovered by the latest scientific research:

➢ The consumption of honey is beneficial in lowering the risk of heart disease. It lowers C-reactive protein (usually associated with high risk of atherosclerosis).[300]

➢ Honey has a lower impact on blood glucose, insulin, and lipid levels compared to glucose or sugar syrups particularly in diabetics and/or people who have high levels of fat in the blood.[301]

➢ Natural honey works as an anti-inflammatory by lowering concentrations of prostaglandin in plasma.[302]

➢ Folklore and anecdotal evidence suggest that honey can prevent and/or provide relief from allergies. In a recent study, researchers found that regular honey consumption results in a statistically significant lowering of allergy symptoms — particularly those symptoms that affect the eyes.[303]

➢ Phenolic compounds in honey increase the antioxidant activity of human plasma and raise the body's defences against oxidative stress. Research suggests that the substitution of honey for other sweeteners can result in an enhanced antioxidant defence system.[304]

➤ Some studies show that honey is, in some cases, a more powerful antibacterial agent than antibiotics.[305] Furthermore, because of its antimicrobial properties, honey has the potential to combat mouth infections and holds promise for the treatment of periodontal and gum disease, mouth ulcers, and other diseases of the mouth.[306]

➤ Honey enhances the growth of human intestinal bifidobacteria and promotes their production of lactic and acetic acid. That is why honey may be considered as a *prebiotic*[307].[308] These bacteria help keep the immune system healthy and reduce the risk of some health problems such as high cholesterol levels and some types of cancer. They also aid in reducing the symptoms of lactose intolerance and shorten the duration of diarrhoea. Hence, honey is an ideal sweetener for fermented dairy products like yogurt and buttermilk.[309]

➤ Recent research suggests the effectiveness of honey as antibacterial agent against Helicobacter pylori, the cause of stomach ulcers.[310]

➤ The benefits of honey extend from its oral use to its valuable anti-microbial actions when applied locally.[311] Studies show that honey is effective in the treatment of wounds colonized by antibiotic-resistant bacteria and in infected post-surgical wounds which do not respond to conventional systemic and local antibiotic treatment. Furthermore, honey demonstrates potent antifungal activity.[312]

Other beneficial by-products of bees:

Honey is not the only healing agent obtained from bees. Bees are the unique source of: bee pollen, *propolis* and *royal jelly*:

1. Bee pollens are the pollen grains collected by the bees from different flowers; they then become a complete nutritional source

rich in vitamins, minerals, and phytonutrients. Bee pollens are convenient source of rutin. One should be cautious in using pollens, as many people are highly allergic to them.[313]

2. Bee propolis is a nutrient from plant origin collected and modified by bees to yield a sticky resinous material which they use in building their hives. It contains flavonoids which are believed to provide most of its healing action. Bee propolis is effective against parasites, fungal infections and viruses — especially herpes, flu and upper respiratory tract infections. It is also an antioxidant and ulcer healer.[314]

3. Royal jelly is the food that turns the queen bee from an ordinary bee into a queen of astonishing size, longevity and reproductive capability.[315] It is a creamy or yellow viscous liquid with a slight bitter flavour representing a concentrated form of vitamins, minerals and some unique nutrients.[316] The consumption of royal jelly improves the absorption of nutrients by the body, increases vitality, and strengthens the immunity.[317] The cancer fighting properties of royal jelly have already been proven in animal studies, but are yet to be tested in humans.[318]

Important information about types of honey:

➢ Honeys from different floral sources may exhibit varied antimicrobial activities.

➢ Commercial honey processing generally involves controlled heating (to destroy yeast and delay granulation) combined with fine straining or pressure filtration. There is concern that the processing of honey may reduce the antioxidant capacity of some varieties. The antioxidant capacity of honey may also be reduced after six months storage regardless of the storage temperature or container type.[319]

Fats

We cannot live without fats. I do not refer here to our love for the flavour of the food, but to their role in how our bodies function. You may be surprised, but this is a well known fact: in moderate amounts, fats are essential for our health. Some vitamins cannot be absorbed unless they are dissolved in fats (vitamins A, D, K and E); fats supply the body with essential fatty acids which keep the brain and nervous system intact and maintain healthy skin. Omega-3 fatty acids found mainly in fatty fish and nuts are linked to a healthy heart and cardiovascular system. Conjugated linoleic acids (CLA) found in dairy and some meat products have the potential ability to reduce certain types of cancer. Even cholesterol is essential for the production of some hormones (namely the sex hormones and cortisols) and for the synthesis of bile acids that is essential for fat digestion.[320]

So, we see that we have to eat fat, but the questions are: How much fat is needed? And which type?

As we mentioned earlier, the general Islamic rule in food consumption is moderation:

﴾ ... وَكُلُواْ وَٱشْرَبُواْ وَلَا تُسْرِفُوٓاْ إِنَّهُۥ لَا يُحِبُّ ٱلْمُسْرِفِينَ ۝ ﴾ (سورة الأعراف:٣١)

﴾...And eat and drink but do not waste by extravagance, certainly He [Allah] does not like those who waste by extravagance.﴿

(Qur'an 7: 31)

According to the recommendation of the USDA, not more than 30% of our calorie intake should be supplied from fat. However, until the age of two years, no restriction should be made on a person's fat intake (provided that it is the right type of fat), as until this age their brain and nervous system are still developing and the fats are needed for the healthy formation of neurons.

No serving range or serving size is given to this group of food by either the USDA or ADA; they just recommend that fats be consumed sparingly. Just to get a general idea about the right amount to be consumed, we can look at the Mayo Clinic's own guidelines for healthy fat intake.[321] Eat a maximum of three to four servings per day, each serving consisting of around 45 calories, preferably from good fat choices. A serving of fats may be found in each of the following:

➢ 4 to 8 nuts or peanuts according to size

➢ a slice of avocado (around the size of an orange slice)

➢ 5 to 8 olives, again according to size

➢ 1 teaspoon vegetable oil: olive oil is the best choice

➢ 1 tablespoonful seeds, but avoid roasted and heavily salted ones

➢ 2 teaspoons commercial[322] mayonnaise, preferably low-fat

Now, we must ask: Which type of fat is the right fat? To answer this question, take a quick glance at how different types of dietary fats affect our blood lipids as summarized in the following table:

Types of Fats

Type of fat	Source	Effects on blood lipids
Saturated fats	Butter, ghee, margarine, meat and poultry	Raise LDL ☹ (bad cholesterol) levels

Type of fat	Source	Effects on blood lipids
Polyunsaturated fats	Most vegetable oils (corn, sunflower, soybean, cottonseed)	Lower both ☹ L LDL & HDL J ☺ (bad & good) cholesterol levels
Monounsaturated fats	Olives & olive oil, canola oil, walnuts and avocado.	Lower LDL & raise HDL J ☺ cholesterol
Trans fats	Hydrogenated oils & deep frying	Increase LDL & reduce HDL
Omega-3 fats	Fatty fish, flax seed oil, some nuts	Lower triglycerides* and total blood cholesterol

☹ LDL cholesterol: cholesterol carried by low density lipoproteins (LDL) which circulate to body cells carrying it where it is needed. If their level in the blood increases beyond natural body needs, they may form deposits on arteries and blood vessels; hence 'bad' cholesterol.

☺ HDL cholesterol: cholesterol carried by high density lipoproteins (HDL) away from body cells to the liver so they can be broken down and excreted; hence 'good' cholesterol.

* Triglycerides are the major component of dietary and tissue fat. A high level in the blood indicates potential cardiovascular risks.

Olives and olive oil

Allah mentions the olive tree in the Qur'an:

﴿وَٱلتِّينِ وَٱلزَّيْتُونِ ۝ وَطُورِ سِينِينَ ۝ وَهَٰذَا ٱلْبَلَدِ ٱلْأَمِينِ ۝ لَقَدْ خَلَقْنَا ٱلْإِنسَٰنَ فِي أَحْسَنِ تَقْوِيمٍ ۝﴾ (سورة التين:١‏:٤)

◆By the fig, and the olive, by Mount Sinai, and by this city of security [Makkah], verily, We created the human of the best stature [or mould].◆
(Qur'an 95: 1-4)

﴿ يُنبِتُ لَكُم بِهِ ٱلزَّرْعَ وَٱلزَّيْتُونَ وَٱلنَّخِيلَ وَٱلْأَعْنَابَ وَمِن كُلِّ ٱلثَّمَرَتِ
إِنَّ فِى ذَٰلِكَ لَآيَةً لِّقَوْمٍ يَتَفَكَّرُونَ ﴿١١﴾ ﴾   (سورة النحل:١١)

◆With it He causes to grow for you the crops, the olives, the date-palms, the grapes, and every kind of fruit. In this is indeed an evident proof and a manifest sign for people who give thought.◆
(Qur'an 16: 11)

Prophet Muhammad (ﷺ) said: «Eat oil and use it as ointment as it comes from a blessed tree.»[323]

It is clear from his statement that he (ﷺ) was referring to olive oil.

As seen in the previous table, olives and their oil are rich in monounsaturated fatty acids. These acids tend to improve blood cholesterol ratio by their double beneficial effect: they raise the level of good cholesterol (HDL) and reduce the level of bad cholesterol (LDL). According to the latest scientific research, a traditional Mediterranean dietary pattern which incorporates fruits and vegetables, whole grains, legumes and fatty fish as well as olive oil is likely to reduce cardiovascular risks. Olive oil's phenolic content seems to reduce the possibility for LDL to form plaque and stick to the artery walls. Furthermore, olive oil is highly effective against chronic constipation and it has been proven effective in expelling gall bladder stones. Ointments prepared from olive oil are good emollients and healing agents for chapped and dry skin.

Olive oil is available in supermarkets in several varieties: light, virgin or extra virgin. All are the same in terms of the type and the amount of fat. The difference lies mainly in the flavour and aroma and perhaps in the phytonutrient content; as we noted earlier, the more processed the food is, the more it loses its beneficial value. The extra virgin type is obtained by cold-pressing the olives and hence it is the most flavoursome and probably the most nutritious type. Remember, although it is healthy, olive oil is still high in calories.

Butter

A hadith states:

«The two children of Busr said: The Messenger of Allah (ﷺ) came by us and we offered him some butter and dried dates, as he used to like eating butter and dried dates.»[324]

Compared to ghee, butter is healthier due to its content of milk solids. In addition, the manufacturing process concentrates the fat in the prepared ghee, thus it contains more fat and calories per spoonful compared to butter.[325] The recommendation of the USDA is to reduce consumption of butter, ghee and animal fats in general, as they are rich in saturated fatty acids and cholesterol — saturated fats are the ones that are solid at room temperature. They could also originate from plant sources, as palm and coconut oils do. This does not mean we have to remove them completely from our diet, but we should decrease the amounts we consume.

A word about cholesterol

Cholesterol is found only in animal-based foods. Although it does not contribute to your calorie intake, the USDA recommends restricting total cholesterol intake to 300 mg per day. This is due to the fact that excess cholesterol in the body may deposit on the arterial walls leading to increased risks of artery damage, plaque formation, atherosclerosis and circulatory problems. Some foods are especially high in cholesterol, such as shellfish, squid, eggs and the organs that we eat. Nonetheless, your total fat intake — especially of saturated and trans-fats — has more effect on blood cholesterol level than dietary cholesterol itself, as the body uses these types of fats to synthesize its own cholesterol.[326]

Nutrition Advice
from the Sunnah

Water

Allah (ﷻ) says in the Qur'an:

(سورة الأنبياء:٣٠)   ﴿ ... وَجَعَلْنَا مِنَ ٱلْمَآءِ كُلَّ شَىْءٍ حَىٍّ ... ۝ ﴾

﴿...And We have made from water every living thing...﴾

(Qur'an 21: 30)

He also says:

(سورة المرسلات:٢٧)   ﴿ ... وَأَسْقَيْنَٰكُم مَّآءً فُرَاتًا ۝ ﴾

﴿...And We have given you to drink sweet water.﴾ *(Qur'an 77: 27)*

Prophet Muhammad (ﷺ) liked to drink cool water. «He used to drink it in three sips, not exhaling into the cup, and said of this method: This is more healthful and better in quenching the thirst.»[327]

Water is the most common substance on earth and it is the most abundant substance in the human body. An average healthy body consists of 50-75% water. The leaner you are, the higher the proportion of water in your body, as fat tissue is less capable of holding water. Every body cell, tissue or organ needs water to perform its normal functions. Besides quenching thirst, water performs several important functions in our bodies:[328]

> ➤ Water regulates body temperature. When it evaporates off our skin, water takes a considerable amount of heat with it, thus cooling the body down. Water holds heat in the body and prevents sudden fluctuations in its temperature.

> ➤ Water acts as a protective cushion represented in the amniotic fluid surrounding the foetus and cerebrospinal fluid surrounding your brain and spinal cord.

> ➤ Water is a lubricant in the form of fluids between the joints as well as in the gastrointestinal tract. It moistens different body tissues such as those of the eyes, mouth and nose.

> ➤ Water is an important part of the hydrolysis reactions occurring in our bodies. An example of such a reaction is the breakdown of complex carbohydrates (like starches) to yield simple sugars.

> ➤ Water is also a solvent for many molecules and ions in the body. For example, after eating a pretzel or a biscuit, water in the saliva dissolves the salt or sugars contents of this food for it to be further processed by the body.

> ➤ Water is the main transport system for the delivery of absorbed nutrients and removal of excreted waste from the cells via the blood and the lymph.

> Water is the main component of every body fluid including blood, gastric juice, saliva and urine.

Drinking water and other beverages is our main source of water, but we also obtain a substantial amount from foods like fruits and vegetables. Celery, lettuce, cucumbers, tomatoes and watermelons hold large amounts of water.

Normally, the body loses around a total of ten cups (or 2½ litres) of water per day. To avoid dehydration and to keep our body functions normal we need to replenish this loss. An average adult needs at least 8 cups of water every day, or around 8-12 cups total fluid intake (that is, including what s/he gets from other juices, drinks and food).[329]

Zamzam water

Zamzam water holds a special place in all Muslims' hearts. It is looked upon as sacred water, a valued gift from the holy land brought each year by pilgrims to their relatives and friends. Prophet Muhammad (ﷺ) said: «It is a nutritious food and a cure from ailments.»[330] He (ﷺ) also said: «Zamzam water is for whatever is intended in drinking it.»[331]

Other drinks

Prophet Muhammad (ﷺ) loved sweet, cold drinks. He used to drink honey at his wife Zainab's house. He also drank the water that either dates or raisins had been soaked in.[332] We should note here that the Prophet (ﷺ) did not drink very hot drinks until they cooled down; he never blew on his food or drink and never breathed into pots or cups.

Vinegar

Vinegar has been used for thousands of years. Vinegar is made by two distinct biochemical processes, both the result of the action of micro-organisms. The first process is obtained through the yeast fermentation of natural fruits or grains sugars into alcohol. This is called alcoholic fermentation. The second process results from the action of a group of bacteria (*Acetobacter*) converting the alcohol to acid. This is the acid fermentation that forms vinegar. Proper bacterial cultures are important, timing is important, and fermentation should be carefully controlled. Vinegar can be made from any fruit, or from any substance containing sugar. Apple juice is most commonly used.[333]

Vinegar has long been recognized as a cleaning and sanitizing agent effective against a broad range of bacteria, yeasts and moulds. The shelf life of vinegar is almost indefinite. Because of its acid nature, vinegar is self-preserving and does not need refrigeration. White vinegar does not show any alteration over time, while naturally produced vinegar may show some physical changes like darkening in colour or the development of cloudiness or sediment, but still it is perfectly safe for consumption.[334]

Prophet Muhammad (ﷺ) liked unprocessed natural vinegar: he used to dip cooked chicken in it. He once said to his wife when she told him that they had only vinegar for dinner: «What an excellent condiment is vinegar!»[335] Scientific research has shown that the effects of potato meals on insulin and blood sugar levels can be reduced by use of vinegar dressing.[336] It was also proved that supplementing a carbohydrate meal with vinegar lowers glucose and insulin responses and increases satiety (the feeling of being full or satisfied after eating).[337]

Vinegar has been widely used as a home remedy and house cleaning agent for ages:[338]

198   *Healing Body & Soul*

> It is used with warm water as gargle in sore throat or added to honey and taken by spoon to relieve throat infections and productive cough.

> It reduces itch when rubbed on mosquito bites.

> It can be diluted and used locally to relieve many fungal infections either the *thrush* in the mouth, which is sometimes caused by long-term antibiotic use, or the athlete's foot and nail fungus.

> When added to beef or poultry soup stock, vinegar help leach the calcium from the bones into your stock.

> When vinegar is repeatedly applied to cold sores, it speeds healing and prevents further outbreaks.

> Vinegar is a mild disinfectant with no side effects, so it can be safely added to water for washing fruits and salad vegetables or for rinsing countertop surfaces and refrigerator shelves.

More advice

Bless your food first:

There are numerous hadiths that command us to do this:

«'Umar ibn Abi Salamah narrated: When I was a boy I was under the care of the Messenger of Allah (ﷺ), and I used to eat with him and my hand used to move around the dish while eating. The Prophet told me: Child, pronounce the Name of Allah (say *bismillâh*), eat with your right hand, and eat from what is nearer to you in the dish.»[339]

The Prophet (ﷺ) also said:

«The Devil eats from the food on which Allah's Name was not mentioned.»[340] «When one of you eats let him mention Allah's Name before starting, and if he forgets, let him say: 'In the Name of Allah at its beginning and at its end' (*bismillâh awwaluhu wa âkhiruh*).»[341]

Dr. Andrew Weil, in his book *8 Weeks for Optimum Health*, recommends taking some time before eating to feel grateful for the food you consume. Remember your connection to the universe, your dependence on all other living things and most importantly remember the ultimate source of all these blessings.[342] These few seconds raise your spiritual awareness and improve your sense of responsibility and connectedness to the world and to your Creator; these few seconds revive in you the idea of 'holism' we are discussing in this book, the meaning that you are not a mere physical body and your life has a vast meaning beyond the material world.

Use your right hand:

Prophet Muhammad (ﷺ) said:

«When one of you eats let him use his right hand and if he drinks let him drink with his right hand, as the Devil eats and drinks with his left hand.»[343]

Eat slowly and sit up properly:

Bukhâri narrated that the Prophet (ﷺ) said: «I do not recline while eating.»

Another piece of advice from the wise people of long ago goes, "Dissolve your food by remembering Allah and prayers (ṣalât), do not sleep immediately after it as your hearts will harden, do not move too much while eating as this may harm you and do not skip dinner or you might age early."

Studies show that the increase in blood sugar levels (BSL) is less drastic when we eat more slowly. If BSL shoots up suddenly, the level of insulin also rises rapidly, leading to a sudden reduction in BSL. An even BSL sustains an even production of the neurotransmitter serotonin. If the level of the latter falls, it causes irritability and mood swings.[344] It is also important to note here that the production of serotonin is further stimulated by good relationships and social communication and collaboration.[345] So gathering and chatting at dinner time with family is a great opportunity to lift our spirits after a long working day, restoring energy and generating strong family ties. In his *Medicine of the Prophet*, Adh-Dhahabi advised families to eat their meals together, in order to gain more blessings and benefits.[346]

Be grateful:

When the Prophet (ﷺ) completed his meals, he used to say:

Alhamdu lillâh hamdan katheeran tayyiban mubârakan feehi, ghair makfee wa lâ maudi'i, wa lâ mustaghnee 'anhu rabbanâ. «All praise be to Allah, Blessed is He! Allah, we cannot reject Your Bounty, nor leave it nor suffice ourselves without it.»[347]

Do not skip dinner:

Remember this part of that wise saying: "Do not skip dinner even if you just eat some dates, as whoever skips dinner, ages."

According to Dr. Barry Sears, eating a healthy snack before going to bed at night ensures the adequate release of growth hormone during sleep.[348] Growth hormone is secreted by the pituitary gland; it is secreted during the deep sleep stages when the body repairs itself in preparation for the next day. Growth hormone has been found to be responsible — among other things — for the burning of fat and the building of new muscles. Dr. Sears further advices not to eat a carbohydrate-rich meal before going to bed, as this raises the insulin level which in turn retards the secretion of growth hormone. A balanced light snack composed of both carbohydrate and protein is advisable. Remember the advice mentioned above: "Do not sleep immediately after it as your hearts will harden." Some physical movement, a relaxing walk or even offering two *raka'ah* of *ṣalât* (two units of prayer) after your dinner will help digestion before you retire.

Environment

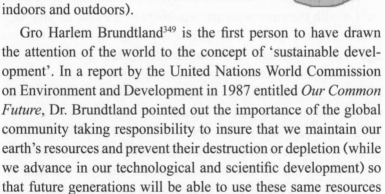

$\mathcal{T}$o reach and maintain a state of good health for our biochemical bodies, it is crucial to pay full attention to both our internal environment (food and nutrition) as well as our external environment (exposure to surrounding chemicals and pollutants, both indoors and outdoors).

Gro Harlem Brundtland[349] is the first person to have drawn the attention of the world to the concept of 'sustainable development'. In a report by the United Nations World Commission on Environment and Development in 1987 entitled *Our Common Future*, Dr. Brundtland pointed out the importance of the global community taking responsibility to insure that we maintain our earth's resources and prevent their destruction or depletion (while we advance in our technological and scientific development) so that future generations will be able to use these same resources and further their own development.[350]

From that day forward, the world began to become more aware of environmental problems and started to take serious steps towards the protection of the environment. The international community finally recognized that we are facing serious hazards, including air pollution from the production of nuclear and other forms of energy, motor vehicle exhaust and waste disposal; the pollution of our food by pesticides, additives and genetically modified crops; health concerns resulting from the depletion of the ozone layer, oil spills, global warming and acid rain. Moreover, the global community began to recognize the links between all these issues and a variety of other problems including increasing levels of poverty in the third world, regional over-population and the drastic, rapid depletion of natural resources.

The recommendation made by the United Nations contained many suggested solutions to solve our environmental crisis, starting with social justice and equality, environmental protection, improvement of the economic status of developing countries, prevention of deforestation, protection of biodiversity and conservation of natural resources.

This sudden environmental awareness is rather late if we compare it with the environmental teachings of the Qur'an and Sunnah, declared and practiced by the early Muslims over 1400 years ago. The Qur'an and Prophetic Hadith contain a component of environmental education: they teach Muslims about their environment and urge them to protect it and respect its different elements; and they teach us to keep an eye on environmental balance, to prevent any disturbance or waste and stop any pollution or corruption. In the Islamic view, humans are seen as the major factor disturbing the natural balance of the universe. Humans interfere intentionally or unintentionally in the earth's ecosystems, leading to a serious impairment in its perfect balance and ordered sequence. Allah teaches us that mischief on the land and in the sea is inflicted by humankind's unwary interference with the natural laws created by Allah for their own benefit.

﴿ ظَهَرَ ٱلْفَسَادُ فِى ٱلْبَرِّ وَٱلْبَحْرِ بِمَا كَسَبَتْ أَيْدِى ٱلنَّاسِ لِيُذِيقَهُم بَعْضَ ٱلَّذِى عَمِلُوا۟
لَعَلَّهُمْ يَرْجِعُونَ ﴿٤١﴾ ﴾   (سورة الروم:٤١)

﴾Evil has appeared on land and sea because of what the hands
of people have earned [by oppression and evil deeds], that Allah
may make them taste a part of that which they have done, in order
that they may return.﴿   *(Qur'an 30: 41)*

Environmental pollution, which is tantamount to the disruption
of the natural balance, is a major form of hu-
man corruption and mischief on earth. This
verse is a clear warning from Allah to human kind ﴾*because of what the hands
of people have earned*﴿. Air pollution,
deforestation, pollution of the soil, seas
and rivers, and all the resulting disasters on this earth are direct conse-
quences of the actions of human beings. ﴾*Allah may make them
taste a part of that which they have done*﴿ This is a lesson from
Allah, a warning showing us the results of our bad deeds reflected
as the spread of diseases, famines, floods, earthquakes and many
other physical, economic and psychological hazards to human
health. ﴾*In order that they may return*﴿. This is the solution: to
repent and refer back to Allah's law on earth, to protect all Allah's
creatures and to take care of the whole environment.

According to Islam, the relationship between humankind and the
environment involves four fields:

One:

To live in harmony and enjoy natural beauty. The Qur'an opens
the door for meditation; it even draws our attention to His various
magnificent creations that we should admire and enjoy:

The skies

﴿وَلَقَدْ جَعَلْنَا فِي ٱلسَّمَاءِ بُرُوجًا وَزَيَّنَّاهَا لِلنَّاظِرِينَ ﴾ ⑯   (سورة الحجر:١٦)

﴿We have put constellations in the sky and We have beautified it
for the beholders.﴾   *(Qur'an 15: 16)*

﴿ أَفَلَمْ يَنظُرُوٓا۟ إِلَى ٱلسَّمَاءِ فَوْقَهُمْ كَيْفَ بَنَيْنَاهَا وَزَيَّنَّاهَا وَمَا لَهَا مِن فُرُوجٍ ﴾ ①
(سورة ق:٦)

﴿Have they not looked at the sky above them, how We have made
it and adorned it, and there are no rifts in it?﴾   *(Qur'an 50: 6)*

The earth

﴿أَلَمْ تَرَ أَنَّ ٱللَّهَ أَنزَلَ مِنَ ٱلسَّمَاءِ مَاءً فَأَخْرَجْنَا بِهِۦ ثَمَرَٰتٍ مُّخْتَلِفًا أَلْوَٰنُهَا ۚ وَمِنَ ٱلْجِبَالِ
جُدَدٌۢ بِيضٌ وَحُمْرٌ مُّخْتَلِفٌ أَلْوَٰنُهَا وَغَرَابِيبُ سُودٌ ﴾ ㉗   (سورة فاطر:٢٧)

﴿Do you not see that Allah sends down water [rain] from the sky,
and We produce therewith fruits of varying colours, and among
the mountains are streaks white and red, of varying colours and
[others] very black.﴾   *(Qur'an 35: 27)*

The human being

﴿لَقَدْ خَلَقْنَا ٱلْإِنسَٰنَ فِىٓ أَحْسَنِ تَقْوِيمٍ ﴾ ④   (سورة التين:٤)

﴿Verily, We created the human being of the best stature [mould].﴾
(Qur'an 95: 4)

The plants

﴿ وَهُوَ ٱلَّذِىٓ أَنزَلَ مِنَ ٱلسَّمَاءِ مَاءً فَأَخْرَجْنَا بِهِۦ نَبَاتَ كُلِّ شَىْءٍ فَأَخْرَجْنَا مِنْهُ
خَضِرًا نُّخْرِجُ مِنْهُ حَبًّا مُّتَرَاكِبًا وَمِنَ ٱلنَّخْلِ مِن طَلْعِهَا قِنْوَانٌ دَانِيَةٌ وَجَنَّٰتٍ مِّنْ

أَعْنَابٍ وَالزَّيْتُونَ وَالرُّمَّانَ مُشْتَبِهًا وَغَيْرَ مُتَشَبِهٍ ۗ انظُرُوٓاْ إِلَىٰ ثَمَرِهِۦٓ إِذَآ أَثْمَرَ وَيَنْعِهِۦٓ ۚ إِنَّ فِى ذَٰلِكُمْ لَءَايَٰتٍ لِّقَوْمٍ يُؤْمِنُونَ ﴿٩٩﴾ ﴾ (سورة الأنعام:٩٩)

❰It is He Who sends down water [rain] from the sky, and with it We bring forth vegetation of all kinds, and out of it We bring forth green stalks, from which We bring forth thick clustered grain And out of the date palm and its spathe come forth clusters of dates hanging low and near, and gardens of grapes, olives and pomegranates, each similar [in kind] yet different [in variety and taste]. Look at their fruits when they begin to bear, and the ripeness thereof. Verily, in these things there are signs for people who believe.❱ *(Qur'an 6: 99)*

The animals

﴿أَفَلَا يَنظُرُونَ إِلَى الْإِبِلِ كَيْفَ خُلِقَتْ ﴿١٧﴾ ﴾ (سورة الغاشية:١٧)

❰Do they not look at the camels, how they are created?❱
(Qur'an 88: 17)

﴿ وَلَكُمْ فِيهَا جَمَالٌ حِينَ تُرِيحُونَ وَحِينَ تَسْرَحُونَ ﴿٦﴾ ﴾ (سورة النحل:٦)

❰And wherein is beauty for you, when you bring them home in the evening, and as you lead them forth to pasture in the morning.❱
(Qur'an 16: 6)

Two:

To teach and remind people to deepen their faith and comprehension of Allah's Powers, of His Beauty, Wisdom and Mercy.

﴿ سَنُرِيهِمْ ءَايَٰتِنَا فِى الْآفَاقِ وَفِىٓ أَنفُسِهِمْ حَتَّىٰ يَتَبَيَّنَ لَهُمْ أَنَّهُ الْحَقُّ ... ﴿٥٣﴾ ﴾ (سورة فُصِّلَت:٥٣)

❰We will show them Our Signs in the universe, and in their own selves, until it becomes manifest to them that this [the Qur'an] is the truth...❱   *(Qur'an 41: 53)*

Three:

To benefit from its various elements:

﴿وَتَحْمِلُ أَثْقَالَكُمْ إِلَىٰ بَلَدٍ لَّمْ تَكُونُوا۟ بَٰلِغِيهِ إِلَّا بِشِقِّ ٱلْأَنفُسِ إِنَّ رَبَّكُمْ لَرَءُوفٌ رَّحِيمٌ ۝ وَٱلْخَيْلَ وَٱلْبِغَالَ وَٱلْحَمِيرَ لِتَرْكَبُوهَا وَزِينَةً وَيَخْلُقُ مَا لَا تَعْلَمُونَ ۝﴾   (سورة النحل:٧-٨)

❰And they carry your loads to a land that you could not reach except with great trouble to yourselves. Truly, Allah is full of kindness, Most Merciful. And [He has created] horses, mules and donkeys for you to ride, and as an adornment. And He creates [other] things of which you have no knowledge.❱   *(Qur'an 16: 7-8)*

﴿وَمِنَ ٱلْأَنْعَٰمِ حَمُولَةً وَفَرْشًا كُلُوا۟ مِمَّا رَزَقَكُمُ ٱللَّهُ ... ۝﴾

(سورة الأنعام:١٤٢)

❰And of the cattle [are some] for burden [like camels] and some [like sheep and goats] for [food and their hair for] coverings. Eat of what Allah has provided for you...❱   *(Qur'an 6: 142)*

Four:

To build a spiritual connection between human beings and nature, from which we can acquire an endless supply of spiritual energy by feeling the beauty of the wondrous inimitable creation:

﴿ ... وَإِن مِّن شَىْءٍ إِلَّا يُسَبِّحُ بِحَمْدِهِۦ وَلَٰكِن لَّا تَفْقَهُونَ تَسْبِيحَهُمْ ... ۝﴾

(سورة الإسراء:٤٤)

❨...there is not a thing but glorifies and praises Him. But you do not understand their glorification...❩   *(Qur'an 17: 44)*

﴿ وَلِلَّهِ يَسْجُدُ مَا فِى ٱلسَّمَوَٰتِ وَمَا فِى ٱلْأَرْضِ مِن دَآبَّةٍ وَٱلْمَلَٰٓئِكَةُ وَهُمْ لَا يَسْتَكْبِرُونَ ۩ ﴾   (سورة النحل:٤٩)

❨And to Allah prostate all that is in the heavens and all that is in the earth, of the live moving creatures and the angels, and they are not proud [they worship Allah with humility].❩   *(Qur'an 16: 49)*

Islam prohibits all sorts of corruption. Here, Muslims are urged to take care of the environment and, as we benefit from it, we have to remember the rights of others.

﴿ ... كُلُوا۟ مِن ثَمَرِهِۦٓ إِذَآ أَثْمَرَ وَءَاتُوا۟ حَقَّهُۥ يَوْمَ حَصَادِهِۦ وَلَا تُسْرِفُوٓا۟ إِنَّهُۥ لَا يُحِبُّ ٱلْمُسْرِفِينَ ۩ ﴾   (سورة الأنعام:١٤١)

❨...Eat of their fruit when they ripen, but pay the due thereof [its Zakat, according to Allah's Orders] on the day of its harvest, and do not waste by extravagance. Verily, He does not like those who waste by extravagance.❩   *(Qur'an 6: 141)*

Once a man named Akhnas ibn Shareeq came to Prophet Muhammad (ﷺ) to ask about Islam, but as he turned to leave, he happened to pass by a pasture and grazing animals. He set it alight and killed the cattle. The following verse was revealed as a sign of Divine disapproval:[351]

﴿ وَإِذَا تَوَلَّىٰ سَعَىٰ فِى ٱلْأَرْضِ لِيُفْسِدَ فِيهَا وَيُهْلِكَ ٱلْحَرْثَ وَٱلنَّسْلَ وَٱللَّهُ لَا يُحِبُّ ٱلْفَسَادَ ۩ ﴾   (سورة البقرة:٢٠٥)

❨And when he turns away [from you O Muhammad], his effort in the land is to make mischief therein and to destroy the crops and the cattle, and Allah does not like mischief.❩   *(Qur'an 2: 205)*

Islamic recommendations for environmental protection

1. Protect plants

𝒫rophet Muhammad (ﷺ) said:

«If anyone cuts down a tree of the desert, Allah will direct his head into hell fire."[352] What is meant by this hadith was clarified by Abu Dâwood: "Whoever cuts a tree in the desert that travellers or cattle use for shade, without a reason, will be punished by Allah.»

This hadith demonstrates the importance of the preservation of the components of the environment and of safeguarding the Divine natural balance.

The Prophet (ﷺ) also encouraged planting in several hadiths:

«Whoever plants a seedling, earns a reward whenever any human or any of Allah's creatures eats from it,»[353] and «If the Day of Resurrection comes while a seedling is in the hand of one of you, let him plant it.»[354]

Islam also forbids wastefulness with plants or any kind of resource, for Allah says in His Qur'an:

﴿ ... وَكُلُواْ وَٱشْرَبُواْ وَلَا تُسْرِفُوٓاْ إِنَّهُۥ لَا يُحِبُّ ٱلْمُسْرِفِينَ ٣١ ﴾ (سورة الأعراف:٣١)

﴿...And eat and drink but do not waste by extravagance, certainly He [Allah] does not like those who waste by extravagance.﴾

(Qur'an 7: 31)

2. Protect animals

As Muslims we are forbidden from killing any living creature without a good reason. This belief is supported by the fact that our Prophet (ﷺ) once said:

«If a human kills a bird or any higher form of creature without good reason, Allah will ask him (or her) about it.»[355]

As Allah (ﷻ) says:

﴿ وَمَا مِن دَآبَّةٍ فِى ٱلْأَرْضِ وَلَا طَٰٓئِرٍ يَطِيرُ بِجَنَاحَيْهِ إِلَّآ أُمَمٌ أَمْثَالُكُم ... ﴿٣٨﴾ ﴾

(سورة الأنعام:٣٨)

﴿There is not a moving [living] creature on earth, nor a bird that flies with its two wings, but forms communities like you...﴾

(Qur'an 6: 38)

Islam views each of these natural communities as a living entity that deserves our respect, and any violation of this law of mutual respect will disturb the perfect balance of the ecosystems that Allah has made interdependent. Respect for animals is also evident in the ruling that we must show mercy to all living creatures.

Allah's Messenger (ﷺ) said:

«A prostitute was forgiven by Allah, because, passing by a panting dog near a well and seeing that the dog was about to die of thirst, she took off her shoe, and tying it with her head-cover she drew out some water for it. So, Allah forgave her because of that.»[356]

3. Protect water resources

Environmental protection extends to water resources. The Prophet (ﷺ) prohibited urination in stagnant water, and science

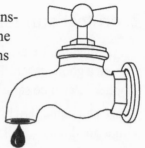

has discovered that many diseases are transmitted through this unhealthy habit. The contamination of water by sewage systems causes the spread of many bacterial, viral and amoebic waterborne diseases like gastroenteritis, typhoid, cholera, amoebic dysentery and hepatitis. At present there is disastrous abuse of the earth's fresh water supply. Rivers and lakes have become a handy dump site for industrial waste and biological contaminants. The clearest example is the contamination of the Great Lakes. The largest reserve of fresh water on the surface of the earth is suffering from a striking deterioration of its water quality. The whole ecosystem is suffocating as a result of industrial and municipal contamination in addition to the discharge from sewage treatment plants. The Great Lakes Basin's population has been subjected to increasing health hazards manifested as higher incidences of cancer and lower fertility rates. This is accompanied by the huge threat to the area's wildlife and marine resources.[357]

> Our Prophet (ﷺ) also prohibited us from wasting water. «One day he (ﷺ) found a man performing ablution using too much water. The Prophet commented: What is this extravagance? The man asked: Does this also apply to water? The Prophet replied: Even if it comes from a running river.»[358]

4. Take care of the home environment

The environmental aspects of homes and workplaces are very crucial factors affecting human health. Many of the Prophet's (ﷺ) recommendations lead the way to healthy home comfort, for example:

«Cover the pots and water bottles.»[359] This advice aims at preventing the contamination of food and drink through contact with microbes, insects or dust.

«Do not leave the fire lit in your homes while you are sleeping: this fire is your enemy so put it out before you sleep.»[360] This hadith is explained by the fact that fire can blaze out of control while the occupants of the house are sleeping; but we can also interpret it another way. Fire causes the release of carbon monoxide, an odourless gas which has a high binding affinity to human haemoglobin in the red blood cells. The resulting bond makes the cells lose their ability to bind to the oxygen molecules, leading to a reduction in the level of blood oxygen which, if continued, leads to certain death. Furthermore, if we apply this advice to our modern home environment, we will see that many toxic chemicals are generated from gas cookers, furnaces and boilers, so turning these off at bedtime is a safeguard against potential hazards.

The Prophet (ﷺ) also said:

«Turn off the lamps while sleeping.»[361]

The use of electric lights with the subsequent elongation of the 'daylight' hours causes the pineal gland to release hormones that (among other potentially harmful changes) stimulates early puberty in young females[362]. So turning off all lamps, even dim lights, when we sleep saves us from many problems caused by hormonal imbalances.

A recently discovered household pollutant is electromagnetic radiation. Living, working or sleeping in the vicinity of power or telephone lines, or any major source of electromagnetic field, and the increased use of mobile phones will negatively affect our health. Until recently, medical science has not paid much attention to the health hazards of energetic toxins, as their effects are not recognisable in the short term. Dr. Andrew Weil warns that the danger of damage to your brain and the rest of your body associated with exposure to electromagnetic radiation is directly proportional to the cumulative amount of radiation received over your lifetime. So do not underestimate any small dose of radiation, as it adds to your total exposure and increases your risk of health problems.[363]

Although the electromagnetic field produced by the appliances we have in our homes may be weak, it can still adversely affect our biological system, impairing

---

Protection against Microwave Hazards

- Do not stand close to an operating microwave as it emits electromagnetic rays.
- Do not cook in it for an extended period of time as this tends to change the food chemistry, creating a potentially harmful unnatural molecule.
- Do not use plastic warppings or plastic containers in the microwaves (even if labelled microwave safe — safety here is meant for the plastic, not for you), as they release carcinogenic plasticizer polymers inside your food.

our immunity and causing serious, sometimes irreversible genetic damage. According to Dr. Weil, the farther we are from an electric appliance, the safer we are, as the strength of the electromagnetic field decreases by moving away from its emitting source.

Examples of the equipment commonly used in our homes that release electromagnetic radiation are: mobile phones, computer monitors, electric blankets, electronic clocks, alarms and radios and microwave ovens[364]. So remember to leave a distance of at least half a meter between any electronic or electric device and your bed.

The cleanliness of the home environment is of major concern to Muslims, and cleanliness in turn is of prime importance in preventative medicine. Prophet Muhammad (ﷺ) said:

«Allah is Beautiful and He loves beauty, He is Good-hearted and He loves goodness, He is Clean and He loves cleanliness; so clean your backyards.»[365]

He (ﷺ) also said:

«Whenever one of you goes to bed, dust off your bed with your clothes, as you never know what was on it after you.»[366]

In the early seventies, science revealed the presence of dust mites: tiny organisms present in house dust and bed covers that cause allergies and itchy skin. To prevent their proliferation, proper aeration is essential. It is also important to clean your home and bedding frequently, and to allow the sun and fresh clean air into rooms daily.[367]

Remember this piece of advice from the Medicine of the Prophet (ﷺ): "Burn incense in your homes with frankincense and thyme." Aromatherapy has been used for centuries in many cultures for both healing and relaxation. Vaporizers and different essential oils are now generally available in health shops, where hundreds of scents are promoted for calming, uplifting, general healing or purifying purposes. Frankincense is widely known for its cleansing and purifying powers; some cultures also use it for spiritual enhancement. Other essential oils like chamomile, sage, lavender and jasmine have calming effects, while grapefruit, rosemary and rose are popular for their uplifting nature. Peppermint, ginger and eucalyptus and perhaps even thyme are said to have stimulating essences.[368]

5. Control noise pollution

Noise is highly stressful and can lead to physical and psychological harm; it is probably the worst disadvantage of living in a big city or near a crowded or industrialized area.

Constant exposure to high levels of noise causes gradual weakness in hearing capacities, affecting the ear drum and sometimes even damaging the auditory nerve. The negative effects of noise exceed this physical damage to the ears, and extend to more serious nervous system problems. The clamorous nature of a busy city life may lead to permanent agitation, moodiness, vexation, stress and headaches. Besides these effects on the central nervous system, noise has also been shown to affect the delicate balance of the body's hormones. Studies show that exposure to noise increases the body's production of corticosteroids and adrenaline hormones.[369] These abnormally high hormonal levels lead to an increase in cholesterol and triglycerides levels, which in turn produces serious heart and circulatory problems in addition to many digestive system disorders.

Islam teaches us that calmness relaxes the nerves and noise ir-ritates them. Allah says in His Qur'an:

﴿ ... وَلَا تَجْهَرْ بِصَلَاتِكَ وَلَا تُخَافِتْ بِهَا وَابْتَغِ بَيْنَ ذَلِكَ سَبِيلًا ﴿١١٠﴾ ﴾

(سورة الإسراء:١١٠)

﴿...And offer your Ṣalât [prayer] neither loudly nor in a low voice, but follow a way between those.﴾   *(Qur'an 17: 110)*

In the Qur'an we read the advice that the wise man Luqmân taught his son; among other things, he told him:

﴿ ... وَاغْضُضْ مِن صَوْتِكَ إِنَّ أَنكَرَ ٱلْأَصْوَٰتِ لَصَوْتُ ٱلْحَمِيرِ ﴿١٩﴾ ﴾(سورة لقمان:١٩)

﴿...And lower your voice. Verily, the harshest of all voices is the voice [braying] of the donkey.﴾   *(Qur'an 31: 19)*

The Prophet (ﷺ) liked to hear people reciting the Glorious Qur'an with beautiful voices; he said about Abu Moosâ who had a sonorous voice:

«This one has the gift of a pipe like those of Prophet Da-vid's family.»[370]

He (ﷺ) advised Muslims to «Embellish the Qur'an with your voices.»[371] Qur'an and the Sunnah enjoin quietude as well as con-sideration for the comfort and feelings of others by avoiding any-thing that can hurt them, even a loud voice. They encourage con-templation, meditation, reflection and creativity, all of which need calmness and relaxed nerves.

Our duty as Muslims

It should be clear from the examples above that Islam empha-sizes the importance of caring for the environment. Sadly, this sense of responsibility and respect for the environment seems to have diminished since the time of the rightly-guided Khulafâ' (Caliphs), so that the Muslim Ummah (community) has shamefully neglected its share of responsibility in caring for and preserving the earth's natural resources and the other living beings that share this planet with us. Only very recently have Muslims again begun to talk of conservation and preservation. It is hoped that Muslim individuals and their leaders will make up for those centuries of inaction and once more take the lead in proactively working to restore the earth's environmental balance. Each day ask yourself: *What did I contribute today to the welfare of my environment? Did I recycle my waste? Did I plant a seed or economise on my water and electricity consumption? Did I shop wisely? Did I clean my backyard, feed a stray cat or help in embellishing my neighbourhood?* You will find something to add everyday and you will certainly feel good about your contribution. To stay healthy, we need a healthy environment on our planet, and its protection is the duty of each one of us.

CHAPTER 3

INTELLECTUAL BODY

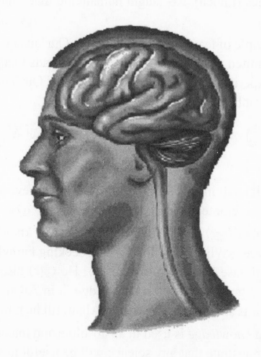

$\mathcal{I}$slam, perhaps more than any other religion, stresses the importance of learning for all humankind. The first verse of the Qur'an that was revealed to Prophet Muhammad (ﷺ) says, «Read!»

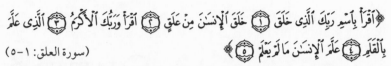

(سورة العلق: ١-٥)

《Read! In the Name of your Creator, Who has created [all that exists], has created the human from a clot [a piece of thick co-agulated blood]. Read! And your Creator is the Most Generous, Who has taught [writing] by the pen [the first person to write was Prophet Idrees [Enoch], has taught humankind that which he did not know.》   *(Qur'an 96: 1-5)*

The principle of learning as taught by the Qur'an and the Sunnah is not limited to religious sciences, but extends to all aspects of human experience. This is very clear in many Qur'anic verses and in the Prophetic Hadith:

﴿ ... يَرْفَعِ ٱللَّهُ ٱلَّذِينَ ءَامَنُوا۟ مِنكُمْ وَٱلَّذِينَ أُوتُوا۟ ٱلْعِلْمَ دَرَجَٰتٍ ... ﴾

(سورة المجادلة: ١١)

《...Allâh will exalt in degree those of you who believe and those who have been granted knowledge...》   *(Qur'an 58: 11)*

The Prophet (ﷺ) said, urging people to seek knowledge everywhere: «Whoever follows a path seeking knowledge, Allah will ease his way to paradise.»[1] He (ﷺ) also said: «Whoever goes out seeking knowledge is in Allah's protection (or is striving for the sake of Allah) till he returns.»[2]

The word *knowledge* is used in an absolute and unconditional sense to demonstrate that any science will be useful to society if it contributes to its development — whether spiritual, economic (material) or intellectual.

In Islam, science is the Muslim's path to certainty about Allah's existence through His magnificent creations; that is why we are ordered to meditate and to think deeply about our creation and the creation of the heavens and earth. Science is also our way to carry out the purpose of our creation as vicegerents on earth.

﴿وَإِذْ قَالَ رَبُّكَ لِلْمَلَـٰئِكَةِ إِنِّى جَاعِلٌ فِى ٱلْأَرْضِ خَلِيفَةً ...﴾ ﴿٣٠﴾

(سورة البقرة: ٣٠)

﴿And [remember] when Allah said to the angels: I will create a vicegerent on earth...﴾
(Qur'an 2: 30)

Knowledge is our way to successfully inhabit and develop a harmonious lifestyle on our planet. Our Muslim ancestors understood this intent very well and applied it as Allah and His Prophet (ﷺ) ordered; that is why they prospered and built the early Muslim civilization that flourished for centuries with justice, peace, knowledge and power. They were pioneers in all scientific fields: from medicine, chemistry, pharmacy, physics and mathematics to philosophy, sociology, astronomy, history and geography.

This intellectual part of the human body is as essential to our life as food and water. Allah distinguished humans from other beings with intellect, power of choice and conscience. If one ignores any of these, a human will regress to the level of an animal, losing an essential aspect of his or her creation and disrupting the perfect balance of his or her health.

Use it or lose it!

Scientist have known for years now that the brain and nervous system cells — unlike other body cells — do not multiply or regenerate: their number does not increse over time, and if some of these cells die away they are not replaced. Hold on now, do not panic: *neurons* (nerve cells) are completely different from other body cells; they do not deteriorate from excess use, on the contrary, the more you 'exercise' your brain, the sharper it becomes.[3]

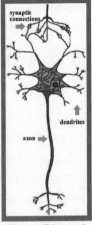

From birth until the age of two years, human brain continues to develop and generate new cells; that is why paediatricians stress the importance of essential fats in the infant's diet as they are the foundation for the nerve cells. After the second year of age, your brain becomes fully developed and the neurons you possess now are the ones that you are going to use for the rest of your life. Still, the brain has a tremendous ability for regenera-

Nerve cell (neuron)

tion. It is true that the brain cells cannot increase in number anymore, but they still can increase their *synaptic connections*. These are the branching systems connecting the nerve cells together and through which information is transferred. The more synaptic connections, the faster the speed of information transfer and the easier will be your ability to retrieve any information when you need it. This marvellous capability is available to you at any age, providing that you give your brain the proper conditions.[4]

The more we engage in intellectual activity, the more we learn and acquire new knowledge and constantly challenge our brains, the stronger the neuron stimulation will be to build more connections among them and speed up the transmission of impulses. Adh-Dhahabi wrote:

> Any organ strengthens and becomes active when it is exercised regularly, and so does the mind; if you want to sharpen your memory and boost your intellect, increase learning, memorize the Qur'an, keep on thinking and meditating and persist in remembrance of Allah (*dhikr*).[5]

So keep your brain active all the time. Your brain needs constant challenge — whatever your age. It needs new ideas and fresh experiences. Try engaging in a new learning task: in my own experience, the best brain and memory boosting exercise is learning and reciting the Holy Book, the Qur'an. Prophet Muhammad (ﷺ) said:

«The person who recites the Qur'an and masters it by heart will be with the honourable and obedient scribes (angels in heaven). And the person who exerts diligent efforts to learn it by heart, and recites it with great difficulty, will have a double reward.»[6]

Apart from its tremendous spiritual, emotional and psychological benefits, this gives your brain a wonderful challenge, enhancing neuron connections and increasing the density of brain receptor sites. Remember: «It will be said to the reader of the Qur'an (who had memorized it and acted upon it): Read, ascend, and recite as you used to recite in life, for your status will be as high as the last verse you recite.»[7]

Keep your brain healthy

$\mathcal{H}$ere are nine ways to keep your brain healthy:

1. Never stop learning

According to Dr. Richard Restak in his book *Older and Wiser*, education is the most important factor in achieving optimum brain potential.[8] The more you learn and acquire new skills, the better the protection you are offering to your brain in the future. Our brain's cognitive functions (various brain activities such as memory, intelligence, and attention span) are much less at risk of deterioration if we continually use them. By education here, I certainly do not mean college degrees or even high school diplomas, but the degree of brain stimulation achieved. The most knowledgeable and honoured human being, our dear Prophet Muhammad (ﷺ) was illiterate; nevertheless, he sought knowledge in all fields. He was taught by Allah the Almighty and he urged his companions to seek knowledge and education wherever possible.

«Seeking knowledge is obligatory on every Muslim.»[9]

In addition, Imam Shâfi'i said: "Seeking knowledge is better than a non-obligatory prayer."

In the Qur'an Allah instructed Prophet Muhammad (ﷺ),

(سورة طه: ١١٤)   ﴿ ...وَقُل رَّبِّ زِدْنِي عِلْمًا ۝ ﴾

﴿...And say: Allah, increase me in knowledge [*rabbi zidnee 'ilman*]﴾   *(Qur'an 20: 114)*

To urge us to seek knowledge, Prophet Muhammad (ﷺ) promised us the reward of learning in this life and in the afterlife:

«When a person passes away, his or her deeds are halted except three of them: a continuous charity (*sadaqah jâriyah*), or useful knowledge, or a pious son (or daughter) who prays for him or her.»[10]

However, as with everything we do, we should always purify our intention. Seek with your learning only Allah's way to gain the benefit of that knowledge in this life, and the reward for it in Paradise. Early Muslims remembered and applied this advice properly, which led them to build a great Islamic empire that lasted for centuries and spread rays of knowledge — in all fields of the sciences — to the whole world.

Adopt the habit of reading at least twenty minutes each day. Read in all fields, expand your knowledge, and apply what you learn in your everyday life.

Learning stimulates the brain to build more synaptic connections, thus the higher the level of learning — especially during early years of life — the greater the protection later in life against brain degeneration by aging, as the brain will take much longer to lose the dense neural connections acquired over the years.[11]

2. Seek mental challenges

Your brain, like your muscles, needs constant exercise, so always keep it busy: read a lot, attend seminars and organize discussion groups with friends and family members.

Prophet Muhammad (ﷺ) said: «The angels lay down their wings for the student (knowledge seekers), pleased with what he is doing; and all creatures in the heavens and on earth, even the whales in the water, ask forgiveness for the scholar.»[12]

Seeking new knowledge especially in challenging fields and unfamiliar subjects encourages the brain to increase in mental capacity and reach higher performance levels, and creates incentives, attention and perseverance.[13] In Western societies, it is not strange to find a college student in his or her seventies or even eighties, while in contemporary Muslim countries, it is sad to say, at that age, we tend to just take it easy and give our brains a nap.

Studies show that too much spare time is one of the main factors associated with dementia.[14] The brain needs constant challenges, fresh experience and novelty in order to keep healthy, and this is totally independent of your age. Think of all the time people waste in front of the television or chit-chatting about useless subjects.

Prophet Muhammad (ﷺ) said: «There are two blessings whose reward many people lose: good health and free time.»[15]

You need to receive and absorb a constant supply of useful knowledge to give your brain connections a continuous boost and activation. Never underestimate your intellectual and cognitive abilities. Try to engage in new learning experiences, and remember the Prophet's (ﷺ) hadith: «Whenever people gather in one of Allah's houses, memorizing Allah's Book and studying it, the angels surround them, mercy envelops them and Allah mentions them among the ones who are with Him.»[16] He (ﷺ) also said: «The best among you are those who learn the Qur'an and then teach it.»[17]

Another important advice for mental challenge is the habit of thinking. When I was young, I attended a school run by nuns; one very important thing I was taught there was to reserve ten minutes every night to reflect on my day, to consider all my actions and assess them. I acquired the habit of thinking, of trying to determine my positive and negative behaviours and then making the intention to take serious steps towards self-improvement.

3. Keep physically active

The old Arab saying, 'the healthy brain lies in a healthy body' is very true. As mentioned in earlier chapters, the importance of exercise is emphasized and Muslims are urged to teach their kids different sports: "Teach your children javelin throwing, swimming and horse riding."

Although scientists have not yet proven any direct link between physical activity and brain performance, human experience and observations prove the benefits of a healthy body for proper brain function.

Aerobic exercises — likewalking, swimming jogging, biking and playing team sports like football, for example — are known to improve blood cholesterol image and lower blood pressure, leading to a better circulatory system and a healthier, stronger heart. With a healthier cardiovascular system, your heart will be able to pump blood more efficiently to all body parts — including the brain. Exercise improves respiratory function and is also a natural mood booster: it increases the release of *endorphins*, which are hormone-like substances responsible for the feeling of wellbeing.[18]

Keep physically active, walk as much as you can everyday, take the stairs instead of the elevator, park the car two blocks away from your destination, so you can benefit from a good walk, and do not forget your breathing exercises. This will enhance lung function, relax you and boost blood circulation with a fresh supply of oxygen to all body parts.

Gerontologist Gene Cohen suggests that mature (elderly) people should develop four different types of activities:[19]

➢ Active group activities such as hockey and football, which keep you active while allowing you to strengthen your social connections.

➢ Passive group activities like art or cooking classes and discussion groups, which do not involve much physical effort but still encourage social gathering.

> Individual active activities as walking, or bicycle riding, for some useful, active time by yourself.

> Individual passive activities like reading, drawing, writing, or cooking — for a more relaxing time alone.

4. Eat right and avoid harmful habits

Follow the food guide pyramid and the Prophet's (ﷺ) healthy nutrition guidelines. In addition, there are some beneficial foods especially for the brain which will be discussed in more detail later on in this chapter.

Avoid all harmful substances such as alcohol and tobacco. Allah states in His Qur'an:

﴿يَٰٓأَيُّهَا ٱلَّذِينَ ءَامَنُوٓاْ إِنَّمَا ٱلۡخَمۡرُ وَٱلۡمَيۡسِرُ وَٱلۡأَنصَابُ وَٱلۡأَزۡلَٰمُ رِجۡسٌ مِّنۡ عَمَلِ ٱلشَّيۡطَٰنِ فَٱجۡتَنِبُوهُ لَعَلَّكُمۡ تُفۡلِحُونَ ۝ إِنَّمَا يُرِيدُ ٱلشَّيۡطَٰنُ أَن يُوقِعَ بَيۡنَكُمُ ٱلۡعَدَٰوَةَ وَٱلۡبَغۡضَآءَ فِي ٱلۡخَمۡرِ وَٱلۡمَيۡسِرِ وَيَصُدَّكُمۡ عَن ذِكۡرِ ٱللَّهِ وَعَنِ ٱلصَّلَوٰةِ فَهَلۡ أَنتُم مُّنتَهُونَ ۝﴾

(سورة المائدة: ٩٠-٩١)

﴿O you who believe! Intoxicants [all kinds of alcoholic drinks], gambling, stone altars [used for sacrificing to idols] and arrows [for seeking luck or decision] are an abomination of Satan's handiwork. So avoid [strictly all] that [abomination] in order that you may be successful. Satan wants only to excite enmity and hatred between you with intoxicants [alcoholic drinks] and gambling, and to hinder you from the remembrance of Allah and from *ṣalât* [the prayer]. So, will you not then abstain?﴾   *(Qur'an 5: 90-91)*

5. Get a good night's sleep

No one can deny that not getting enough sleep affects your brain performance. Sleep restores, replenishes and rebuilds the areas of the brain and body which may become tired after a long day.

Scientists believe that sleep gives the body's cells and neurons suitable time to regenerate and restore their energy.[20] A regular sleeping pattern is especially important for children and adolescents, because growth hormone is secreted during the deep sleep period.

Stages of sleep

There are five stages of sleep; each one is characterized by different brainwave patterns which may be measured by an electroencephalogram (EEG). Stages 1 to 4 are collectively called non-REM sleep. During these stages, the body's metabolism slows down: the brain is least active, and blood pressure, heart rate and breathing are lower than when a person is awake. Hormones are secreted, among them growth hormone, which enables new proteins to work on renewal where required in the bones and skin.[21]

Then comes the fifth stage (known as the Rapid Eye Movement or REM stage), which represents one quarter of total time spent asleep. This is the period during which dreaming occurs.[22] We switch between REM and non-REM sleep involuntarily throughout the night. Each cycle lasts for about 90 minutes.

The amount of sleep needed varies with age. Young infants sleep approximately 16 hours per day compared to adults who need as little as six hours. This difference in the amount of sleep has led scientists to deduce the actual role of sleep in one's life. REM sleep in early infancy may play a crucial role in brain development and stimulation.[23]

For adults, REM sleep is important in memory function. In an experiment in the 1970s, researchers presented individuals with some information just before they went to bed. Then some of them were awakened just before entering the REM stage and the others were left to finish their sleeping cycle. The individuals who were awakened before entering REM sleep were less likely to remember the information the next morning.[24] Recent studies show that sleep is crucial for different memory functions; this is probably due to the fact that during sleep, your brain is not engaged in other sensory or intellectual activities, thus it is more capable of working on memory associations, integrations and storage[25].[26]

When I was young, I used to have a hard time remembering poems learnt at school. My mum once told me, "Read the poem a few times thoroughly just before going to bed, then go to sleep and you will remember it the next morning." I tried it and it worked wonderfully.

Our Prophet (ﷺ) taught us that we should wake up at dawn to pray *fajr* (dawn) prayer, then start the day by some quiet meditation during which we remember Allah with the morning dhikr. After sunrise, we pray the *ḍuḥâ'* prayer (a Sunnah prayer), then start our working day. At this time, your body releases large doses of the hormone *cortisol* which helps you to wake up, and bright sunlight increases your wakefulness.

«The Prophet (ﷺ) disliked sleeping just before *'ishâ'* (the night prayer) or staying up to chat or engage in entertainment after it.»[27]

At night, the *pineal gland* in the brain secretes the hormone *melatonin*, which helps to adjust our sleeping pattern. This hormone is also a known antioxidant, so during the night it protects and restores healthy cells and neurons. If we sleep just before *'ishâ'*, this will delay our night sleep time and probably cause insomnia.

Furthermore, *dopamine*, a neurotransmitter secreted by the brain, is supplied in the greatest quantities during the two hours before midnight. Dopamine is responsible for giving us energy, motivation and increased interest and focus. Therefore, if you sleep late you lose your dopamine reserve for the next day, and this cannot be replenished until the next night.

Get into the habit of going to bed early at a fixed time, and keep to a consistent sleeping routine. Perform your prayers and recite your bedtime remembrance of Allah just before sleeping. Do not try to plan the next day's events before going to bed: just relax and depend totally on Allah:

«O, Allah, The Ever Living, The Sustainer of all that exists, I call for Your Mercy, rectify all my affairs for me and do not make me depend on myself (nor on another human being), even for an instant." (*Yâ ḥayyu yâ qayyoom, bi raḥmatika astagheethu, aṣliḥ-lee sha'nee kullahu wa lâ takalnee ilâ nafsee tarfata 'ayn.*)»[28]

Avoid heavy meals in the evening: just have a light supper and drink milk or (even better) buttermilk, as our Prophet (ﷺ) used to do. Perform ablution just before going to bed, Prophet Muhammad (ﷺ) said:

«Whenever you go to bed, perform ablution as you do for prayer.»[29]

Napping or relaxing for a few minutes in the middle of the day can replenish your energy. The midday siesta is mentioned many times in the Qur'an. One verse in particular points to it as a regular habit:

﴿ يَٰٓأَيُّهَا ٱلَّذِينَ ءَامَنُوا لِيَسْتَـْٔذِنكُمُ ٱلَّذِينَ مَلَكَتْ أَيْمَٰنُكُمْ وَٱلَّذِينَ لَمْ يَبْلُغُوا ٱلْحُلُمَ مِنكُمْ ثَلَٰثَ مَرَّٰتٍ مِّن قَبْلِ صَلَوٰةِ ٱلْفَجْرِ وَحِينَ تَضَعُونَ ثِيَابَكُم مِّنَ ٱلظَّهِيرَةِ وَمِنۢ بَعْدِ صَلَوٰةِ ٱلْعِشَآءِ ... ۝ ﴾ (سورة النور: ٥٨)

❨O you who believe! Let your servants and those who have not reached puberty ask leave of you at three times [before they come into your presence]: Before the prayer of dawn, and when you lay aside your clothing for the heat of noon, and after the prayer of night...❩   *(Qur'an 24: 58)*

The phrase 'when you lay aside your clothing for the heat of noon' is a clear reference to the period of rest at midday. This provides a short withdrawal from the stresses of the day, helps regenerate your energy, improves alertness and gives a mood boost. However, in no way should naps be used to try to compensate for staying up late, especially when people regularly stay up for hours after nightfall, just to watch TV or for other unnecessary activities.

6. Keep a positive state of mind

A decline in brain activity and loss of function has a lot to do with one's state of mind — especially in the elderly. As we think of ourselves as incapable of certain faculties, our subconscious mind[30] accepts this idea and we end up in effect unable to do something just because we believe we cannot! High self-esteem, belief in oneself, in one's potential and the realization of one's achievements are essential in keeping a healthy brain and a positive state of mind. As our Prophet (ﷺ) advised:

«The strong believer is more loved by Allah than the weak one, and there is benefaction in both.»[31]

If we stop using one of our brain functions (especially at a young age), it will gradually cease to develop and we can lose this faculty forever. We all have the ability to boost our brain performance and even our intelligence — we only have to believe in it and work at it.

7. Practice deep thinking

Deep thinking is essential to boost your brain's potential. The Qur'an urges us to use all our senses to understand and believe the truth of our creation and the creation of the earth and the universe. In many verses of the Qur'an, Allah refers to those who use their minds for deep thinking as 'people of understanding or intelligence'.[32]

﴿ كِتَٰبٌ أَنزَلْنَٰهُ إِلَيْكَ مُبَٰرَكٌ لِّيَدَّبَّرُوٓاْ ءَايَٰتِهِۦ وَلِيَتَذَكَّرَ أُوْلُواْ ٱلْأَلْبَٰبِ ﴾

(سورة ص: ٢٩)

﴿[This is] a Book [the Qur'an] which We have sent down to you, full of blessings that they may ponder over its verses, and that people of understanding may remember.﴾ *(Qur'an 38: 29)*

«Our mother 'Â'ishah reported that one night, Prophet Muhammad (ﷺ) woke up to pray and he cried till his tears wet his beard, then he bowed and cried, and prostrated himself and cried, till Bilâl came to start the call for the *fajr* (dawn) prayer and asked him the reason for his tears. Prophet Muhammad (ﷺ) said: How could I not cry, when today these verses of Qur'an have been revealed to me:

﴿ إِنَّ فِى خَلْقِ ٱلسَّمَٰوَٰتِ وَٱلْأَرْضِ وَٱخْتِلَٰفِ ٱلَّيْلِ وَٱلنَّهَارِ لَءَايَٰتٍ لِّأُوْلِى ٱلْأَلْبَٰبِ ۝ ٱلَّذِينَ يَذْكُرُونَ ٱللَّهَ قِيَٰمًا وَقُعُودًا وَعَلَىٰ جُنُوبِهِمْ وَيَتَفَكَّرُونَ فِى خَلْقِ ٱلسَّمَٰوَٰتِ وَٱلْأَرْضِ رَبَّنَا مَا خَلَقْتَ هَٰذَا بَٰطِلًا سُبْحَٰنَكَ فَقِنَا عَذَابَ ٱلنَّارِ ۝ ﴾

(سورة آل عمران: ١٩٠-١٩١)

﴿Verily! In the creation of the heavens and the earth, and in the alternation of night and day, there are indeed signs for people of understanding. Those who remember Allah [always, and in prayers] standing, sitting, and lying down on their sides, and think deeply about the creation of the heavens and the earth, [saying]: O Allah! You have not created [all] this without purpose, glory to You! [Exalted be You above all that they associate with You as partners.] Give us salvation from the torment of the Fire. 》   *(Qur'an 3: 190-191)*

Then he (ﷺ) said, "Woe unto him who reads it and does not reflect."》[33]

There is no special time, place or condition necessary for thought. You can think while walking, cooking, driving, eating, or even lying in your bed. Try to think positively and sincerely to find your way towards Allah and reach the right conclusions.

More than anything, do not get swept away by the flow of daily life. The struggle to acquire a good education, earn your living, raise your children... all these consume a great deal of your time and effort; despite this, do not forget in your rush, the purpose of your creation:

(٥٦ :سورة الذاريات)   ﴿ وَمَا خَلَقْتُ ٱلْجِنَّ وَٱلْإِنسَ إِلَّا لِيَعْبُدُونِ ﴾

《And I [Allah] created the jinns and humans only so they should worship Me [Alone].》   *(Qur'an 51: 56)*

8. Social activity

Family life is of great concern in Islam. One of Islam's primary goals is to build a strong and lasting family life with firm bonds of intimacy, true security and unity.[34] This outlook corresponds with what science tells us: a happy environment, natural social contacts, support from family and friends, satisfaction with one's life and strong ethical standards are all important factors in ensuring healthy brain performance.

Studies show that a happy family environment gives rise to healthy, intelligent and productive kids. An atmosphere that encourages constant communication between parents and children in the first three years of their lives has been linked to higher IQ levels in children.[35] Providing an intellectually stimulating environment for young children is essential for boosting their intelligence. The quality of interactive care given to kids from an early age and time spent talking, reading stories and playing with them have a crucial role in their brain development. The effect is even believed to be long lasting, which means that the first three years in a child's life can affect his or her brainpower for the rest of his or her life.[36] This in effect puts a great deal of responsibility on the mother, and emphasizes her important and irreplaceable role in raising young people with healthy minds. Prophet Muhammad (ﷺ) said:

«You are all guardians and are responsible for those under your care: a man is a guardian for his family and a woman is a guardian over her husband's household and their children.»[37]

Studies demonstrate that elderly people living alone, receiving no family care or support, are more prone to deterioration of their cognitive faculties, which can be manifested as dementia and memory loss.[38] In the Qur'an, Allah orders us to take care of our parents in their old age, as they took care of us when we were little:

﴿ ۞ وَقَضَىٰ رَبُّكَ أَلَّا تَعْبُدُوٓا۟ إِلَّآ إِيَّاهُ وَبِٱلْوَٰلِدَيْنِ إِحْسَٰنًا إِمَّا يَبْلُغَنَّ عِندَكَ ٱلْكِبَرَ أَحَدُهُمَآ أَوْ كِلَاهُمَا فَلَا تَقُل لَّهُمَآ أُفٍّ وَلَا تَنْهَرْهُمَا وَقُل لَّهُمَا قَوْلًا كَرِيمًا ۝ وَٱخْفِضْ لَهُمَا جَنَاحَ ٱلذُّلِّ مِنَ ٱلرَّحْمَةِ وَقُل رَّبِّ ٱرْحَمْهُمَا كَمَا رَبَّيَانِى صَغِيرًا ۝ ﴾ (سورة الإسراء:٢٣-٢٤)

❲And Allah has decreed that you worship none but Him, and that you be dutiful to your parents. If one of them or both of them attain old age in your life, do not say to them a word of disrespect, nor shout at them, but address them in terms of honour. And lower unto them the wing of submission and humility through mercy, and say: O Allah! Bestow on them Your Mercy as they did bring me up when I was small.❯   *(Qur'an 17: 23-24)*

Notice here the word عندك means not only 'in your life', but 'with you', meaning that they should not be left alone: strong and continuous family ties and support are very important for the mental, psychological and physical health of the elderly, as well as being advantageous for the younger generations of the family.

Social commitment in Islam ranges from blood ties and marital commitments to the brotherly connections between all Muslims in society, laying the foundation for an extended Muslim family that fosters a mature sense of love, nurturing and security. In the Qur'an and the Sunnah, we find many reminders of the importance of Muslim unity — and indeed of the unity of all humankind by nature and origin. We all came from one father and one mother: Adam and Eve; thus, there is no room in Islam for racial discrimination and social injustice.

Allah (ﷻ) says:

﴿ إِنَّمَا ٱلْمُؤْمِنُونَ إِخْوَةٌ فَأَصْلِحُوا بَيْنَ أَخَوَيْكُمْ وَٱتَّقُوا ٱللَّهَ لَعَلَّكُمْ تُرْحَمُونَ ۝ ﴾

(سورة الحُجُرات: ١٠)

❰The believers are truly brothers. So make reconciliation between your brothers, and fear Allah, that you may receive mercy.❯
(Qur'an 49: 10)

This principle for the foundation of a true Muslim society is considered by many scholars to be a religious duty and a commitment that is essential for building a secure, happy and prosperous society. This in turn has a noticeable effect on the individual's happiness, contentment and peace of mind.[39]

9. Reduce stress

Research shows that continuous stress raises the blood corticosteroids and adrenaline levels, which has an adverse effect on the neural connections, preventing the effective transfer of information[40]. To make matters worse, continuous stress has also been found to increase the production of free radicals in the body, which attack body cells — including the neurons — and cause even more damage.

An excellent way to reduce stress is to keep in mind that everything you own is a gift from Allah, so that you do not grieve over what you lose nor do you delight in what you earn. Allah says in His Holy Book:

﴿وَمَآ أَصَابَ مِن مُّصِيبَةٍ فِى ٱلۡأَرۡضِ وَلَا فِىٓ أَنفُسِكُمۡ إِلَّا فِى كِتَـٰبٍ مِّن قَبۡلِ أَن نَّبۡرَأَهَآ إِنَّ ذَٰلِكَ عَلَى ٱللَّهِ يَسِيرٌ ۝ لِّكَيۡلَا تَأۡسَوۡا۟ عَلَىٰ مَا فَاتَكُمۡ وَلَا تَفۡرَحُوا۟ بِمَآ ءَاتَىٰكُمۡ وَٱللَّهُ لَا يُحِبُّ كُلَّ مُخۡتَالٍ فَخُورٍ ۝﴾ (سورة الحديد: ٢٢-٢٣)

﴿No calamity befalls on the earth or in yourselves but is inscribed in the Book of Decrees before We bring it into existence. Verily, that is easy for Allah. In order that you may not be sad over that which has eluded you, nor rejoice because of that which has been given to you. And Allah does not like prideful boasters.﴾

(Qur'an 57: 22-23)

Give your best effort to everything you do, and then do not hold yourself responsible for the results whether good or bad. Keep your faith, reformulate frustrations into challenges and anger into acceptance. Keep in mind that while you may not be able to change what is happening to you, you can certainly change your attitude towards it. Your way of looking at your problems can help you generate more energy and enthusiasm.

Ibn al-Qayyim says in his book Key to the Door of Happiness:

"The brain's activity is spoiled by the burning heat of anger, lust or overwhelming care, by fatigue and the violent movements of physical and psychological powers."[41]

Practice relaxation to rebalance your nervous system and reduce stress. By relaxation, I certainly do not mean sitting on the couch watching television (especially the news, which is a major source of stress). Instead, learn how to relax.

There are different techniques of relaxation:

> Physical relaxation: this is a kind of release or 'let go' technique that achieves mental wellbeing by relaxing the body's muscles. A well-known example is yoga.[42]

> Mental relaxation: this is another release technique that achieves a relaxed state through visualizing a pleasant picture or view. It works like this: The left-brain hemisphere is responsible for intellectual faculties and rational ability, while the right-brain hemisphere is the source of inspiration and feelings. During our daily life, we usually use our left side more often. This visualization technique is based on the idea that recalling pleasant and peaceful images through our right hemisphere brings about a general feeling of wellbeing, and counters the stressful thoughts that result from the over-engagement of the left side of the brain. Involving our brain's right side is like adding bright colours to a black and white picture, or flavouring a bland, tasteless food.

> Meditation: this is a deep relaxation technique with a more lasting effect than that of those mentioned above. Meditation is explained in more detail in Chapter Five, which deals with the spiritual body.

Food for thought

*A*s we have learnt so far, our body is one whole system. To deliver good 'food' to the brain, you have to feed the whole body in a healthy way. So the first step in our optimum brain nutrition plan is to follow a healthy eating regime that conforms to the principles of the food guide pyramid. To review briefly: choose your basic food from the complex carbohydrates group; eat lots of fresh fruits and vegetables; reduce your consumption of red meat and instead eat fish and beans as a main protein source; drink your milk and reduce your intake of fats and sweets.

Above all, remember this divine rule:

﴿ ... وَكُلُوا وَاشْرَبُوا وَلَا تُسْرِفُوٓا إِنَّهُ لَا يُحِبُّ ٱلْمُسْرِفِينَ ﴾ (٣١) (سورة الأعراف: ٣١)

﴿...And eat and drink but do not waste by extravagance, certainly He [Allah] does not like those who waste by extravagance.﴾

(Qur'an 7: 31)

These holy words are especially useful for our brain health. According to Dr. Richard Restak, if we eat a balanced diet of complex carbohydrates, proteins and essential fats without consuming any extra calories, we will get all our nutrient needs, and preserve the youthful functions and vitality of our bodies for longer.[43] This caloric restriction is believed to reduce the amount of free radicals generated in the body; by doing so we protect our DNA (the genetic material present inside every cell) from possible damage.

In the 1930s Clive McCay, a Cornell University scientist, conducted an animal study proving that a diet containing all needed nutrients while restricting caloric intake by almost 60% caused the rats to live healthier and longer.[44] Now scientists believe that a reduction in calorie intake is the best way to protect your body and brain by giving them both the chance to regenerate and to repair the damage caused by nutritional and environmental hazards on a daily basis, instead of leaving it to accumulate over the years. If performed properly, fasting during Ramadan as prescribed in the Qur'an, and at other times of the year as encouraged in the Sunnah, is an excellent application of this concept.

In addition to the general guidelines for healthy nutrition (described in Chapter Two), our brains may benefit from some more specific advice:[45]

Ten ways to feed your brain

1. Switch to whole grains and cereals

To reach optimum brain performance, it is crucial to keep an even blood sugar level (BSL). Our brain feeds only on glucose, of which it needs a steady supply: it is very sensitive to any rise or fall in the BSL.[46] Therefore, to keep your BSL steady you have to consume carbohydrates that do not cause a sharp or sudden rise in blood glucose; these are the low glycemic index (GI)[47] carbohydrates.

Allah mentions grains with their husks among His many gifts to us:

(سورة الرحمن: ١٢)   ﴾ وَٱلْحَبُّ ذُو ٱلْعَصْفِ وَٱلرَّيْحَانُ ۝ ﴿

﴾And also corn, with [its] leaves and stalk for fodder, and sweet-scented plants.﴿   *(Qur'an 55: 12)*

Complex carbohydrates in the form of whole grain products are usually a good choice. Whenever possible, avoid refined carbohydrates like white flour, processed sugars and syrups and the foods made from them. In addition, try to avoid highly processed and over-cooked food. Remember that adding vinegar to carbohydrate-rich foods may help minimize the rise in BSL.[48]

Eating refined sugars causes a sudden rise in your blood sugar level (BSL); the body responds with a rapid release of insulin, which in turn causes a sudden fall in BSL. The results are mood swings, weak mental performance and poor concentration. This effect is especially obvious in young children who show signs of hyperactivity and sometimes agitation when they consume too much sugar. To make matters worse, for the refined carbohydrates to be metabolized and assimilated by the body, they use up the stores of vitamins and minerals and supply only empty calories.

Allah has supplied our bodies with a perfectly balanced nature: if we try to change it, we just hurt ourselves. For example, the mineral chromium present in abundance in cane and beet sugar has a critical role in controlling BSL and assisting insulin function. When the plants are processed and refined to extract white sugar (sucrose), most of this essential mineral is lost.[49]

2. Eat the right kinds of fats

Our body needs a constant supply of two types of fats: omega-3 and omega-6 fatty acids. These fats are essential for — among other things — brain performance, memory and intelligence. The balance between both types of fats is very critical for brain structure and function[50]. We all seem to consume more omega-6 (mainly from common vegetable oils), than omega-3 (present in nuts, seeds and oily fish).

Allah mentions fish meat in the Qur'an, naming it 'tender meat':

﴿ وَهُوَ ٱلَّذِى سَخَّرَ ٱلْبَحْرَ لِتَأْكُلُوا۟ مِنْهُ لَحْمًا طَرِيًّا ... ﴿ ١٤ ﴾ ﴾

(سورة النحل: ١٤)

﴿And He it is Who has subjected the sea [to you], that you eat fresh tender meat [fish] from it...﴾   *(Qur'an 16: 14)*

Stick to the recommended daily amounts of these fats (see Chapter Two), and minimize your intake of saturated fats and hydrogenated fats — especially from fried and processed foods and red meat.

Olive oil is rich in another type of good fat: *monounsaturated* fatty acids. These fats, as mentioned in Chapter Two, increase HDL cholesterol in the blood and reduce levels of LDL cholesterol, thus protecting your circulatory system and enabling it to efficiently supply your brain with the needed oxygen and nutrients. Recall the saying of the Prophet (ﷺ):

«Eat (olive) oil and use it as an ointment, as it comes from a blessed tree.»[51]

3. Your brain needs protein

Many amino acids (protein building blocks) contribute to mind and mood behaviour. Tryptophan is one that has already been discussed in the previous chapter. *Phenyl alanine* is the starter for the formation of dopamine, adrenaline and *noradrenaline*, which keep you motivated and energized. *Gamma amino butyric acid* (GABA) is in itself an anti-anxiety, relaxing and calming neurotransmitter.[52]

Try to get most of your amino acid supply from combinations of nuts, beans and whole grains such as wheat, barley and

oats. As we mentioned in the previous chapter, Prophet Muhammad (ﷺ) ordered *talbeenah* (porridge made from barley) to improve the mood of someone recuperating from an illness.

Again, be careful of getting too much of a good thing. Excess protein intake, especially if it is of animal origin, can result
in the competition of the amino acids for absorption: usually the
amino acid most affected is tryptophan, which negatively affects
your mood. In addition, if too much acid is circulating in your
blood, the body responds by leaching the bones'
calcium to neutralize it. Furthermore, the
breakdown of these amino acids results
in a by-product of ammonia putting too
much stress on your kidneys.[53]

Research has found that the consumption of high quantities of
red meat, when compared to following a vegetarian diet, is linked
to an increased risk of old age dementia.[54] Red meat contains large
amounts of saturated fats, which adversely affect your circulatory
system, as explained in Chapter Two. In addition, the increased
iron load in the body increases free radical generation, causing
further damage. To repeat the Prophet's (ﷺ) warning:

«Beware of meat, as it has a ferocity like that of wine.»[55]

4. Remember your micronutrients

Micronutrients (vitamins and minerals) are
needed by the body in small amounts to perform important metabolic functions. The
body cannot synthesize most of them, so a
constant supply in the diet is very important.
They are essential in glucose metabolism,
to produce energy, and to synthesise many

neurotransmitters, prostaglandins (hormone-like substances) and phospholipids.[56] Please refer to the Table of Micronutrients at the back of this book for more details concerning their dietary sources and the role each of them performs in the body.

To get an adequate supply of vitamins and minerals:

➢ Eat your daily servings of fruits and vegetables. Vary the types, enjoy the different colours and include lots of dark green leafy vegetables.

➢ Make nuts, seeds, beans and lentils part of your daily regime. Be aware that they are rich in calories, so if you are watching your weight, limit quantities to the lower amounts that may be recommended for your age and weight.

➢ Replace refined grains with whole ones that are rich in B vitamins, the vital vitamins for mental performance, memory, mood, and energy production. We can now further understand why our Prophet (ﷺ) stressed the importance of eating whole grains rather than refined ones.

➢ Avoid nutrient-robbers: these are the empty calorie foods like overly refined or processed food, fat-loaded fast foods, and foods with added synthetic flavouring and colouring.

5. Do not forget the antioxidants

We face daily attacks from pollutants, chemicals, smoke, junk foods, pesticides and additives that generate a tremendous amount of free radicals (oxidants) — not to mention stress — in our bodies. If they encounter no defence or opposition, these free radicals start a chain reaction that causes the body's cells to reproduce abnormally, affecting body tissues and eventually its organs. Since brain cells do not divide, it is very crucial to protect them by consuming antioxidants.[57]

As detailed in the previous chapter, a wide range of antioxidants is found in foods of plant origin, and a balanced, healthy diet can supply you with your body's needs. Some examples of powerful antioxidants are:

➢ Vitamin E, found in nuts, seeds, whole grains that include the germ, and vegetable oils. It is fat soluble, so it protects the membranes and lipids of nerve cells.

➢ Vitamin C, found in citrus fruits, broccoli, coloured bell peppers, kiwi fruit, berries, tomatoes, dark green leaves and the cabbage family. It is water soluble, so it protects the inside of the cells and helps to regenerate vitamin E.

➢ Selenium, found in nuts, seeds, seafood, organ meat, eggs, mushrooms and molasses. Selenium is an essential part of an antioxidant enzyme, *glutathione peroxidase*, which protects the body from oxidative damage and reduces the requirement for vitamin E.[58]

➢ Beta-carotenes found in carrots, sweet potato, apricots, peaches, squashes, broccoli, and green leafy vegetables.

6. Eat more fruits and vegetables

As mentioned above, fruits and vegetables are your main source of vitamins, minerals and antioxidants. Besides, fruits are excellent source of potassium, which protects you from the risk of hypertension that in turn would negatively affect your brain performance. Moreover, some fruits mentioned in the Qur'an or the Sunnah have specific mental benefits, for example:

> Bananas are a good source of tryptophan, which is the source of the mood elevating neurotransmitter serotonin.

> Raisins are exceptional antioxidants. According to the ORAC scale, (oxygen radical absorbency capacity) raisins are one of the best antioxidants found in the plant kingdom.[59]

> Watermelons are rich in lycopene, another very helpful antioxidant. Lycopene is abundant in many other red fruits like tomatoes for example.

7. Eat your eggs!

I have a hard time convincing my eight-year-old son to eat his egg every morning. "I can't believe that what is in this egg I can't get from any other food!" He screams each day at the breakfast table.

Actually, egg yolks are the richest and most compact source of what we call *phospholipids*: these constitute an essential part of the *myelin sheath* surrounding our nerve cells. The myelin sheath form a kind of insulation for the transfer system among nerve cells: the better the insulation, the more efficient the transfer will be. *Phospholipids* play a major role in memory function, mood elevation and general intellectual ability.[60] They are especially important for children in their growing years when their brain is still developing.

Other rich sources of phospholipids are organ meat (liver, spleen and kidneys). As mentioned in Chapter Two, Prophet Muhammad (ﷺ) said: «We are allowed two dead animals and two bloods: fish and locust; and liver and spleen.»[61]

The *choline* content of the eggs and organ meat is also an important building block for the neurotransmitter *acetylcholine*, a multifunction hormone-like substance essential for proper memory performance. Other good sources of choline include whole wheat, sardines, peanuts, cauliflower and cabbage.[62] Furthermore, eggs contain all the essential amino acids and they are a good source of vitamin B_{12}, which is important for nerve function.[63]

Eggs and organ meat are avoided by many people due to their high cholesterol content. However, recent studies have proved that the cholesterol consumed in diet contributes only slightly to high levels of it in the blood; the main cause of high cholesterol is the cholesterol synthesized in the body itself due to the increased intake of saturated fats. So, in moderation, eggs and organ meat are a healthy food source of choline, which in addition to its benefits for the brain, aids in the reduction of *homocysteine*[64] levels in the blood.[65]

8. Drink your milk

According to the American Dietetic Association (ADA), milk and other dairy products are the best sources of calcium: not only do they contain an abundant amount of the mineral, but the calcium in milk is readily absorbed and assimilated in the body. Recall that Prophet Muhammad (ﷺ) said:

«I do not know of a more complete food or drink than milk.»[66]

Why is calcium important for the brain? It used to be thought that calcium was only essential for strong bones and teeth and for the proper function of muscles, but new studies show that, besides being a nerve and muscle relaxant,[67] calcium plays a crucial role in memory formation. Calcium facilitates the communication between brain neurons upon receiving new input information. It encourages the development of new connections at the *synaptic levels* (nerve junctions) thus strengthening the pattern of the acquired knowledge.[68] Milk and dairy are also very good sources of B vitamins, which, as mentioned above, are essential for brain health.

9. Avoid intoxicants

The dangers of smoking and tobacco use have already been discussed in Chapter One. Here we are concerned with its effects on the brain. Smoking generates thousands of oxidants in your body and delivers heavy metals, notably cadmium, which depletes other minerals essential for brain function, like zinc.[69] Allah (ﷻ) commands:

(سورة البقرة: ١٩٥)   ﴿ ... وَلَا تُلۡقُوا۟ بِأَيۡدِيكُمۡ إِلَى ٱلتَّهۡلُكَةِ ... ۝ ﴾

﴿...And do not throw yourselves into destruction...﴾ *(Qur'an 2: 195)*

Alcohol is another brain enemy. According to Patrick Holford, alcohol depletes your body vitamins and essential fatty acids, affecting your memory and general brain performance.[70]

10. Go easy on brain stimulants

Stimulants in tea, coffee, chocolate and cola raise the levels of the body stress hormones adrenaline and *cortisol.* The more you consume, the more addicted your system will become to these stimulants and you will eventually need to increase your daily 'dose' to relieve stress and keep you going.[71]

Remember what Prophet Muhammad (ﷺ) commanded:
«There should be neither harming nor reciprocating harm.»[72]

The subconscious mind

Our mind has the most amazing powers, most of which are yet to be discovered and learned. Only you can tap your mind's seemingly unlimited potential.

There are two levels to the mind: the conscious level, which is our perception of what happens around us, our rational thinking and our behaviours; and the subconscious level, which can be considered as our back-up system, the storage unit of our emotions. Positive thoughts generate prosperity and bliss, while negative ones result in troubles and distress. What is meant by that is that every thought or emotion directly affects your physical body.[73] Cells cannot discriminate between true or false suggestions sent to them by the mind — whether conscious or subconscious; they accept them as they are. Therefore, the key here is belief: whatever you really believe in, your subconscious mind will take as an undoubted fact and it will directly show on your physical health and emotions.

This interior consciousness is an attribute of the soul: the source of power, intelligence and wisdom. Allah (ﷻ) says in His Qur'an:

﴿ فَإِذَا سَوَّيْتُهُ وَنَفَخْتُ فِيهِ مِن رُّوحِى فَقَعُوا۟ لَهُۥ سَٰجِدِينَ ۞ ﴾   (سورة الحِجر: ٢٩)

﴿When I have fashioned him [the human] and breathed into him of My spirit, fall down in obeisance unto him.﴾   *(Qur'an 15: 29)*

So, through the humble wisdom of your own mind, you can change your whole life. It has the potential to lift you to happiness, abundance and security. All you need is Faith, and the reaction or the response you will get from your subconscious mind will be determined by the nature of your thoughts and beliefs. The power of your subconscious mind is not subject to logical thinking; it executes whatever you have true faith and belief in.[74] Thus, it is crucial to give it consistently positive, and harmonious thoughts; if you keep concentrating on how poor, unhappy, weak or incapable you are, mental images of vulnerability and weakness along with apprehension and incompetence will be conveyed to all the body tissues, which in their turn will be affected by these destructive vibrations and your body will keep hindering you with illnesses, imbalances in the various physical systems and lack of motivation or energy.

The idea of subconscious suggestion can be seen in the behaviour of many early Muslims. The Prophet (ﷺ) even taught his own daughter, Fâṭimah, this technique when she came with her husband, 'Ali (may Allah be pleased with them) asking the Prophet (ﷺ) to help them hire a servant, as the housework was becoming too much for them to bear.

«Prophet Muhammad (ﷺ) sat gently beside them and taught them a dhikr to say every night just before going to bed:

33 times سبحان الله *Subḥân Allah* (Glory be to Allah),

33 times الحمد لله *Alḥamdu lillâh* (All praise is for Allah),

and 34 times الله أكبر *Allâhu akbar* (Allah is the Greatest).

He told them: The following morning, you will find within yourself the strength to perform all the needed work. They tried it with total faith and it worked; they no longer felt that they needed a servant.»[75]

The same *autosuggestion* principle worked for Abu Dardâ', a Companion of Prophet Muhammad (ﷺ). When people came rushing to inform him that his house was on fire, Abu Dardâ' replied: "No, it isn't." They told him that they just come from his neighbourhood, and that all the houses there were on fire. Again, in total faith, he repeated that his house was perfectly safe. They all went back to check, and to their surprise, the whole area had completely burnt down except for a single house — Abu Dardâ's home. He then explained that Prophet Muhammad (ﷺ) had taught him this dhikr: "O Allah! You are my Master and Protector! None has the right to be worshipped except you. I place my trust in You; You are the Owner of the Mighty Throne. What Allah wills, happens, and what He does not will, does not happen. There is neither might nor power except with Allah, the Sublime, and the Most Great. I know that Allah is the All Powerful, and He is the All Knower of everything. O Allah! I seek refuge in You from the evil in myself and from the evil in any beast you master. Allah is on the straight path."[76]

The Prophet (ﷺ) had told Abu Dardâ' that whoever said these words in the morning would be protected till night, and whoever said them at the end of the day would be protected till the following morning. These are not mere words: Abu Dardâ' totally believed in them and in Allah's power and will. Remember, <u>Faith</u> is the key!

The subconscious mind perceives through intuition, or what we sometimes call the 'sixth sense'. You can see and hear with your usual senses, you conscious mind understands the material images and worldly facts that you are faced with; but true interpretation, real perception of the hidden meanings behind all creations can only be grasped with your internal instinct: a built-in insight that is not limited to what you have learned or even experienced in your life.

Allah (ﷻ) tells us about those who do not use their internal instinct to reach His true Path:

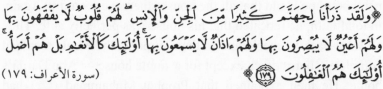

(سورة الأعراف: ١٧٩)

❰And surely, We have destined many of the jinns and humans for Hell. They have hearts with which they do not understand, they have eyes with which they do not see, and they have ears with which they do not hear [the truth]. They are like cattle, nay even more astray: those, they are the heedless ones!❱   *(Qur'an 7: 179)*

Your internal instinct is a Divine gift. Many of the Companions of the Prophet (ﷺ) experienced this gift; they earned it through their deep faith and devotion to Allah and through purification of their bodies and souls, so that they could free their minds and their intuition.

The subconscious mind is very sensitive to suggestions: it does not have the ability to negotiate or barter; it simply receives whatever is sent by the conscious mind and accepts it. Your conscious mind is the only passage through which any information can reach the subconscious mind.[77] This means that with your will, you have the ability to filter the suggestions received, stored and executed by your subconscious.

When I reached the age of eighteen, I started urging my parents to teach me to drive. I took lessons for weeks and practiced for months, but all in vain. I could not control the car — I was too scared. Once, I sat on my bed thinking and trying to figure out what was wrong with me. I realized that no female members of my family could drive: my mum, aunts and cousins had all tried to learn and failed miserably. So that was the problem. Without realizing it, I subconsciously believed that since I was a female member of this family, I would not be able to learn to drive either. It took me a while to erase this negative attitude from my mind and to replace it with a powerful belief that I was capable of doing it. It was only when I mentally accepted this new suggestion that my subconscious powers began to act accordingly, and *alhamdulillâh*, I soon got my license.

There are two types of mental suggestion. The first is *autosuggestion*, in which a person makes a suggestion to herself or himself, which may be either positive or negative. The subconscious mind accepts these kinds of suggestions, executes them and acts upon them to bring to our lives either success and prosperity or failure and misery[78]. Sometimes, these autosuggestions can be involuntary, as in my case with the driving experience. A negative suggestion can only be overcome through the force of a positive one when strengthened with true faith in Allah, then by belief in our own capabilities and potential. A hypnotherapist tries to deliver these suggestions to his or her clients while they are in a state of trance. In my humble opinion, I would not trust surrendering my conscious to a total stranger, to fill it (while I am in a state of unawareness) with whatever s/he liked. We all have the power to correct our beliefs and convictions, this is a built-in mechanism in every human being; we only have to learn how work with it to get the full benefit from it.

Prophet Muhammad (ﷺ) taught us to make remembrance of Allah, and gave us dozens of examples of dhikr Allah. Some of these are to be recited specifically in the morning and evening. These are not just meditation exercises; they are a continuous active remembrance of Allah's power, a regeneration of our faith and belief. If you practice them regularly and faithfully, they constitute a type of autosuggestion, protecting you from poverty, disease and evil thoughts, and opening in front of you the doors to a prosperous, happy and healthy life in this world, and to a promised eternal reward beyond all human limitations and boundaries.

The second type of suggestion is known as *heterosuggestion*. Heterosuggestions are ideas delivered by other persons, or by our cultural environment, like socially held beliefs, customs and traditions.[79] These also may involve either constructive or destructive information. We have the right to accept or reject them; we have the will and the power to choose, and then to take responsibility for our choices.

One example of a form of heterosuggestion is fortune-tellers. Some people like to visit fortune-tellers, or insist on reading their horoscope each morning in the newspapers, thinking they can predict and foresee events in their future. This is totally contradictory to the teaching of our religion, as Prophet Muhammad (ﷺ) said: «Whoever goes to a fortune-teller and believes him (or her), has disbelieved in what was revealed to Muhammad.»[80] The type of information the diviner is providing are mere suggestions, they cannot see into the future. In the Qur'an, the *Jinn* say of themselves:

﴿وَأَنَّا لَا نَدْرِىٓ أَشَرٌّ أُرِيدَ بِمَن فِى ٱلْأَرْضِ أَمْ أَرَادَ بِهِمْ رَبُّهُمْ رَشَدًا ۝﴾ (سورة الجن: ١٠)

❰And we do not know whether evil is intended for those on earth, or whether Allah intends for them a Right Path.❱ *(Qur'an 72: 10)*

Their predictions of failure can turn true if you believe in them, as your subconscious mind will work upon them until it executes them. It is a pity that, ignorance and unawareness lead so many people to this path. Hypnotism, tea leaves, astrological formulas, and other forms of heterosuggestion have no power over us; it is people who choose to give these things the power to control their lives.

Let us take an example of a useful, positive heterosuggestion as found in this statement by the Messenger of Allah (ﷺ):

«When you visit a sick person, say good words to him for the sake of Allah, for although that does not prevent any harm, it still brings relief to the patient's heart."[81] In a sound hadith, the Messenger of Allah (ﷺ) used to supplicate for a sick or afflicted person, and say to them: "It is all right, you will be purified (through this affliction), Allah willing.»[82]

These two hadiths demonstrate the important role the emotional state of the patient plays in his or her recovery; this is the main secret behind the miraculous recovery of some people who were not expected to survive particularly destructive illnesses such as with difficult cases of cancer. New research suggests the importance of psychological treatment along with conventional remedies prescribed for chronic diseases, in order to strengthen the patient's immunity. Relieving the anxiety of the affected person by some simple but honest words enhances his or her resolve and gives them hope and energy to fight the illness.

Try your own suggestions. Before going to bed, think of something pleasant — a favourite holiday spot, something you have always dreamed of doing or having — always visualize a prosperous, happy life, relieve yourself from your daily hassles and worldly distress. Leave your subconscious mind to execute your matters for you and depend on and trust in Allah. Do not be impatient for the results; just keep practicing it every night with total faith, contentment and patience. Then, when your problems are solved and your happy ending is reached, always remember and give thanks and praises to Almighty Allah who can, by His Will, make anything happen.

（سورة يس: ٨٢）   ﴿إِنَّمَآ أَمْرُهُۥ إِذَآ أَرَادَ شَيْـًٔا أَن يَقُولَ لَهُۥ كُن فَيَكُونُ ۝﴾

❨Verily, His Command, when He intends a thing, is only that He says to it: Be! And it is.❩　　　　*(Qur'an 36: 82)*

Finally, always remember that any calamity that befalls you is of your own doing (although at first you may not recognize it), and that anything good is from Allah (ﷻ).

$$\text{﴿مَّا أَصَابَكَ مِنْ حَسَنَةٍ فَمِنَ اللَّهِ وَمَا أَصَابَكَ مِن سَيِّئَةٍ فَمِن نَّفْسِكَ ... ﴾ ۝}$$

(سورة النساء: ٧٩)

❨Whatever of good reaches you, is from Allah, but whatever of evil befalls you, is from yourself...❩　　　　*(Qur'an 4: 79)*

Neurolinguistic Programming (NLP)

𝒯he concept of *neurolinguistic programming* (NLP) was introduced in the 1970s by Richard Bandler, a mathematician and computer programmer who was also interested in psychology. He developed these ideas further after collaborating with Dr. John Grinder, an assistant professor in linguistics. NLP is a behavioural technique that boosts your emotional intelligence and helps better understand and deal with your thoughts, feelings and emotions. When you have a better understanding of what is going on inside your mind and heart, you will surely be more capable of having better relationships and more fruitful communication with others. This technique aims at allowing a person to change or eliminate bad thoughts and behaviours, control desires, choose his own mental and psychological state of wellbeing and adopt constructive beliefs and attitudes. It is a guide for better quality of life simply by programming your own 'biological computer'.[83]

NLP is a new term, but it is not really a new idea. As we mentioned earlier, Islamic dhikr is meant to perform the same role by positively reprogramming your mind, thus adjusting your emotional status and constantly reminding you of your final ultimate goal: Allah's pleasure. The practice of dhikr Allah keeps open an everlasting link between you and your spiritual source of energy.

To better understand the concept, let us take a look at a typical start to the day: Most of us wake up in the morning and automatically reach for the kettle or the coffee maker to take our morning dose of caffeine. Caffeine helps the release of the motivating neurotransmitters *dopamine* and *adrenaline*, thus gradually waking you up. However, the more caffeine you consume, the more irresponsive your brain becomes to it and to the action of the natural 'in-house' stimulants dopamine and adrenaline; consequently, more caffeine is needed to achieve the same level of stimulation.[84]

Another way some people start their day is to stay in bed for a while, remembering their problems, occupations and engagements.[85] *I have to meet my unfair boss again today, I have a deadline that I need to work on, I have to help the kids study for their exams, my husband will keep torturing me about my weight problem*, and the list goes on and on. This stressful exercise naturally raises your adrenaline level, which pushes you to jump out of bed and face the new day. However, you face this day as an automated anxiety machine, loaded with stress hormones and ready to explode in the face of the first unfortunate human being you encounter.

Now look at the Islamic way to 'program' your day. There is a dhikr you say upon awaking: "All praise and thanks are due to Allah who brings us to life after he caused us to die (during sleep)[86] and unto Him is the resurrection." (*Alḥamdu lillâh alladhee aḥyânâ ba'da an amâtanâ wa ilayhin-nushoor.*)[87]

The pronunciation of this dhikr first thing in the morning constitutes a quick yet powerful reminder of our unlimited blessings. By giving praise and thanks to Allah, we soundly remind ourselves that there are hundreds of gifts in our lives that we need to thank Him for. One is the gift of breath, or life itself, as the words of this dhikr make reference to the state of unconsciousness that we are in while we sleep, a state not unlike being 'dead' for a while. Another day alive means another opportunity to work and give — another chance to fulfil our duty to ourselves, our surroundings and our Creator. Mentioning the Resurrection every morning is a continuous reminder of our ultimate goal in life, of the unimportance of this mortal life, and thus the unimportance of all our seemingly insurmountable problems. This simple yet powerful dhikr gives us the motivation and the enthusiasm we need to start the day — without the intoxicating effects of caffeine and stress. If we add to this the Prophet's (ﷺ) habit of drinking a spoonful of honey dissolved in half a cup of warm water, we are giving our brain the amount of glucose needed to help it synthesize the serotonin neurotransmitter — an effective and potent mood booster. Now there is the ultimate Islamic way to start your day!

Another example of brain reprogramming is the 'mirror supplication (du'â'). Prophet Muhammad (ﷺ) taught us that when we look in the mirror we should say:

«O Allah! Perfect my manners as you have perfected the creation of me (*Allâhumma kamâ aḥsanta khalqee, iḥsan khuluqee*).»[88]

Again, when you look in the mirror, what do you see? A pleasant, good looking, relaxed and self-confident human being, or an ugly, dissatisfied, unhappy creature? When they look at themselves in the mirror, some people see only their apparent physical defects, upon which they build their self-image and behavioural responses: *I have a huge, ugly nose, I wish I had more hair, I'm too short* (from men), *and I am too fat, who on earth would wish to marry someone like me?*

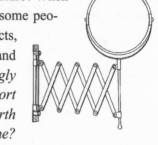

My husband's going to leave me for another woman (from women). In contrast, the Islamic mirror dhikr gives us a recurring boost of self-esteem. We are the creation of Allah: how can we be ugly?

Allah (ﷻ) says:

﴿ ... وَصَوَّرَكُمْ فَأَحْسَنَ صُوَرَكُمْ ... ۞﴾   (سورة غافر: ٦٤)

﴿...And He has given you shape and made your shapes good [looking]...﴾   *(Qur'an 40: 64)*

This is an assurance from Allah that we are beautiful — each and every one of us. Along with this confidence lesson, another lesson is delivered to us: Do not get too confident. Arrogance is a sin in Islam, so supplicate for good manners, as this is what really matters to a true Muslim.

There are hundreds of examples of dhikr Allah that our beloved Prophet (ﷺ) taught us. He did not leave one detail of human action without teaching us what to say upon performing it. There is a dhikr or du'â' (supplication) to be said for waking up, for going to bed, for putting on new clothes, for undressing, for entering and leaving the toilet, for entering or leaving the mosque and for entering the market (or mega mall, as the case may be). There are supplications and remembrances for eating, visiting the sick, sneezing and travelling and others said in cases of fear, physical pain, panic, anger or distress; and others in case of delight, amazement or upon receiving pleasant news.[89]

CHAPTER 4

EMOTIONAL BODY

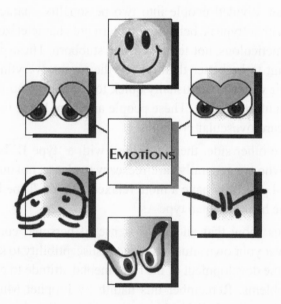

$\mathcal{I}$t has been proven that mental and emotional stresses affect body tissues and secretions. Destructive emotions like fear, resentment, worry, envy, boastfulness and egotism truly poison the body. Dealing with crisis, stress and problematic events is a recurring aspect of daily life. How we adapt and cope with these challenges affects not only our psychology and emotions, but also our physical body and immune system.

Sources of stress

$\mathcal{T}$here are three major sources of stress:[1]

1. Personality factors

In the seventies, two American cardiologists, Friedman and Rosenman, divided people into two personality characteristics: People with a 'type A' behaviour pattern are characterized as fastidious, meticulous, hot-tempered, and stubborn. These people always want to be better than others; they want everything to be done their way and are usually quick to get angry and frustrated at the slightest mistake. These people are more liable to develop various cardiovascular problems.

On the other side, there are those with a 'type B' behaviour pattern, who are generally carefree, easy to please, not quick-tempered and generally have a more relaxed attitude. Type B people tend to be healthier than type As.[2]

Studies show that an overall sense of personal control and power over your own situation reduces susceptibility to stress and leads to the development of the right mental attitude to cope with your problems. Remember this hadith by Prophet Muhammad (ﷺ): «The strong believer is more loved by Allah than the weak one, and there is benefaction in both.»

I recall here an interesting study performed in Israel following the Iraqi launched missiles during the Gulf War of 1991. The study of Israeli civilians found that the mortality rate increased alarmingly after the attack. Surprisingly, the increased number of deaths was not caused by the physical effect of the missiles — which were practically ineffective, probably due to the great distance of the target. Rather, it was caused by heart failure and other cardiovascular problems induced by the fright, apprehension and panic these missiles had induced in the hapless civilians.[3] It should be noted here, though, that the mental state was not the main cause of these deaths; most

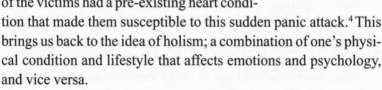

of the victims had a pre-existing heart condition that made them susceptible to this sudden panic attack.[4] This brings us back to the idea of holism; a combination of one's physical condition and lifestyle that affects emotions and psychology, and vice versa.

The lack of a sense of power is an essential factor in this incident. A positive sense of power that primarily arises from faith and social unity, so that when those two elements are missing, people feel fear and insecurity, as we have been taught in the Qur'an:

﴿لَأَنتُمْ أَشَدُّ رَهْبَةً فِى صُدُورِهِم مِّنَ ٱللَّهِ ذَٰلِكَ بِأَنَّهُمْ قَوْمٌ لَّا يَفْقَهُونَ ۝ لَا يُقَٰتِلُونَكُمْ جَمِيعًا إِلَّا فِى قُرًى مُّحَصَّنَةٍ أَوْ مِن وَرَآءِ جُدُرٍ بَأْسُهُم بَيْنَهُمْ شَدِيدٌ تَحْسَبُهُمْ جَمِيعًا وَقُلُوبُهُمْ شَتَّىٰ ذَٰلِكَ بِأَنَّهُمْ قَوْمٌ لَّا يَعْقِلُونَ ۝﴾

(سورة الحشر: ١٣–١٤)

﴿Verily, you [believers in the Oneness of Allah — Islamic monotheism] are more awful as a fear in their breasts than Allah. That is because they are a people who do not comprehend [the Majesty and Power of Allah]. They do not fight against you even together, except in fortified townships, or from behind walls. Their enmity among themselves is very great. You would think they were united, but their hearts are divided, that is because they are a people who do not understand.﴾ *(Qur'an 59: 13-14)*

The following are important qualities or personality traits that enable you to manage stress:

> strong faith
> a feeling of power
> independence
> having a sense of commitment
> self control
> the perception of problems as challenges

2. Environmental[5] factors

Stress is inevitable in our lives. In the modern world, we face daily mental and emotional challenges that tend to leave us caught and struggling between our needs and ambitions on one side and our actual circumstances and reality on the other. Whether these are big challenges like divorce, job loss or the death of a loved one, or just everyday minor hassles like lack of time, traffic jams and juggling responsibilities, all these are stress-inducing factors that we experience on a daily basis, and they put the body in a continuous state of anxiety. This feeling depletes your energy, tenses your muscles, disrupts your blood circulation and most dangerous of all, it damages your immunity. Researchers found that people who are faced with stressful circumstances on an everyday basis are more prone to microbial attacks and various immuno-compromised conditions than they would be if they were living under reduced tension.[6]

The way people cope with these events is a major factor in whether or not their health is affected. Take the example of divorce. Most people would say that divorce is one of the most devastating life crises; it affects the whole family, and generates a highly stressful environment. Yet look at the *soorah* (chapter) in the Qur'an named *Ṭalâq* or 'Divorce'. Reading these verses makes you feel as if a kind, merciful hand is caressing you and giving you hope for the future. The verses are filled with positive attitude — assurances from Allah that things will get better, that there is a foreseeable end to the current misery.

﴾ ... وَمَن يَتَّقِ ٱللَّهَ يَجْعَل لَّهُۥ مَخْرَجًا ۝ وَيَرْزُقْهُ مِنْ حَيْثُ لَا يَحْتَسِبُ وَمَن يَتَوَكَّلْ عَلَى ٱللَّهِ فَهُوَ حَسْبُهُۥٓ إِنَّ ٱللَّهَ بَٰلِغُ أَمْرِهِۦ قَدْ جَعَلَ ٱللَّهُ لِكُلِّ شَىْءٍ قَدْرًا ۝ ﴾

(سورة الطلاق: ٢-٣)

﴿...And whosoever fears Allah and keeps his duty to Him, He will make a way for him to get out [from every difficulty], and He will provide for him from [sources] he never could imagine. And whosoever puts his trust in Allah, then He will suffice for him. Verily, Allah will accomplish His purpose. Indeed Allah has set a measure for all things.﴾

(Qur'an 65: 2-3)

(سورة الطلاق: ٤)   ﴾ ... وَمَن يَتَّقِ ٱللَّهَ يَجْعَل لَّهُۥ مِنْ أَمْرِهِۦ يُسْرًا ۝ ﴿

﴿...And whosoever fears Allah and keeps his duty to Him, He will make his matter easy for him.﴾

(Qur'an 65: 4)

﴾ ... وَمَن يَتَّقِ ٱللَّهَ يُكَفِّرْ عَنْهُ سَيِّئَاتِهِۦ وَيُعْظِمْ لَهُۥٓ أَجْرًا ۝ ﴿   (سورة الطلاق: ٥)

﴿...And whosoever fears Allah and keeps his duty to Him, He will remit his sins from him, and will enlarge his reward.﴾

(Qur'an 65: 5)

﴾ ... لَا يُكَلِّفُ ٱللَّهُ نَفْسًا إِلَّا مَآ ءَاتَىٰهَا سَيَجْعَلُ ٱللَّهُ بَعْدَ عُسْرٍ يُسْرًا ۝ ﴿

(سورة الطلاق: ٧)

❨...Allah puts no burden on any person beyond what He has given him. Allah will grant after hardship, ease.❩   *(Qur'an 65: 7)*

Reading this soorah — with a deep belief and trust in Allah's promises and His complete Power, Mercy and Wisdom — will reduce stress and give hope, helping a person to cope with a disturbing situation, even in the most difficult circumstances.

3. Social factors

It helps to have someone close to you, whom you trust and to whom you feel free to talk about your problems and share your feelings. Being surrounded by a happy, loving and caring environment, whether at home, in the neighbourhood or at work, increases the ability to cope with stress. Prophet Muhammad (ﷺ) said:

«The believers are to each other like a solid building, they strengthen each other.»[7]

Conversely, living in a hostile environment, feeling out of place, rejected or lonely increases stress.

Another important source of tension, for individuals as well as the family and the whole society, is poverty.[8] Long-term exposure to difficult circumstances like a stressful social situation, insecure working conditions, inadequate shelter, and financial worries compound otherwise ordinary problems.[9] Furthermore, studies indicate a strong relationship between low socioeconomic status and poor health conditions, family disunity and unhappiness.

Knowing this, we can understand the wisdom behind this supplication taught to us by the Prophet (ﷺ), to be repeated three times every morning and evening:

«O Allah! I seek refuge with You from the trials of poverty. *(Allâhumma a'oodhu bika min fitnat il-faqr).*»[10]

Sometimes, poverty causes such stress that it may lead to disbelief in Allah's Mercy and Justice if not dealt with properly emotionally and psychologically as well as on the social level.

Are we dealing properly with our stress?

When you are subjected to stress, there are two types of responses occurring inside your body: involuntary cellular and hormonal reactions (*physiological response*) and your conscious reaction to the stressful experience, which is manifested in your mental or emotional state and your coping attitude (*cognitive response*)[11].

1. Physiological response

It is normal to feel stress while facing danger or unpleasant situations. In fact, Allah created your body to be highly adaptable; this enables it to deal with normal pressures. Nevertheless, the way your body responds to stress is dependent primarily on the type of stress you are facing, that is, whether it is acute or chronic. The acute stressors trigger the sympathetic nervous system to release adrenalin and noradrenaline whose role is to prepare the body to face the incoming danger. This response is activated within a few seconds of the stress alarm and subsides shortly after the disappearance of the stressor.

Other key players in the stress response are the steroid hormones[12] (mainly *cortisol*) released from the *adrenal cortex*. This response is slower, but its effect is more persistent.

The high levels of cortisol associated with chronic stress have a devastating suppressing effect on the immune system;[13] they reduce the number of white blood cells, interfere with the production of lymphocytes, suppress the production of some other immune system regulators and hence increase vulnerability to illnesses, cellular malfunctions and tumours. Chronic stress also elicits a 'down-regulation' of the immune response. That is, the immune cells are constantly being stimulated with high levels of stress hormones but they are not actually facing any real danger or any threatening pathogen, so they get used to the high level of the stress hormones circulating in the body. When the body is faced with a real threat, the immune cells no longer become stimulated, and lose their ability to deal effectively with the invader.[14] Furthermore, the constant stimulation of the sympathetic nervous system leads to a permanent rise in blood pressure, rapid heart rate, inactive digestion, increased blood sugar levels and increased breakdown and mobilization of stored fat. If you are overweight, you might look at this last effect as beneficial, but this is not the case. The increased mobilization of body fuel reserves entails the rapid release of fatty acids into the bloodstream, which build up on the artery walls, contributing to coronary heart problems. In contrast, in the acute stressful situation response noted above, there can be a short-term increase in adrenalin and noradrenaline levels without necessarily raising the level of cortisol.

2. Cognitive response

Richard Lazarus[15] uses the term 'cognitive appraisal' to describe how different changes and various encountered circumstances influence individuals. Some people perceive any problem as menacing, imminent, and troublesome; while others approach their problem with a fighting spirit, favouring adjustment and adaptation. Perceiving stressful situations as harmful hinders our ability to analyse and subsequently cope with these situations. On the other hand, seeing them as challenging enables us to deal effectively with the events.[16]

Our way of coping with our emotions depends primarily on our degree of faith. A deep trust in and love for Allah, coupled with the realization that this world is transient, can give us strength and peace of mind. This is an internal serenity that comes from the realization that each event (no matter how difficult or tragic) must include something good for us; we draw a lesson out of every experience, and turn each failure into challenge and each loss into hope. A true believer never falls into despair, as s/he is simply never enslaved by worldly passions. Allah promises to reward patience and the acceptance of His Will in this life and in the hereafter. The believer should always remember this verse of the Qur'an:

$$ ﴿ قُل لَّن يُصِيبَنَآ إِلَّا مَا كَتَبَ ٱللَّهُ لَنَا هُوَ مَوْلَىٰنَا وَعَلَى ٱللَّهِ فَلْيَتَوَكَّلِ $$

$$ ٱلْمُؤْمِنُونَ ۝ ﴾ (سورة التوبة: ٥١) $$

❨Say: Nothing shall ever happen to us except what Allah has ordained for us. He is our Maulâ [Allah, Helper and Protector]. And in Allah let the believers put their trust.❩ *(Qur'an 9: 51)*

The cognitive view can dramatically influence our physiological response to a stressful situation. By changing the mental image and improving our coping attitude, we initiate a relaxing feeling, calming down the 'fight, flight and fright' response triggered by the hypothalamus centre in the brain and executed by the sympathetic nervous system. This proactive behaviour saves us from a load of physical risks.

I once read a story about a group of
alumni, highly established in their ca-
reers, who got together to visit their old
university lecturer. Conversation soon
turned into complaints about stress at work
and in daily life. Offering his guests coffee,
the lecturer went to the kitchen and returned
with a large pot of coffee and an assortment of cups: porcelain,
plastic, glass, some plain-looking and some expensive and exqui-
site, telling them to help themselves to hot coffee. When all the
students had a cup of coffee in hand, the lecturer said: "If you noticed, all the nice-looking, expensive cups were taken up, leaving
behind the plain and cheap ones. While it is normal for you to want
only the best for yourselves, that is the source of your problems
and stress. What all of you really wanted was coffee, not the cup,
but you consciously went for the better cups and are eyeing each
other's cups. Now, if life is coffee, then the jobs, money and position in society are the cups. They are just tools to hold and contain
life, but the quality of life doesn't change. Sometimes, by concentrating only on the cup, we fail to enjoy the coffee in it. So don't let
the cups distract you...enjoy the coffee instead."[17]

Be happy

Happiness is an inner feeling; it is the contentment and satisfaction of one's soul. You are the only one responsible for your
own happiness. Happiness is a decision that you can make any-
time and stick to it. I know many people who keep saying, *If I was
richer, I would have been happier; If I pass this exam, I will be
happier.* There is always an 'if' involved; their happiness is dependent on some materialistic objective in their lives, and let me
assure you that even 'if' this objective is reached, there will al-

ways be another one waiting, further postponing their happiness. Prophet Muhammad (ﷺ) said: «Seek the help of Allah, do not be frustrated and if something befalls you, do not say: If I had done this, so and so would have happened, but say: Allah decreed, and what Allah wills, He does. Indeed, 'if' opens the door for evil.»[18]

Ibn al-Qayyim classified happiness into three types:[19]

➤ External happiness, resulting from wealth, power, prestige or the possession of worldly material goods. This type, he noted, is the lowest stage of happiness, as it is a momentary pleasure that can vanish in an instant.

Allah (ﷻ) says:

﴿ ٱعْلَمُوٓا۟ أَنَّمَا ٱلْحَيَوٰةُ ٱلدُّنْيَا لَعِبٌ وَلَهْوٌ وَزِينَةٌ وَتَفَاخُرٌ بَيْنَكُمْ وَتَكَاثُرٌ فِى ٱلْأَمْوَٰلِ وَٱلْأَوْلَٰدِ كَمَثَلِ غَيْثٍ أَعْجَبَ ٱلْكُفَّارَ نَبَاتُهُۥ ثُمَّ يَهِيجُ فَتَرَىٰهُ مُصْفَرًّا ثُمَّ يَكُونُ حُطَٰمًا وَفِى ٱلْأَخِرَةِ عَذَابٌ شَدِيدٌ وَمَغْفِرَةٌ مِّنَ ٱللَّهِ وَرِضْوَٰنٌ وَمَا ٱلْحَيَوٰةُ ٱلدُّنْيَآ إِلَّا مَتَٰعُ ٱلْغُرُورِ ﴾

(سورة الحديد: ٢٠)

﴿Know that the life of this world is only play and amusement, pomp and mutual boasting among you, and rivalry in respect of wealth and children, as the likeness of vegetation after rain, thereof the growth is pleasing to the tiller; afterwards it dries up and you see it turning yellow; then it becomes straw. But in the Hereafter [there is] a severe torment [for the disbelievers, evil-doers], and [there is] Forgiveness from Allah and [His] Good Pleasure [for the believers who do good works], whereas the life of this world is only a deceiving enjoyment.﴾   *(Qur'an 57: 20)*

➤ The second type of happiness originates from the physical body — its health, mood and strength. This one is more related to who we are than the first type, but still, it is an external type of happiness and it can come to an end at any time.

Allah (ﷻ) states in His Holy Book:

$$﴿لَقَدْ خَلَقْنَا ٱلْإِنسَٰنَ فِىٓ أَحْسَنِ تَقْوِيمٍ ۝ ثُمَّ رَدَدْنَٰهُ أَسْفَلَ سَٰفِلِينَ ۝﴾$$

(سورة التين: ٤-٥)

◆Verily, We created the human of the best stature [mould], then We reduced him to the lowest of the low.﴿   *(Qur'an 95: 4-5)*

> The third type is moral happiness, which originates from the heart and the soul. This is true happiness, and it results from useful knowledge, good manners, content of character and faith. Allah teaches us in His Holy Book:

$$﴿ قُلْ بِفَضْلِ ٱللَّهِ وَبِرَحْمَتِهِۦ فَبِذَٰلِكَ فَلْيَفْرَحُوا۟ هُوَ خَيْرٌ مِّمَّا يَجْمَعُونَ ۝﴾$$

(سورة يونس: ٥٨)

◆Say: In the Bounty of Allah, and in His Mercy [Islam and the Qur'an]; therein let them rejoice. That is better than what [the wealth] they amass.﴿   *(Qur'an 10: 58)*

Ibn al-Qayyim interpreted the 'Bounty of Allah' as the faith of the believer; and His 'Mercy' as the Glorious Qur'an.

According to Ghazâli (the Younger), the real reasons for happiness reside in the soul; this happiness can be served by the physical body (health and strength), and then by other external worldly desires like wealth and children. Whoever follows this order adjusts their priorities and attains real bliss.[20]

Here are some guidelines from the Qur'an and the Sunnah that if properly applied and faithfully believed, will ensure your way to a happy, prosperous life on earth and in the hereafter.

Twenty tips to bring you happiness

1. Be grateful

$\mathcal{B}$e grateful to Allah and be grateful to His creatures. There is a hadith of the Messenger of Allah (ﷺ) that states:

«One who is not grateful to people is not grateful to Allah.»[21]

«Suhayb reported that the Prophet (ﷺ) said: The believer's affair is amazing: it is all for the good, and that is not the case of anyone other than a believer. If good times come to him, he is thankful and thus it is good for him, and if bad times befall him, he is patient, and thus it is also good for him.»[22]

Allah's blessings are countless. Think about your sense of sight, hearing, touch, smell; think about your health, wealth, family and friends; think about your kids, your parents, and your spouse.

The following story may clarify the importance of this: Prophet Muhammad once told the story of a worshipper who lived in total isolation for 1000 years, doing nothing but worshipping Allah. When this man died, Allah ordered the angels to take him to Heaven by the Mercy of Allah. The man disagreed, stating that he should go to Heaven as a result of his own work, his 1000 years of worship. Allah then ordered His angels to settle the man's account. The angels put the worshipper's work on one scale of the balance and on the other they started by putting the blessing of eyesight. The scale carrying only the eyesight blessing was much heavier. The man then shouted: By your mercy, O Allah, by your mercy! Allah replied: Take my servant to Heaven by my mercy.[23]

Allah (ﷻ) says in His Book:

﴿وَءَاتَىٰكُم مِّن كُلِّ مَا سَأَلْتُمُوهُ وَإِن تَعُدُّواْ نِعْمَتَ ٱللَّهِ لَا تُحْصُوهَآ ... ﴿٣٤﴾ ﴾

(سورة إبراهيم: ٣٤)

﴾And He gave you of all that you asked for, and if you count the Blessings of Allah, never will you be able to count them...﴿

(Qur'an 14: 34)

Even if you are encountering some problems or inconveniences, think about those who are in a worse condition: The Prophet (ﷺ) advised:

«Look at those who are inferior to you and do not look at the ones above you, this is worthier of you so you do not despise Allah's blessings.»[24]

Once Imam Mâlik was walking when he met an old, blind, handicapped person sitting on the side of the road praying and thanking Allah for his blessings. The Imam stopped and asked the old worshipper, "What are you giving thanks for?" The old man replied, "Didn't Allah bless me with a healthy heart to glorify Him with?"[25]

I love these verses sung by Ahmed Bukhatir:[26]

With feet to take me where I'd go;
With eyes to see the sunset's glow;
With ears to hear what I'd know,
O God, forgive me when I whine.
I've been blessed indeed, the world is mine!

Remember, there is always a divine blessing that we need to be thankful for; there is always a benefaction, a grace that we need to glorify and praise Allah for. Do not eye other people's blessings thinking that you are deprived in some way.[27]

Allah is the Most Just. Each and every one of us has his appropriate gifts, you just have to feel and enjoy them. Do not let your life speed before your eyes like a video clip. Enjoy each and every moment, celebrate each and every boon. Stop for a while and reflect; what did you encounter today that brought a sense of happiness and satisfaction to your heart? It does not have to be a big thing: did you see the beautiful sunrise, did you smell the breeze of fresh air or may be notice the smile on your little child's face? You will find a lot to thank Allah for.

«A man once asked 'Abdullah ibn 'Amr ibn al-'Âs: Am I not one of the poor immigrants? 'Abdullah replied: Do you have a wife to go back to? The man said: Yes; then 'Abdullah asked: Do you have a house to live in? Again the man nodded. 'Abdullah said: Then you are one of the rich ones. The man added: And I have a servant. 'Abdullah said: Then, you are one of the kings!»[28]

2. Do not wait for a reward

Allah (ﷻ) says in the Qur'an:

(سورة البقرة: ١٤٨)   ﴿ ... فَٱسْتَبِقُوا۟ ٱلْخَيْرَٰتِ ... ﴿١٤٨﴾ ﴾

﴿...So hasten towards all that is good...﴾   *(Qur'an 2: 148)*

He (ﷻ) also tells us:

﴿يَـٰٓأَيُّهَا ٱلَّذِينَ ءَامَنُوا۟ ٱرْكَعُوا۟ وَٱسْجُدُوا۟ وَٱعْبُدُوا۟ رَبَّكُمْ وَٱفْعَلُوا۟ ٱلْخَيْرَ لَعَلَّكُمْ تُفْلِحُونَ ۩ ﴿٧٧﴾ ﴾

(سورة الحج: ٧٧)

﴿O you who believe! Bow down, and prostrate yourselves, and worship Allah and do good, that you may be successful.﴾

(Qur'an 22: 77)

In the same verse of the Qur'an ordering us to bow and prostrate and worship Allah, He directed us to perform good deeds for others. Acts of worship fill your heart with mercy and compassion, compelling you to serve your society and the whole of humanity. Benefaction to others is a sign of the acceptance of your acts of worship.[29] The Messenger of Allah (ﷺ) related this *hadith qudsi*:[30]

«A man from among those who were before you was called to account. Nothing in the way of good was found for him except that he used to have dealings with people and, being well-to-do, he would order his servants to let off the man in straitened circumstances (from repaying his debt). He [the Prophet (ﷺ)] said that Allah said: We are worthier than you of that (being generous). Let him off.»[31]

The first beneficiary of your acting to help others is yourself; this pure act of unselfishness feeds your soul, boosts your sense of self-worth and brings you closer to Allah. Psychological studies show that people's happiness greatly improves with the level of their altruistic activity[32] and a close, supportive social system significantly increases gratification.[33] Do not wait for any human thanks or worldly benefits — your real reward will be from Allah Himself:

﴿وَيُطْعِمُونَ ٱلطَّعَامَ عَلَىٰ حُبِّهِۦ مِسْكِينًا وَيَتِيمًا وَأَسِيرًا ۝ إِنَّمَا نُطْعِمُكُمْ لِوَجْهِ ٱللَّهِ لَا نُرِيدُ مِنكُمْ جَزَآءً وَلَا شُكُورًا ۝ إِنَّا نَخَافُ مِن رَّبِّنَا يَوْمًا عَبُوسًا قَمْطَرِيرًا ۝ فَوَقَىٰهُمُ ٱللَّهُ شَرَّ ذَٰلِكَ ٱلْيَوْمِ وَلَقَّىٰهُمْ نَضْرَةً وَسُرُورًا ۝ وَجَزَىٰهُم بِمَا صَبَرُواْ جَنَّةً وَحَرِيرًا ۝﴾

(سورة الإنسان: ٨–١٢)

❰And they give food, in spite of their love for it [or for the love of Him], to the needy, the orphan, and the captive, [saying]: We feed you seeking Allah's Countenance only. We wish for no reward, nor thanks from you. Verily, We fear from Allah a Day, hard and distressful, that will make the faces look horrible [from their extreme dislike for it]. So Allah saved them from the evil of that Day, and gave them a light of beauty and joy, and their recompense shall be Paradise, and silken garments, because they were patient.⟩   *(Qur'an 76: 8-12)*

The positive effects of helping others and comforting them will show directly in your life on earth and will also benefit your afterlife. Allah says in His Holy Book:

﴿ مَنْ عَمِلَ صَلِحًا مِّن ذَكَرٍ أَوْ أُنثَىٰ وَهُوَ مُؤْمِنٌ فَلَنُحْيِيَنَّهُ حَيَوٰةً طَيِّبَةً وَلَنَجْزِيَنَّهُمْ أَجْرَهُم بِأَحْسَنِ مَاكَانُوا۟ يَعْمَلُونَ ۝ ﴾   (سورة النحل: ٩٧)

⟨Whoever works righteousness, whether male or female, while he [or she] is a true believer [in Islamic monotheism] verily, to him We will give a good life [in this world with respect, contentment and lawful provision], and We shall pay them certainly a reward in proportion to the best of what they used to do [Paradise in the Hereafter].⟩   *(Qur'an 16: 97)*

You will find happiness in feeding the hungry, sheltering the homeless; you will feel comfort in the smile of an orphan and the felicity of the poor. Ghazâli the Younger said, "Benefaction to others is a delight to the heart."[34]

Imam Ahmed ibn Hanbal once told a story about a woman who left her son to look for a shady place to feed him a loaf of bread. While she was looking around, a kidnapper came and took the boy to sell him into slavery. When she returned and discovered that her little boy was gone, she burst into tears. Meanwhile, a beggar passed by asking for food; despite her pain and fears, she handed the man the loaf of bread she had been carrying for her son. In just a few minutes, the kidnapper came back with her little boy.

He told her, "As I was trying to sell him, a strange voice from within said to me, 'Don't you have a son? Aren't you afraid that he might face the same fate one day?' So, I came back to return your boy."

The woman took her child in her arms and said: "Glory be to Allah, who has accepted my loaf of bread (as charity)!"[35]

Prophet Muhammad (ﷺ) said: «Allah will help His servant as long as he helps his brother.»[36]

One of Allah's Names is 'The Multiplier of Rewards' (*Ash-Shakoor*) He rewards even a small good deed with an abundant recompense both in this life and in the Hereafter.

Imam Ahmed ibn Miskeen told the story of Abu Nâṣr, a fisherman who was so poor that he could not even feed his family. One day when the fisherman passed by the Imam, the Imam asked him to follow him to the sea. There, the Imam pronounced the Name of Allah the Most Gracious, the Most Merciful, and ordered Abu Nâṣr to cast his fishAing net. Out came a big fish. Abu Nâṣr sold the fish and bought some food for his wife and child. While heading home, Abu Nâṣr passed by a woman and her little child crying from hunger; he could not help but hand them the food he had bought for his family. Once again, he was going home to his hungry boy, grieved and penniless. Before reaching his house, Abu Nâṣr heard a man calling his name; that stranger handed him a small parcel and said,

'Your father had lent me some money years ago before he passed away. I did not have the means to return it. As soon as I could afford it, I came looking all over for you until I finally found you. Here you are, this is your money, my son."

The poor fisherman opened the parcel, and to his surprise, it contained 30,000 dirhams (pieces of silver)![37]

This is no fairy tale, this is a true story; and there is certainly no coincidence, believe me! The grieving mother who lost her little boy and the poor fisherman had one thing in common: They were both very sincere in their altruistic act and were both really faithful to Allah.

Remember!
Always make your intention right

In every community, there are innumerable different ways to help others. Anything you do will not only help the world, it will also help you. You will experience rewards that cannot be attained in any other way. It does not have to be money; you can give of your time or your skills. Remember, though: always be sincere in your actions and seek only Allah's reward.

3. Be a believer

You experience what you believe in. You only need to adjust your inner feelings, keep your self-esteem and confidence and above all, have Faith and true belief in your Creator — in Allah. As I said in the previous chapter, it is all in your mind; the power of your thoughts generates your sentiments upon which your reactions will depend. Every great action started with just an idea, a mere thought or an opinion that came into awareness to result in effective changes in people's lives. Our belief generates a tremendous power, a driving force that achieves great results and actualizes our visions.[38]

If you anticipate abundance and prosperity, benefaction will follow, but if your thoughts are gloomy and pessimistic, evil will follow. Allah says in this hadith qudsi: «I am as My servant thinks I am, and I am with him if he calls for Me...»[39]

Thoughts and beliefs are not merely things that we do; they are effective tools which, if properly applied and scrupulously nourished, can become our reality. The more we choose to have gracious, wholesome, constructive, and inspirational thoughts towards ourselves and others and towards every event that we encounter in our daily living, the more we will generate blissful reactions in our lives. Your wisdom resides within yourself: stop seeking answers elsewhere, purify your heart and soul, believe in yourself and your abilities and have total unconditional faith in your Creator; only then you will reach enlightenment and change your life for the better.

Dr. Albert Ellis outlined an 'ABC' system to help people adjust their state of mind:[40]

A= Action

B= Belief

C= Consequential feeling

We usually think that actions (or encountered events) are the only causative agents behind our feelings. For example, if I lost my job, this would lead to a feeling of low self-esteem: *I am not good enough and I won't ever be successful in my life.* This shows the importance of 'B' in the formula. If I believe in myself, I will have confidence, and I can change my consequential feelings 'C' in a positive direction: *This is a new challenge, a given opportunity to learn and to further improve myself and reveal my hidden talents and gifts.*

Do not accept failure, it is only up to you to turn your failure into success by always trying one more time.[41] It is not what happens that matters, but how you choose to respond to it. Learn from your experience and have total belief in your abilities and potential. I remember that during a Kindergarten interview with my friend's four-year-old daughter, the teacher asked her about an alphabet letter that she did not recognize. The little girl replied immediately: "You don't expect me to know everything, do you? Otherwise why should I come to school in the first place?" Needless to say, the girl was immediately accepted in the school.

To create change in our lives we have to start working on our sense of self-worth, inner spirituality and self-awareness. Allah teaches us this in the Qur'an:

﴿ ... إِنَّ ٱللَّهَ لَا يُغَيِّرُ مَا بِقَوْمٍ حَتَّىٰ يُغَيِّرُوا۟ مَا بِأَنفُسِهِمْ ... ۝ ﴾   (سورة الرعد: ١١)

﴿...Verily, Allah will never change the condition of a people until they change what is in themselves...﴾   *(Qur'an 13: 11)*

Remember, it is all up to you; no one else can hurt your feelings or make you feel sad. All you need to do to change your situation is to adjust your thoughts and beliefs; your attitudes and reactions will then be changed for the better. Learn a lesson from each failure, search for the message behind every problem. Believe that Allah wills only what is best for you and that the door to His Guidance and Mercy is always open. Visualize a perfect life and surroundings, and you will find yourself subconsciously working on that perfection once you believe in it. Remember that your thoughts are neither limited nor controllable by anyone except yourself; they are not restricted by time or place;[42] they are not even subjected to material world reality. Did anyone in the early twentieth century imagine that a man would walk on the moon, that we would be able to see and speak directly to our friends living on the other side of the globe or that one could retrieve any desired information within seconds just by pushing a little button?

Always remember Allah's promise, that He rewards good deeds by keeping evil and distress away, leading to a pleasant life.

(سورة طه: ١٢٣)   ﴿ ... فَمَنِ ٱتَّبَعَ هُدَايَ فَلَا يَضِلُّ وَلَا يَشْقَىٰ ۝ ﴾

❲...Then whoever follows My Guidance shall neither go astray, nor fall into distress and misery.❳   *(Qur'an 20: 123)*

Conversely, He warns:

(سورة طه: ١٢٤)   ﴿ وَمَنْ أَعْرَضَ عَن ذِكْرِى فَإِنَّ لَهُۥ مَعِيشَةً ضَنكًا ... ۝ ﴾

❲But whosoever turns away from My Reminder [i.e., neither believes in this Qur'an nor acts on its orders] verily, for him is a life of hardship...❳   *(Qur'an 20: 124)*

4. Live in the moment

We cannot change the past; memories may only serve us as guides, warnings or lessons for the future. Regretting events long past and dwelling on tragic incidents will cripple us and compromise our psychological wellbeing.

By the same token, we cannot control the future. However confident you are, whatever resources you have, you can never predict the next moment. We do not even own a single breath, so why waste the time and energy worrying?

«Prophet Muhammad (ﷺ) taught 'Abdullah ibn 'Umar: When you wake up, do not talk to yourself about the evening, and if you enter into evening, do not talk to yourself about the morning; take from your life for your death and from your health for your sickness, as you never know, 'Abdullah, what your fate will be tomorrow.»[43]

Lee Schnebly noted in her book *Nurturing Yourself and Others*, that fretting about our future and dwelling over our past deny us the joy of noticing and appreciating what we are experiencing at present.[44] Prophet Muhammad (ﷺ) taught us:

«He who wakes in the morning while healthy in his body, safe in his residence and having his day's sustenance, will be as if the entire world was granted to him.»[45]

When I was a little girl, I used to complain a lot about almost everything, and my mother used to respond with these French verses by Victor Hugo:

Naître désirant la mort,
Grandir regrettant l'enfance où le coeur dort
Vieillir regrettant la jeunesse ravit
Et mourir regrettant la vieillesse et la vie.

We are born wishing for death
We grow up regretting the loss of childhood where
    the heart is as pure as gold
We grow old regretting the loss of our happy, healthy youth,
And we die regretting growing old, and life itself.

I did not truly understand their meaning until years later. My mother was right: I have to enjoy the moment, for each has its own taste and its own beauty. Each stage in our life has its bitter and its sweet: why look at the empty part of the glass? Why feel that the sun is always brighter on the other side? Enjoy your life, think about all the blessings you have got — and for sure you have got many. Allah is the Most Just.

We say our daily dhikr Allah and supplications to remind us that each morning we are facing a new life; thus we reconfirm our faith and devotion to Allah and supplicate for health, wealth and happiness in this new day:

«We have reached the morning while the dominion of the universe belongs to Allah. All praise is due to Allah. None has the right to be worshipped except Allah, Who has no partner. All praise and thanks are due to Allah, Who is able to do all things. O Allah! I ask You to give me the best of this day and the best of what follows it, and I seek refuge in you from the evil of this day and the evil of what follows it. I seek refuge in You from laziness and senile old age, and I seek refuge in You from the torment of the fire and the punishment of the grave." (*Aṣbaḥnâ wa aṣbaḥal-mulku lillâh, wal-ḥamdu lillâh, lâ ilâhah illâ Allâh, waḥdahu lâ shareeka lahu, lahul-mulku wa lahul-ḥamd, wa huwa 'ala kulli shay'in qadeer. Rabbi as'aluka khaira mâ fee hâdhal-yawmi wa khaira mâ ba'dahu, wa a'oodhu bika min sharri hâdhal-yawmi wa sharri mâ ba'dah. Rabbi a'oodhu bika minal-kasal wa soo' il-kibar; rabbi a'oodhu bika min 'adhâbin fin-nâr wa 'adhâbin fil-qabr.*)»[46]

«O Allah! I ask You for knowledge which is useful, for provision which is lawful and for deeds which You accept." (*Allâhumma innee as'aluka 'ilman nâfi'an wa rizqan ṭayyiban wa 'amalan mutaqabbalan.*)»[47]

There is a similar du'â' to be said each evening:

«"We have reached the evening, while all dominion belongs to Allah, the Creator and Master of humankind, the jinn and all that exists. O Allah! I ask You to give me the good of this night, its triumph and victory, its light, its blessing and guidance. I seek refuge with You from its evil and the evil which follows it." (*Amsayna wa amsal-mulku lillâhi rabbil-'alameen. Allâhumma innee as'aluka khaira hâdhihil-laylah, fat-ḥahâ wa naṣrahâ wa noorahâ wa barakâtahâ wa hudâhâ, wa a'oodhu bika min sharri mâ feehâ wa sharri mâ ba'dahâ*).»[48]

No one knows if he or she will wake up the next morning. Allah (ﷻ) says:

$$ ﴿ اللَّهُ يَتَوَفَّى الْأَنفُسَ حِينَ مَوْتِهَا وَالَّتِي لَمْ تَمُتْ فِي مَنَامِهَا فَيُمْسِكُ الَّتِي قَضَى عَلَيْهَا الْمَوْتَ وَيُرْسِلُ الْأُخْرَى إِلَى أَجَلٍ مُّسَمًّى ... ﴾ $$ (سورة الزُّمَر: ٤٢)

﴿It is Allah Who receives the souls at the time of their death, and those that do not die during their sleep. He keeps those [souls]for which He has ordained death and sends the rest [back to their bodies] for a term appointed...﴾ *(Qur'an 39: 42)*

Since no one can ever know what waits for them tomorrow, why worry? Just keep faith and renew your vows each night before you go to bed; ask Allah for protection, forgiveness and mercy.

«O Allah! Verily, You created my soul, and You are able to take its life. To You belong its life and death. If You keep it alive, guard it; and if You cause its death, forgive it. O Allah! I ask You to grant me wellbeing.

(*Allâhumma innaka khalaqta nafsee wa anta tawaffâhâ, laka mamâtuha wa maḥyâhâ; in aḥyaytahâ faḥfadh-hâ, wa in amattahâ faghfir lahâ. Allahumma innee as'alukal 'âfiyah).*»[49]

When I feel depressed or if I am going through a difficult situation, I always remind myself of these verses by Imam Shâfi'i:

Let the fates run with their sufferings,
And sleep only with a peaceful mind.
Between the blink of the eye and its alertness,
Allah changes one state to another.

Living in the moment brings the peace of mind we all struggle to achieve. It is a relaxing state of mind that helps us to meet and surmount everyday challenges.[50]

5. Apply detachment

Detachment simply means that you enjoy your blessings and belongings, appreciate all the gifts constantly appearing in your life, but do not get too attached to them.[51] Do not be interested merely in your material possessions; do not use these external possessions as a measure of your happiness, satisfaction, and success in life. The more generous you are, the more prosperous you will become. This is certainly not an invitation for indifference, complacency, or carelessness, it is just an attempt to put our priorities straight, to realise that we have no control over anyone or anything in our lives, whether it is money, job, person or even health; so do not allow these things to own you. Attachment to goods, people or belongings results in an alarming sense of insecurity that hinders our ability to appreciate our innumerable gifts, the things that truly matters in our lives.

As Allah (ﷺ) says:

﴿ فَمَآ أُوتِيتُم مِّن شَىْءٍ فَمَتَـٰعُ ٱلْحَيَوٰةِ ٱلدُّنْيَا ۖ وَمَا عِندَ ٱللَّهِ خَيْرٌ وَأَبْقَىٰ لِلَّذِينَ ءَامَنُوا۟ وَعَلَىٰ رَبِّهِمْ يَتَوَكَّلُونَ ۝ ﴾ (سورة الشورى: ٣٦)

◆Now whatever you have been given is but a passing comfort for the life of this world, and that which Allah has is better and more lasting for those who believe and put their trust in Allah.◆

(Qur'an 42: 36)

Once the Caliph Haroon Rasheed asked a wise man for advice. The man looked at the glass of water in the Caliph's hand and said, "If you are denied this sip of water, will you give away your entire kingdom to have it?"

The Caliph nodded.

The wise man continued, "And if after drinking it, it was withheld inside your body, would
you give your entire kingdom to get it out?"

Again the Caliph answered in the affirma-
tive.

The wise man concluded, "So what is the
value of a kingdom that is not worth a sip of water or even a drop of urine?"[52]

The Glorious Qur'an teaches us the meaning
of detachment in many verses:

﴿ وَلَا تَمُدَّنَّ عَيْنَيْكَ إِلَىٰ مَا مَتَّعْنَا بِهِۦ أَزْوَٰجًا مِّنْهُمْ زَهْرَةَ ٱلْحَيَوٰةِ ٱلدُّنْيَا لِنَفْتِنَهُمْ فِيهِ وَرِزْقُ
رَبِّكَ خَيْرٌ وَأَبْقَىٰ ﴿١٣١﴾ ﴾   (سورة طه: ١٣١)

﴾And strain not your eyes in longing for the things We have given
for enjoyment to various groups of them [polytheists and disbelievers in the Oneness of Allah] — the splendour of the life of this
world — that We may test them thereby. But the provision [good
reward in the Hereafter] of Allah is better and more lasting.﴿

(Qur'an 20: 131)

﴿ وَٱضْرِبْ لَهُم مَّثَلَ ٱلْحَيَوٰةِ ٱلدُّنْيَا كَمَآءٍ أَنزَلْنَٰهُ مِنَ ٱلسَّمَآءِ فَٱخْتَلَطَ بِهِۦ نَبَاتُ
ٱلْأَرْضِ فَأَصْبَحَ هَشِيمًا تَذْرُوهُ ٱلرِّيَٰحُ وَكَانَ ٱللَّهُ عَلَىٰ كُلِّ شَىْءٍ مُّقْتَدِرًا ﴿٤٥﴾ ٱلْمَالُ وَٱلْبَنُونَ
زِينَةُ ٱلْحَيَوٰةِ ٱلدُّنْيَا وَٱلْبَٰقِيَٰتُ ٱلصَّٰلِحَٰتُ خَيْرٌ عِندَ رَبِّكَ ثَوَابًا وَخَيْرٌ أَمَلًا ﴿٤٦﴾ ﴾

(سورة الكهف: ٤٥-٤٦)

﴾And put forward to them the example of the life of this world,
it is like the water [rain] which We send down from the sky, and
the vegetation of the earth mingles with it, and becomes fresh and
green. But [later] it becomes dry twigs, which the winds scat-
ter. And Allah is Able to do everything. Wealth and children are

the adornment of the life of this world. But the good righteous deeds [five compulsory prayers, deeds of obedience to Allah, good speech, remembrance of Allah with glorification, praises and thanks] that last, are better with Allah for rewards and better in terms of hope.❯   *(Qur'an 18: 45-46)*

An early scholar who analysed detachment was the Muslim philosopher, Al-Farabi (870-950 CE). He divided the power of awareness of one's soul into three levels: the senses, the imagination and the intellect. Using our senses, we draw a specified picture of a person or an object; this is a physical being that can be seen and detected. Then with our imagination, we add our own meanings and descriptions of this thing, whether we love it, need it or hate it. Finally comes the role of the intellect, which — according to Al-Farabi — is an awareness level independent of any physical matter; it is a level of enlightenment totally detached from the materialistic aspect of life. This detachment converts the imagined picture into pure logic. A wise intellect perceives the meanings beyond the materials, frees it from the world of form and apprehends the rational unimportance of these materials in one's life.[53]

In this hadith qudsi, Allah (ﷻ) says: «O human, devote yourself to worshipping Me, I will fill your heart with prosperity, and meet your needs; but if you do not, I will keep your hands busy and I will not fulfil your needs.»[54] (Remember the true meaning of worship discussed in the Introduction.)

The Almighty also said: «Whoever's main concern is the Hereafter, Allah will put wealth and prosperity into his heart and unify his affairs, and the world will be driven to him. And whoever's main concern is this worldly existence, Allah will bring his poverty between his eyes and disperse his affairs, and what will reach him from this world is only what is predestined for him.»[55]

The most common attachment in one's life is to wealth. Having money is a great bliss from Allah, and working hard to get money is an absolutely normal part of our life. What is not normal is to let this money control us.

Prophet Muhammad (ﷺ) said: «The bounty of this life is green and beautiful, whoever takes it with open-handed-ness, his sustenance will be blessed; and whoever takes it with haughtiness, it will not be blessed for him, and he will be like one who eats and never reaches satiety.»[56]

Letting money have power over our lives creates a sort of attachment that cannot be satisfied, an obsession that gives a continuous feeling of dissatisfaction.

Allah warns us against avarice in many verses of the Qur'an, and encourages believers to spend their money on the needy, seeking Allah's approval.

﴿ ٱلشَّيْطَٰنُ يَعِدُكُمُ ٱلْفَقْرَ وَيَأْمُرُكُم بِٱلْفَحْشَآءِ ۖ وَٱللَّهُ يَعِدُكُم مَّغْفِرَةً مِّنْهُ وَفَضْلًا ۗ وَٱللَّهُ وَٰسِعٌ عَلِيمٌ ﴾ (سورة البقرة: ٢٦٨)

❝Satan threatens you with poverty and orders you to commit sins; whereas Allah promises you Forgiveness from Himself and Bounty, and Allah is All-Sufficient for His creatures' needs, All-Knower.❞
(Qur'an 2: 268)

﴿ فَٱتَّقُوا۟ ٱللَّهَ مَا ٱسْتَطَعْتُمْ وَٱسْمَعُوا۟ وَأَطِيعُوا۟ وَأَنفِقُوا۟ خَيْرًا لِّأَنفُسِكُمْ ۗ وَمَن يُوقَ شُحَّ نَفْسِهِ فَأُو۟لَٰٓئِكَ هُمُ ٱلْمُفْلِحُونَ ﴿١٦﴾ إِن تُقْرِضُوا۟ ٱللَّهَ قَرْضًا حَسَنًا يُضَٰعِفْهُ لَكُمْ وَيَغْفِرْ لَكُمْ ۚ وَٱللَّهُ شَكُورٌ حَلِيمٌ ﴿١٧﴾ ﴾ (سورة التغابن: ١٦-١٧)

◀So keep your duty to Allah and fear Him as much as you can; listen and obey; and spend in charity; that is better for yourselves. And whosoever is saved from their own covetousness, then they are the successful ones. If you lend to Allah a goodly loan [i.e., spend in Allah's Cause] He will double it for you, and will forgive you. And Allah is Most Ready to appreciate and to reward, Most Forbearing.▶   *(Qur'an 64: 16 - 17)*

Ibn Mas'ood, a Companion of the Prophet (ﷺ), once said, "Everyone is a guest in the world, and their money is but a loan. The guest must go sooner or later, and the loan must be returned."

Another sort of attachment is the attachment to our own looks, the belief that this physical body is what you are all about. Some people are completely obsessed with their appearance, which makes them unaware of their true essence: the beauty of their souls. The sheer numbers of people — especially women — undergoing plastic surgery nowadays is clear proof of this terrible preoccupation. Some people believe that wrinkles, hair loss or obesity are valid reasons for depression; they consider their physical appearance to be a measure of their self-worth. This creates an unnecessary life-long fear that can only lead to suffering.

The Qur'an teaches that the body is only a temporary packaging; the most important part of a person is one's soul. This of course does not mean that we neglect our looks; on the contrary, we should appreciate, respect and care for our physical appearance, while at the same time concentrating on the beauty of our souls. The rule is to take care of your body so that it can effectively serve the true purpose it has been created for. Recall this du'â' each time you look in the mirror:

«O Allah! Perfect my manners as You have perfected the creation of me.

(*Allâhumma kamâ aḥsanta khalqee, iḥsan khuluqee*).»[57]

Detachment invokes the true meaning of *Islam*: surrender to Allah's will. Have total, unconditional faith and trust in His absolute Wisdom and Judgment; believe in His total domination of all things, He is the Trustee, the All-Sufficient, the Supporter. Do not get tense, calm down and work in harmony with this perfect universe. Relax.

There is a reminder in this hadith of the Messenger of Allah (ﷺ) about why we should not become too attached to our possessions:

«The human being says: My wealth! My wealth! But verily only three things are his out of (all) his wealth: what he has consumed and used up, or worn and worn out, or given away and acquired (a reward instead); and what is besides these shall be gone, and he shall leave it for (other) people (when he dies).»[58]

6. Love

We live on the same planet, breathe the same air, enjoy the same moon and are warmed by the same sun, yet our hearts are so disconnected from one another. Love is the only true feeling that can bring peace back into our lives, the only sentiment that can unite our efforts and combine our hearts, yet we can hardly find it in our present existence.

There are two kinds of love: metaphorical love, which is transient love related to the material world and the bodily life; and Divine love, the love of Allah — this is the real, eternal and infinite love. The writings of the Muslim philosopher Rumi demonstrate that both kinds of love should ultimately lead the way to Allah.[59] Metaphorical love can lead to Divine love.

The admiration of nature's beauty, the pure sacred feelings between a man and his wife and unconditional parental love are reflections of great blessings from Allah, a manifestation of His Divine Names and Attributes; this love is a bridge that leads a wise
mind to the All-Powerful, All-Compassionate Creator.

To love Allah we have to feel His existence through our mod-
est humble minds. Our reason and reflection should confess total
submissiveness and awe. For Muslims, love of Allah comes first;
it is the purest and truest kind of affection, the essence of every
creation. It is the requirement of faith for the true Muslim. Allah
says in His Holy Book:

﴿ قُلْ إِن كَانَ ءَابَآؤُكُمْ وَأَبْنَآؤُكُمْ وَإِخْوَٰنُكُمْ وَأَزْوَٰجُكُمْ وَعَشِيرَتُكُمْ وَأَمْوَٰلُ
ٱقْتَرَفْتُمُوهَا وَتِجَٰرَةٌ تَخْشَوْنَ كَسَادَهَا وَمَسَٰكِنُ تَرْضَوْنَهَآ أَحَبَّ إِلَيْكُم مِّنَ
ٱللَّهِ وَرَسُولِهِۦ وَجِهَادٍ فِى سَبِيلِهِۦ فَتَرَبَّصُواْ حَتَّىٰ يَأْتِىَ ٱللَّهُ بِأَمْرِهِۦ وَٱللَّهُ لَا يَهْدِى ٱلْقَوْمَ
ٱلْفَٰسِقِينَ ۝ ﴾

(سورة التوبة: ٢٤)

❮Say: If your fathers, your sons, your brothers, your wives, your
kindred, the wealth that you have gained, the commerce in which
you fear a decline, and the dwellings in which you delight are
dearer to you than Allah and His Messenger, and striving hard
and fighting in His Cause, then wait until Allah brings about His
Decision [torment]. And Allah does not guide the people who are
rebellious [disobedient to Allah].❯   *(Qur'an 9: 24)*

M. Fethullah Gulen wrote in *Love and Tolerance* how love has
been forgotten in our daily struggle for survival. How our material
possessions, worldly greed, narrow vision, envy and selfishness
have all replaced these sacred feelings of love and compassion in
our hearts. People's sense of loyalty and moral and ethical commitments have weakened with their preoccupation with the prob-

lems of everyday life. Gulen refers this obvious deterioration to our distance away from the greatest source of love, from our God, Allah. Because we have not followed His Path, because we have not loved Him as we should, the feelings of love are gone from our hearts. In order to love each other again and to live in peace and harmony, we should turn only to Him and love Him with all our hearts.[60]

Allah (ﷻ) says in His Book:

﴿ وَمَا قَدَرُوا۟ ٱللَّهَ حَقَّ قَدْرِهِۦ وَٱلْأَرْضُ جَمِيعًا قَبْضَتُهُۥ يَوْمَ ٱلْقِيَـٰمَةِ وَٱلسَّمَـٰوَٰتُ مَطْوِيَّـٰتٌۢ بِيَمِينِهِۦ سُبْحَـٰنَهُۥ وَتَعَـٰلَىٰ عَمَّا يُشْرِكُونَ ۝ ﴾ (سورة الزُّمَر: ٦٧)

﴾They have not made a just estimate of Allah such as is due to Him. And on the Day of Resurrection the whole of the earth will be grasped by His Hand and the heavens will be rolled up in His Right Hand. Glorified is He, and High is He above all that they associate as partners with Him!﴿ *(Qur'an 39: 67)*

Allah promises us that if we love Him and follow His path, He will love us in return.

﴿ قُلْ إِن كُنتُمْ تُحِبُّونَ ٱللَّهَ فَٱتَّبِعُونِى يُحْبِبْكُمُ ٱللَّهُ وَيَغْفِرْ لَكُمْ ذُنُوبَكُمْ وَٱللَّهُ غَفُورٌ رَّحِيمٌ ۝ ﴾ (سورة آل عمران: ٣١)

﴾Say [O Muhammad to people]: If you [really] love Allah, then follow me [accept Islamic monotheism, follow the Qur'an and the Sunnah], Allah will love you and forgive you your sins. And Allah is Oft-Forgiving, Most Merciful.﴿ *(Qur'an 3: 31)*

Imagine how great this would be — to earn the love of Allah! There is a hadith qudsi that gives us some idea of what that is like:

«If Allah loves a person, He calls out to Gabriel saying: Allah loves so-and-so, therefore love him. So Gabriel loves him, and makes an announcement to the inhabitants of heaven: Allah loves so-and-so, therefore love him also. And the inhabitants of heaven love him, and he is then granted the pleasure and acceptance of the people on earth.»[61]

To love (in the true Islamic meaning) is to relate everything we love to Allah and avoid associating worldly partners and idols with Him. This higher meaning of love takes it beyond mere human relations into a more sacred and spiritual level. I have heard the expression 'to love for the sake of Allah' many times before, but I did not truly understand its meaning until recently. I met a group of enthusiastic young women who were preparing for a conference about true Islamic relationships and morality. The organizers lived in different countries and communicated through e-mail; they had never met before, but they were all so dedicated and believed so much in the Islamic values they were teaching, that they had experienced an incredibly strong bonding, connecting their souls. They met each other for the first time at the conference and lived together for only one week; a week of hard work and extreme dedication. At the end of the conference, I saw them crying because they were soon to be separated. I felt true love, a divine affection that bonded their hearts and freed it from all worldly greed and personal interests; a love that generated an immense energy revealed in their beautiful work and a successful conference. They found their happiness in each other's success, in self-denial and in the Divine love that filled their hearts and overflowed, as if bathing everything and everybody around them in a sacred divine blessing. I then remembered these words by Ghazâli, "Love for Allah envelopes the heart; it rules the heart and it even spreads over everything."

Our Prophet (ﷺ) taught us: «By the One who holds my soul in His Hand, you will not believe until you love each other. Shall I tell you about something that if you do it you will love each other? Spread peace among you (that is, by saying 'Assalâmu 'alaykum').»[62]

He also (ﷺ) said: «None of you (truly) believes until he loves for his brother what he loves for himself.»[63]

There is another important meaning in this hadith. In order to love our brothers and sisters in faith, we need to love ourselves first. This is not an invitation for selfishness, but a call for you to discover and appreciate your true self, to focus on loving what you are and not hating yourself for what you are not. If you think negative thoughts, if you resent your presence, actions, fortune and fate, you will definitely feel the same about others, you will fill your heart with envy and your mind with sorrow and regret. Only when we connect to our inner love, we will find the power within ourselves to help others; we will feel the desire to share this love with the world and we will see this passion purifying our hearts and spreading through our lives, causing them to glow with beauty.

There is an old Egyptian saying: 'If your house is made of glass, do not throw stones at others.' So do not search for people's mistakes or concentrate on their defects and imperfections; instead, try to find the good in everyone. If we accept the other person as she or he is, if we try to love them only for the sake of Allah, it will be easier for us to communicate, understand each other and live peacefully together.

Allah (ﷻ) says in this hadith qudsi: «Those who love each other for My sake, have pulpits of light; the Prophets and the martyrs wish eagerly for their status.»[64]

I once read an old Chinese tale about a young girl named Lin who got married and went to live with her husband and mother-in-law. Lin could not get along with her mother-in-law at all. Their personalities were very different, and Lin was angered by many of her mother-in-law's habits and criticisms. Time went by and Lin and her mother-in-law kept on arguing and fighting. All the anger and unhappiness in the house was causing Lin's poor husband great distress.

Finally, Lin could not stand it any longer, so she went to see her father's friend, Mr. Huang, who was an herbalist. She told him the situation and asked if he would give her some poison so that she could solve the problem once and for all. Mr. Huang thought for a while, and finally said, "Lin, I will help you solve your problem, but you must listen to me very carefully."

Mr. Huang went into the attic, and returned with a package of herbs. He told Lin, "You can't use a quick-acting poison to get rid of your mother-in-law, because that would cause suspicion. Therefore, I have given you a number of herbs that will slowly build up poison in her body. Every other day, prepare a delicious meal and put a little of these herbs in her serving. Now, in order to make sure that nobody suspects you when she dies, you must act very friendly towards her. Don't argue with her, obey her every wish, and treat her like a queen."

Lin was very happy. She thanked Mr. Huang and hurried home to start her plot. Weeks went by, and months went by, and every other day, Lin served the specially-treated food to her mother-in-law. She remembered what Mr. Huang had said about avoiding suspicion, so she controlled her temper, obeyed her mother-in-law, and treated her like her own mother.

After six months, the whole house had changed. Lin had practiced controlling her temper so much that she found that she almost never got mad or upset. She had not had an argument with her mother-in-law in six months, because she now seemed much kinder and easier to get along with. The mother-in-law's attitude toward Lin also changed; she began to love her like her own daughter; and Lin's husband was very happy. Finally, Lin went to see Mr. Huang and asked for his help again — but this time, a different kind of help. She asked him to keep the poison from killing her mother-in-law!

"She has changed into such a nice woman, and I love her like my own mother now," said Lin, "I do not want her to die from that poison I gave her."

Mr. Huang smiled and nodded his head, "Lin, there is nothing to worry about. I never gave you any poison. The herbs I gave you were tonics to improve her health. The only poison was in your mind, but that has been all washed away by the love which you gave her. How you treat others is exactly how they will treat you. There is a wise Chinese saying: *The person who loves others will also be loved in return.*"[65]

7. Keep hope and be optimistic

Over the past few years, the world has faced many terrible natural disasters. The tsunami in the Pacific Ocean, hurricanes in the Atlantic, and mudslides and earthquakes across Asia took tens of thousands of lives, crushed or washed away houses and cars, uprooted trees and crops and destroyed many dreams. Earth, wind and water do not differentiate whether you are living on a tropical Indonesian island, in New Orleans, USA, or on a fault line in Pakistan. The only difference lies in the people themselves.

Consider the case of two people who have survived one of these great calamities; both have lost their entire families, their homes, money — everything. Both are facing the unknown, surrounded by poverty, corruption and serious health hazards. Now, consider that one of them is a believer and the other is not. What do you think their reactions will be? Of course, both will be in a state of deep sorrow and grief — we are human after all; but the believer with his faith and complete trust in Allah will be certain deep inside that all those belongings were never really his: they belong to Allah; He gave them to the believer and He can take them back any time. The believer knows that every event — whatever pain it may bring — also brings with it a valuable lesson and a deeper meaning. S/he is not attached to his worldly acquisitions, s/he knows that this life is but a big test, a transient step that will lead to an ultimate joy if s/he follows Allah's straight path and has kept hope, patience and perseverance. The believer knows that his or her great reward is in Paradise, not on this earth.[66] In contrast, the unbeliever would be totally devastated, overwhelmed by calamity; his or her affliction would be unbounded and unbearable. S/he would keep blaming misfortune, and cursing fate. The unbeliever's worldly possessions are the only meaning in his or her life: losing those means losing all hope. S/he fails to see the meaning behind any test he or she may be faced with during his or her lifetime; s/he feels bitterness, enmity, rancour, and distress and experiences a hostile and resentful attitude towards the whole world, and as a result is likely to fall apart, get depressed, irritable and fall prey to various physical ailments.[67]

The degree of hope and optimism one has depends on one's level of faith. Disasters and tragic events only increase the believers' faith and submission to Allah. They feel an inner peace and are thankful even for difficult situations (seeing them as tests of their faith and patience) and supplicate for Allah's help and guidance.

«It was narrated by Anas ibn Mâlik that the Prophet (ﷺ) passed by a women who was weeping beside a grave. He told her to fear Allah and to be patient. She did not recognize him and said: Go away, for you have not been afflicted with a calamity like mine! When she found out later that he was the Prophet Muhammad, she went to his house and told him: I did not recognize you. He said: Verily, patience should be shown at the first stroke of calamity.»[68]

That is the true sign of faith and belief in Allah. Allah describes these believers, saying:

﴿ تَتَجَافَىٰ جُنُوبُهُمۡ عَنِ ٱلۡمَضَاجِعِ يَدۡعُونَ رَبَّهُمۡ خَوۡفًا وَطَمَعًا وَمِمَّا رَزَقۡنَٰهُمۡ يُنفِقُونَ ۝ فَلَا تَعۡلَمُ نَفۡسٌ مَّآ أُخۡفِيَ لَهُم مِّن قُرَّةِ أَعۡيُنٍ جَزَآءَۢ بِمَا كَانُوا۟ يَعۡمَلُونَ ۝ ﴾

(سورة السجدة: ١٦-١٧)

◆Their sides forsake their beds, to invoke Allah in fear and hope, and they spend [charity in Allah's Cause] out of what We have bestowed on them. No person knows what is kept hidden for them of joy as a reward for what they used to do.◗ *(Qur'an 32: 16-17)*

"During the time of the Prophet (ﷺ), it was related that a woman once cut her finger with a knife, whereupon she smiled with relief. Her servant was beside her and was astonished at her reaction; the woman told her: When I visualized the reward for my patience, I forgot my pain."[69]

Harun Yahya wrote a beautiful book entitled *Hopefulness in Islam*. In his book Yahya explains how the believers see benefits in everything that happens to them. They know deep inside that Allah wills only what is in their best interest. They believe in His unlimited Mercy and precious guidance and are certain that their rewards are somehow there, waiting for them.[70]

From the Qur'an we learn:

﴿ قُل لَّن يُصِيبَنَآ إِلَّا مَا كَتَبَ ٱللَّهُ لَنَا هُوَ مَوۡلَىٰنَا وَعَلَى ٱللَّهِ فَلۡيَتَوَكَّلِ ٱلۡمُؤۡمِنُونَ ۝ ﴾

(سورة التوبة: ٥١)

❴Say: Nothing shall ever happen to us except what Allah has ordained for us. He is our Maulâ [Master, Helper and Protector]. And in Allah let the believers put their trust.❵   *(Qur'an 9: 51)*

Studies show that people who complain a lot — who always worry, disapprove, deprecate, grumble and make a fuss out of every little event in their lives — are the ones who are more prone to encountering difficult situations and events. Pessimism will show in their daily living as troublesome circumstances and recurrent problems.

Each morning upon waking up, remind yourself that you have the choice either to be happy and optimistic or to be in a bad mood. Of course, all of us should choose to be happy, to feel hope and look forward to whatever life is offering that day. Always look for the positive side of each situation you encounter. Each time something goes wrong, you can choose to be the miserable, afflicted sufferer or the strong, unbeatable survivor and 'student of life' — to dwell on your loss or to overcome, to learn a positive lesson from the experience.

Life is all about choices; your attitude, your perception and awareness are the things that really count. You choose how to deal with each event, how to accept your own destiny, how to interpret your lessons and experiences; you even choose how other people affect your feelings. With each rising sun, the newly born day gives you the choice to live your life fully and to be happy. Do not worry about tomorrow — it is enough to learn from and deal with the present moment.

8. Be responsible

Do not blame others for your own mistakes: stop looking for answers outside yourself. Look within you, you will find the right answers. Acknowledge that you are responsible for what you choose to feel or think and that you are solely responsible for the choices in your life, so you cannot make excuses and blame others for the choices you have made. Be confident of your talents, strengths and abilities. Develop a positive, self-affirming personality, believe in yourself, but do not be over-confident. We are all human, we can all make mistakes. Admit your points of weakness; learn from them and try to correct them. This attitude protects and nurtures both your physical health and your emotional wellbeing. Allah says (ﷻ) in the Qur'an:

﴿ مَّآ أَصَابَكَ مِنْ حَسَنَةٍ فَمِنَ ٱللَّهِ وَمَآ أَصَابَكَ مِن سَيِّئَةٍ فَمِن نَّفْسِكَ ... ۝ ﴾

(سورة النساء: ٧٩)

﴿Whatever of good reaches you, is from Allah, but whatever of evil befalls you, is from yourself...﴾ *(Qur'an 4: 79)*

He also says:

﴿ إِنَّ ٱللَّهَ لَا يَظْلِمُ ٱلنَّاسَ شَيْئًا وَلَٰكِنَّ ٱلنَّاسَ أَنفُسَهُمْ يَظْلِمُونَ ۝ ﴾

(سورة يونس: ٤٤)

﴿Verily Allah will not deal unjustly with people in anything: it is people who wrong their own souls.﴾ *(Qur'an 10: 44)*

﴿ وَمَآ أَصَٰبَكُم مِّن مُّصِيبَةٍ فَبِمَا كَسَبَتْ أَيْدِيكُمْ ... ۝ ﴾

(سورة الشورى: ٣٠)

﴿And whatever of misfortune befalls you, it is because of what your hands have earned...﴾ *(Qur'an 42: 30)*

Your life is your choice; it is not what happens that matters, but how you choose to respond to it. In his book *Who moved my cheese?* Dr. Spencer Johnson gives the analogy of two rats and two tiny people living in a maze. When the rats fail to get their piece of cheese, they try again a different way; in contrast, the two men sit in their places, blaming others for their failure and waiting for their cheese to return![71]

Let go of reproach and animosity toward everyone, even towards the ones who once harmed you, abused your feelings or caused you distress. You cannot waste your time blaming bacteria for making you sick: what you can do is to learn the lessons and heed the warnings they bring. If you do not accept personal responsibility, you risk developing a permanent hateful, repugnant, and indignant attitude towards everyone around you. You will become overly dependent on others for praise, endorsement, support, and acceptance. You will feel endless self-pity, low self-esteem, chronic disability and depression.

Being responsible also involves being committed. Commitment means devoting yourself to something and sticking to your plan of choice. Try again and again; do not accept failure. It is up to you alone to change your failure to success. Remember Allah's words:

﴿ ... إِنَّ ٱللَّهَ لَا يُغَيِّرُ مَا بِقَوْمٍ حَتَّىٰ يُغَيِّرُوا۟ مَا بِأَنفُسِهِمْ ... ۝ ﴾ (سورة الرعد: ١١)

❨...Verily Allah will never change the condition of a people until they change what is in themselves...❩   *(Qur'an 13: 11)*

Take the first step and Allah will guide your way:

﴿ ۞ لِّلَّذِينَ أَحْسَنُوا۟ ٱلْحُسْنَىٰ وَزِيَادَةٌ ... ۝ ﴾ (سورة يونس: ٢٦)

❨To those who do right is a goodly [reward] Yes, even more [than in measure]!...❩   *(Qur'an 10: 26)*

Finish what you have started, care about what you are doing. Always do your best, even if it takes extra time and effort. Doing things right gives you a good feeling about yourself. Prophet Muhammad (ﷺ) said:

«Allah likes when one of you does a job, that he perfects it.»[72]

9. Define your objectives

Each and every person has to have a purpose for his or her life: an objective that prevents one's actions from being barren and meaningless. If you do not give it true meaning, life is a total waste. If there is no reason for what you are doing, nothing will be worthwhile. In a study performed on some college students, a comparison was made between those who where displeased with their circumstances, and those who where satisfied and content. One of the major disparities between these two groups was that the unhappy students did not envision a clear goal to live for.[73]

Pause for a moment and ask yourself: *What is my objective? What am I seeking out of this life?* If your answer is anything other than: *to attain Allah's approval*, then you have to reconsider your values and adjust your plans. The ultimate goal for all Muslims is Allah's pleasure. Being sure of this one and only goal leads a person onto the straight path, by adjusting one's values and morals, and submitting one's heart, mind and body to collaborate — to work together to move in the right direction.

It is perfectly fine to have temporary goals that help you through the journey that leads to the final objective, like your studies, your job, your responsibility to spouse, parents, and children, and so on. Always bear in mind, however, that these intermediate goals are mere helpers along the way; the final goal is clear, obvious and irreplaceable. Remember that we are created for a purpose, and each and every event in our lives is well planned and organized to serve this purpose. Allah (ﷻ) says:

(سورة الذاريات: ٥٦)   ﴿ وَمَا خَلَقْتُ ٱلْجِنَّ وَٱلْإِنسَ إِلَّا لِيَعْبُدُونِ ۝ ﴾

﴿And I [Allah] created the jinns and humans only so they should worship Me [Alone].﴾   *(Qur'an 51: 56)*

Worshipping does not mean only praying and fasting; every action in a true Muslim's life is considered an act of worship. As we mentioned, it is right intention and sincerity that turn a mere physical or social ritual into an act of worship and obedience to the Almighty.[74] Preparing your lessons, cooking for your family, working in your office, visiting a friend and even playing with your kids can all be acts of worship to be rewarded by Allah. This is part of the role that we have to perform in this life.

Allah (ﷻ) says:

(سورة هود: ٦١)   ﴿ ... هُوَ أَنشَأَكُم مِّنَ ٱلْأَرْضِ وَٱسْتَعْمَرَكُمْ فِيهَا ... ۝ ﴾

﴿...He brought you forth from the earth and settled you therein...﴾
(Qur'an 11: 61)

We are ordered to develop this earth, to make it flourish and prosper. Remember that this is a Divine order, it is not just a request; this is why we were created!

Allah (ﷻ) also says:

(سورة الطلاق: ٧)   ﴿ ... لَا يُكَلِّفُ ٱللَّهُ نَفْسًا إِلَّا مَآ ءَاتَىٰهَا ... ۝ ﴾

﴿...Allah puts no burden on any person beyond what He has given him...﴾   *(Qur'an 65: 7)*

Since He has given us the order to inhabit, explore, make use of, preserve and develop the earth and our environment, so, with no doubt, has He also given each and every one of us the aptitude and natural ability to fulfil this sacred duty. Every one of us has a 'sacred identity', which includes our own special gifts, powers and talents. They do exist, believe me; the true challenge is to explore and further apply them for our wellbeing and for the welfare of the whole world.

Once a friend of mine was complaining to me about being a true loser; she was convinced that she was good at nothing, that she possessed no talents whatsoever. I sat with her and tried to make her think about all the things that she really enjoys doing, her hobbies and what she was good at. After a long discussion, she only came up with two skills:

"I love shopping at expensive department stores and I enjoy eating in fancy five-star restaurants," she said. I could not conceive of any possible way to help her out, so I left, urging her to think of other more 'useful' things to do.

A few days later, I was reviewing a job recruitment site when my eyes fell on a very strange career category: a renowned company was seeking a 'mysterious shopper'. The job description went as follows: "The person required has to love shopping and dinning in high standard stores and restaurants, he/she will then be charged with writing reports evaluating these places in terms of service quality and employee efficiency."

That was it! There was actually something there waiting especially for my friend, demanding her particular passion and total dedication; with her unique talents, she could excel at helping different companies in the hospitality industry to ameliorate their quality standards.

This example may be an extreme, but it illustrates perfectly how we all have hidden potential waiting to be explored. Never underestimate the value of your hobbies and interests; never think that you cannot do any good. If you still cannot find what you are good at, dig deeper, look around you, ask friends and read in different fields. If you are a parent, try to encourage your kids to uncover their own gifts. Never impose your own ideas on them, just open up new areas, suggest new options, help them explore their talents and interests, and whatever they choose, do not discourage or criticize them, just advise them, give them more to read and monitor their progress.

Another important part of defining your goals is to keep yourself challenged constantly. If your objectives are easy to reach, after a while you get bored and become dissatisfied. As soon as you reach your goals, you might lose your interest, feel unmotivated and lose momentum. On the other hand, if your challenges are well suited for your abilities, and if you are gradually meeting your goals, you are self-fulfilled and satisfied. Constantly realising your short-term goals gives you the required stamina and driving force to continue your pursuit for bigger and higher goals. It will give you the required excitement and delight that will stimulate your will-power and keep you going.

Here is a story that I really think illustrates this concept:

The Japanese have always loved fresh fish, but the waters close to Japan do not hold many fish. So, they built bigger fishing boats and went farther out to sea than ever. The farther out the fishermen went, the longer it took to bring in the fish, and because the fish were not fresh anymore, the Japanese did not like the taste. To solve this problem, fishing companies installed freezers on their boats. They would catch the fish and freeze them at sea. Freezers allowed the boats to go even farther and stay longer.

However, the Japanese could still taste the difference between fresh and frozen, and they did not like frozen fish. So fishing companies installed fish tanks on their vessels, into which they stuffed the live catch. After a little thrashing around, the fish stopped moving; they were tired and dull, sluggish but alive. Unfortunately, the Japanese could still taste the difference: because the fish had not moved freely for days, they lost their fresh-fish taste.

Finally, the Japanese found the solution in a simple saying: 'A person thrives, oddly enough, only in the presence of a challenging environment.' So to keep the fish tasting fresh, fishing companies added a small shark to each tank. The shark ate a few fish, but the rest arrived in a very lively state. The fish were challenged![75]

If you have too many dreams and big ambitions, do not get discouraged or disappointed. Take a moment to assess your capabilities and resources, adjust your priorities and carefully plan your next step.

Allah (ﷻ) says in the Qur'an:

(سورة الشَّرح: ٧)　　　　　　　　﴿ فَإِذَا فَرَغْتَ فَانصَبْ ۝ ﴾

﴿Therefore, when you are free [from your immediate task], still labour hard.﴾   *(Qur'an 94: 7)*

We must always remember the next verse, too, because it completes the meaning of the previous one:

(سورة الشَّرح: ٨)　　　　　　　　﴿ وَإِلَىٰ رَبِّكَ فَارْغَب ۝ ﴾

﴿And to Allah [Alone] turn [all your intentions and hopes and] your supplications.﴾   *(Qur'an 94: 8)*

As we mentioned earlier, you should live in the moment and enjoy your achievements, and at the same time always set your intentions for your future goals. What made the Islamic empire grow and flourish in the early years was great ambition. The Muslims did not stop at spreading the new religion in the Arabian Peninsula; they went out to spread the message of Islam all over the world: from China in the east to Spain in the west. After establishing an empire, the challenge did not stop for these Muslims; they began to research and record their newfound knowledge in all scientific fields: geography, astronomy, philosophy, medicine, and physics, among others. Their challenges kept them alive and kept the empire growing; but when the momentum faded, the whole empire faded away with it.

More importantly, do not devise goals just for your personal material success, think of your whole society, your whole *Ummah* (community of Muslims). Do not rest on your laurels, keep yourself going!

10. Be powerful

When we think of someone who has power, we imagine them to be dominant and controlling, but this is not true power. Our power lies deep within our souls; it is reflected in each action, movement and decision. It radiates love, compassion and understanding; it illuminates our surroundings and our world. Being powerful means overcoming our fears and self-doubts, exploring new challenges and fulfilling our duties and responsibilities.

Each of us is blessed with innumerable talents, faculties and potentials, the true challenge is to dig deep into our souls to explore these faculties and make the most out of them. You cannot be happy unless you improve your sense of self-worth; by doing that, you unlock your potential and free your creative powers. Studies show that a strong belief in our own abilities significantly increases our satisfaction both at home and at work.[76]

Do not get discouraged by other people or try to copy them; do not fear being different. Prophet Muhammad (ﷺ) said:

«Do not be worthless: you say if people behave well, you behave too and if they misbehave, you do the same. Instead,

if people behave well, you behave well too, and if they misbehave, do not act unjustly.»[77]

To repeat another of the Messenger's wise sayings: «The
strong believer is more loved by Allah than the weak one,
and there is benefaction in both.»[78]

To boost your self-esteem, try following these steps:

1. Believe in your self-worth and your potential. Think about
   what your strong points are, write them down and keep the list
   where you can see it to remind yourself. Work on improving
   and adding to them. At the same time, keep your faith in your
   Creator. Always remind yourself that Allah is with you, that
   you certainly are on the right path, and nothing can defeat you.

"Abu 'Abbâs 'Abdullah the son of 'Abbâs narrated: «One
day I was (riding) behind the Prophet (ﷺ) and he said to
me: Young man, I shall teach you some words (of advice).
Be mindful of Allah, and Allah will protect you. Be mindful
of Allah, and you will find Him in front of you. If you ask,
ask of Allah; if you seek help, seek help from Allah. Know
that if the people came together to do you a favour, they
would be unable to unless Allah had prescribed it for you;
and if they united to harm you, they would not do you any
harm unless Allah had prescribed it for you. The pens (that
write destiny) have been lifted and the pages have dried»[79].[80]

Believe deep in your soul that your connection with Allah is
the true source of your powers;

Allah (ﷺ) says:

$$﴿ ... ۞ وَمَن يَتَوَكَّلْ عَلَى ٱللَّهِ فَهُوَ حَسْبُهُۥٓ إِنَّ ٱللَّهَ بَٰلِغُ أَمْرِهِۦ قَدْ جَعَلَ ٱللَّهُ لِكُلِّ شَىْءٍ قَدْرًا ۞ ﴾$$

(سورة الطلاق: ٣)

❴...And whosoever puts his trust in Allah, then He will suffice him. Verily, Allah will accomplish His purpose. Indeed Allah has set a measure for all things.❵   *(Qur'an 65: 3)*

﴿ ۞ ... أَلَيْسَ ٱللَّهُ بِكَافٍ عَبْدَهُۥ وَيُخَوِّفُونَكَ بِٱلَّذِينَ مِن دُونِهِۦ ... ﴾

(سورة الزُّمَر: ٣٦)

❴Is not Allah Sufficient for His slave? Yet they try to frighten you with those [whom they worship] besides Him!...❵   *(Qur'an 39: 36)*

2. Assess your limitations and work with them.[81] Figure out how you perceive yourself, recognize your own personal limits and acknowledge your human limitations. We are all human and we all have our flaws — do not be ashamed of yours. Instead, recognize them so that you can figure out how to deal with them. Practice daily your dhikr and du'â' (think of them as 'fortification') and your self-empowering affirmations, like this one to be said three times:

«In the Name of Allah in whose Name nothing can cause harm in the earth or the heavens. He is the All-Hearer and the All-Knower." *(Bismillâhi alladhee la yaḍurruhu ma'a ismihi shay'un fil arḍi wa lâ fis-samâ'i, wa huwa as-Samee' ul 'Aleem.)»*[82]

Dhikr Allah rectifies your mental image; you visualize in your heart a mental picture of yourself as strong through Allah's Strength and succeeding with Allah's help and blessings. It reformulates any negative thoughts or self-doubts into confidence and strength; it increases your faith in Allah and supports your belief in your abilities.

3. Visualize your personal success. Imagine performing your tasks well. The better you imagine yourself, the bigger the

boost you are giving to your confidence.[83] You are a believer, thus be sure that Allah will always be there for you. Allah (ﷻ) says in His Holy Book:

$$ \text{﴿} \ ... \ يُثَبِّتُ ٱللَّهُ ٱلَّذِينَ ءَامَنُواْ بِٱلْقَوْلِ ٱلثَّابِتِ فِى ٱلْحَيَوٰةِ \ \text{۝} \ \text{﴾} $$

(سورة إبراهيم: ٢٧)

﴿Allah will establish in strength those who believe, with the word that stands firm, in this world and in the Hereafter...﴾

(Qur'an 14: 27)

4. Work to achieve your visualized goal, and remember that your aptitude and performance are directly related to your levels of confidence.[84] When things go wrong, do not get discouraged; perceive it as a challenge and keep trying. Focus on success and always maintain your positive self-image.

11. Forgive and forget

When we are hurt, insulted or faced with injustice, we have two options to deal with our feelings: either to forgive and forget or to hate, harbour grudge and rancour and live to seek revenge. Both choices are hard, but their results are completely opposite. Hatred, bitterness and hostility intoxicate your body.[85] They throw you into frustration, weaken your system and make your nerves tense. Anger, rancour and revenge are debilitating sentiments that poison the soul and add nothing but pain. Harbouring animosity and bitterness consumes a tremendous amount of valuable energy. Why should you put yourself through that?

On the other hand, forgiveness transcends the soul and frees you from your destructive negative energy. Forgiveness heals you not only emotionally but also physically and mentally. Is it not worth it to get rid of the burden of anger, hatred and resentment, to be able to restore your position in social life, giving and receiving support? Is it not more comforting to promote your positive emotions, reduce anxiety and stress and readjust your hormonal balance, blood pressure and heart rate?

Forgiveness was a prevailing feature of the first Islamic nation. Forgiveness practiced by Prophet Muhammad (ﷺ) was the perfect example. When he conquered Makkah, finally having the upper hand over the people who had for so long tortured him and his friends, he (ﷺ) asked them:

«"What do you think I would do to you?"

"O noble brother and generous nephew," they replied, "we expect nothing but goodness from you."

He (ﷺ) said: "I speak to you in the same words as Yoosuf spoke unto his brothers: ﴿No reproach on you this day﴾ Go! You are free!"»[86]

"It was related that 'Abdullah ibn Mas'ood once went to the market to buy food. When he reached for the money he kept in his turban, he discovered it was gone. People gathered and asked 'Abdullah to supplicate and ask for the hand of the thief to be amputated. He quietly raised his hands towards the skies and supplicated: O Allah! If what made him take it is his need, bless it for him and if it was his boldness to perform sins, make this the last of his misdeeds!"[87]

Lots of people refuse to forgive, thinking it a sign of weakness; they think that by forgiving they are surrendering to their offenders. On the contrary, by forgiving you cease to be the victim of hatred and anger and you triumph over your own evil. Now comes the most important question:

How do you forgive?

First, let us confess that it is far from easy. Allah tells us:

﴿ وَلَمَن صَبَرَ وَغَفَرَ إِنَّ ذَٰلِكَ لَمِنْ عَزْمِ ٱلْأُمُورِ ﴿٤٣﴾ ﴾ (سورة الشورى: ٤٣)

﴿And whosoever is patient and forgives, indeed that is of the steadfast heart of things.﴾ *(Qur'an 42: 43)*

It is a challenging task requiring a fight against our own selves, it is considered by Islam as a sacred type of struggle (jihad). Prophet Muhammad (ﷺ) said:

«A *mujâhid* (one who strives in Allah's cause) is one who engages in jihad against his own self in obeying Allah.»[88]

Some helpful hints:

➢ Allow yourself enough time to heal, let yourself fully express your feelings; do not just deny the pain and turn your back on it, expecting it to disappear on its own. You have to recognize and respect your true emotions so you can release them and transcend the whole situation. Abel, the pious son of Adam was true to himself and his feelings when he resented his brother Cain, for intending to kill him[89] and said:

﴿ إِنِّي أُرِيدُ أَن تَبُوٓأَ بِإِثْمِي وَإِثْمِكَ فَتَكُونَ مِنْ أَصْحَٰبِ ٱلنَّارِ وَذَٰلِكَ جَزَٰٓؤُاْ ٱلظَّٰلِمِينَ ﴿٢٩﴾ ﴾ (سورة المائدة: ٢٩)

﴿Verily, I intend to let you draw my sin as well as yours upon yourself, then you will be one of the dwellers of the Fire, and that is the recompense of the wrongdoers.﴾ *(Qur'an 5: 29)*

➢ Perform regular breathing exercises: the easiest one is simply to observe your breathing: do not try to control it or force it; just watch it and relax. You can also make use of meditation techniques to help you relax.

➤ Practice thinking that this life is just a transient path and those little events make up the bridge on which we can cross to the next world. So, take what is absolutely necessary for you to cross it and leave what is not.

Allah (ﷻ) says:

﴿ مَا عِندَكُمْ يَنفَدُّ وَمَا عِندَ ٱللَّهِ بَاقٍ وَلَنَجْزِيَنَّ ٱلَّذِينَ صَبَرُوٓا۟ أَجْرَهُم بِأَحْسَنِ مَا كَانُوا۟ يَعْمَلُونَ ﴿٩٦﴾ ﴾   (سورة النحل: ٩٦)

❨Whatever is with you, will be exhausted, and whatever is with Allah [of good deeds] will remain. And those who are patient, We will certainly pay them a reward in proportion to the best of what they used to do.❩   *(Qur'an 16: 96)*

➤ Honour the Divine Wisdom behind every event. Live in harmony with Allah's Will, rather than fighting it. Focus on your blessings, be grateful for them and release yourself from earthly bonding and material attachments.

➤ Keep your mind engaged with more important things. Think about Allah's Oneness, Justice and Mercy, about the rewards of conquering your anger and forgiving the offender:

﴿ ... فَمَنْ عَفَا وَأَصْلَحَ فَأَجْرُهُۥ عَلَى ٱللَّهِ ... ﴿٤٠﴾ ﴾   (سورة الشورى: ٤٠)

❨...Whoever forgives and makes reconciliation, his reward is due from Allah...❩   *(Qur'an 42: 40)*

﴿ ... وَلْيَعْفُوا۟ وَلْيَصْفَحُوٓا۟ أَلَا تُحِبُّونَ أَن يَغْفِرَ ٱللَّهُ لَكُمْ وَٱللَّهُ غَفُورٌ رَّحِيمٌ ﴿٢٢﴾ ﴾   (سورة النور: ٢٢)

❨...Let them pardon and forgive. Do you not love that Allah should forgive you? And Allah is Oft-Forgiving, Most Merciful.❩

(Qur'an 24: 22)

> Fear the punishment of Allah upon those whose hearts are filled with anger, hatred and resentment.[90] Taking revenge is following the devil's path! A man once came to the Caliph 'Umar ibn 'Abdel Azeez complaining about an unjust act. The Caliph replied: "It is better for you to face Allah as a victim of injustice than to take revenge."[91] "It was narrated that Jesus passed by some Jews who spoke to him badly, and he replied nicely. His followers asked in surprise: They speak with evil and you reply with good? He answered: Everyone spends from what he has."[92]

> Consider each event a lesson and every person a teacher; regardless of how you choose to judge their actions, it is useless to hate them or blame them for the situation you are in. Sometimes blaming our offenders temporarily eases the anger in our hearts and gives us a 'justifiable' reason for our feelings. But this does not last for long, our anger and pain do not dissipate through blame. Take responsibility for your own situation. View your experience as a necessary step in your path towards purification of your heart and soul.

> Hatred is a heavy burden to carry; it does not benefit you or harm your offender in any way. It is a blinding sentiment that can eventually take full control of all your thoughts and actions. It can even redirect its path towards you leading to self-resentment and blame. In order to forgive others, start by forgiving yourself. Be compassionate towards yourself; do not carry all the blame. You probably did the best you could, so go easy on yourself. Love yourself for who you are, appreciate the blessings you are given and let go of your negative emotions.

> Look for the good in everyone. Each person has to have a good side, we are human after all. Try to identify each person's motivations, understand them, show compassion, find excuses for

them, and then release the whole situation once and for all. Just let it go! «It was narrated by 'Abdullah ibn 'Umar that a man once asked the Prophet: O Messenger of Allah, how many times do I forgive my servant? The Prophet replied: Seventy times each day and night.»[93]

> Know that Allah does not love anger, hatred or revenge.[94] On the contrary, He () says:

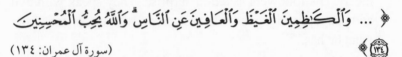

(سورة آل عمران: ١٣٤)

﴿Those...who repress anger, and who pardon people; verily, Allah loves the doers of good.﴾   *(Qur'an 3: 134)*

> Fill your heart with love and spread it all around you to extinguish the fire of rancour and anger;[95] do not leave any place in your heart for the debilitating sentiments that sicken your soul and open the door for evil.

> Know that people who are spreading injustice and animosity usually ignore the effect of their acts on others, they just act selfishly. You cannot blame bacteria for making you sick — they are simply doing what they know how to do, regardless of your opinion about it — you just need to protect yourself from them by building a stronger immunity. Shift your focus from feeling like a poor victim to realise that life has a bigger meaning: a valuable lesson is waiting for you to grasp its fruits.[96] And remember, your thoughts are reflected in your daily life. If you are totally consumed with others' dishonesty, cheating and selfishness, this is what will keep appearing in your life. Instead, if you detach yourself from the need for revenge, if you shift your thoughts to love and compassion, then this is exactly what you will be receiving in return. (Remember the story about Lin and her mother-in-law on page 286.)

Levels of forgiveness

There are three levels of forgiveness. As stated in the Qur'an:

$$ \text{﴾ ... وَإِن تَعْفُوا۟ وَتَصْفَحُوا۟ وَتَغْفِرُوا۟ فَإِنَّ ٱللَّهَ غَفُورٌ رَّحِيمٌ ﴿ ۝ ﴾} $$

(سورة التغابن: ١٤)

❴...If you pardon [them] and overlook, and forgive [their faults], then verily, Allah is Oft-Forgiving, Most Merciful❵ *(Qur'an 64: 14)*

First, stop blaming others for their mistakes and wipe out any trace of resentment left in your heart. The second step is for you to overlook the offence completely, as if it never happened. The final step, and the best response, is to cover up for those who offended you, to veil their mistakes and faults, by never mentioning their offences to anyone.

Two of the five pillars of Islam are practical exercises in forgiveness: pilgrimage (Hajj) and the fast of Ramadan. Tolerance, tolerance, tolerance! This is a valuable lesson that I have learnt personally during the pilgrimage. It is not easy to be offended and let go, to be hurt and kindly forgive and forget; to replace hatred with love, and anger with acceptance. We are faced with these challenges on a daily basis, and with the Hajj comes the practical exercise: a lesson to learn and apply. Overwhelmed by an immense feeling of serenity and peace, nothing else is important anymore except Allah's pleasure and approval. If you have experienced the Hajj, then you are surely familiar with the difficulties posed by the huge crowds there. While trying to perform the rituals, you are pushed around, stepped upon and maybe even verbally insulted (in total contradiction to Islamic teachings, especially concerning one of its most sacred acts of worship). Nevertheless, we are ordered to overlook the offences and mistakes of others, to forgive and forget, and not to argue or resent — even internally. Prophet Muhammad (ﷺ) said:

«Whoever performs the pilgrimage and does not commit any obscenity or wickedness, will return (from it) as (pure and free of sin as) on the day when his mother gave birth to him.»[97]

We all should realise that we actually waste a tremendous amount of energy and time in useless arguments. Just let it go, then enjoy the peace and serenity that fill your heart and mind. Cherish the feelings of love, acceptance and inner happiness.

During the holy month of Ramadan, the same lesson is repeated. Our Prophet (ﷺ) taught us:

«Fasting is like a shield. If one of you is observing a fast, do not commit any abomination, do not shout and do not act out of ignorance, and if someone insults you or fights with you, just say: I am fasting, I am fasting»[98]

So, by observing your duties during worship you are at the same time practicing how to forgive and control your temper; with practice, these seemingly difficult tasks can gradually become much easier.

12. Do not get angry

Anger, like stress and worry, intoxicates your body; it pulls you into a never-ending vicious cycle of unhappiness and rage, which in turn depletes your energy and leaves you devastated and depressed. It is important to realise that anger does not resolve anything.

«A man came to the Prophet (ﷺ) and asked him for advice; the Prophet (ﷺ) replied, repeating several times: Do not get angry.»[99]

﴾ ... وَمَا عِندَ ٱللَّهِ خَيْرٌ وَأَبْقَىٰ لِلَّذِينَ ءَامَنُوا۟ ... ﴿٣٦﴾ ... وَإِذَا مَا غَضِبُوا۟ هُمْ يَغْفِرُونَ

(سورة الشورىٰ: ٣٦-٣٧)   ﴿٣٧﴾﴾

﴾...And that which Allah has is better and more lasting for those who believe...and when they are angry, they forgive.﴿

(Qur'an 42: 36-37)

Controlling one's temper is not an easy task: it needs patience, wisdom and struggle within oneself; that is why Prophet Muhammad (ﷺ) said:

«Who do you count as strong among you? The companions said: The one who throws people down (during fights). He (ﷺ) said: No. The strong one is the he who controls his temper when he gets angry.»[100]

Our Prophet (ﷺ) taught us how to control anger and rage with this advice:

«Anger is from the Devil, and the Devil is made of fire, and fire is extinguished by water; so if anyone of you gets angry, let him perform ablution.»[101]

Today, many psychologists advise patients suffering from anxiety or going through panic or fits of rage to use *hydrotherapy* (water therapy). The amazing calming effect of water has been scientifically proven, and is used all over the world.

«Prophet Muhammad (ﷺ) said when he saw an angry man getting into a fight: I know a du'â' that, if he said it, his anger would fade away: I seek refuge with Allah from the accursed Satan. (*A'oodhu billâhi minash-shaytân ir-rajeem.*)[102]»

Seeking refuge in Allah to help us control our feelings and restore our emotional equilibrium is very important. Controlling one's rage is only the first step in the Islamic approach for responding to offenders, as Allah (ﷻ) says in His Book:

﴿ ... وَٱلْكَـٰظِمِينَ ٱلْغَيْظَ وَٱلْعَافِينَ عَنِ ٱلنَّاسِ وَٱللَّهُ يُحِبُّ ٱلْمُحْسِنِينَ ﴾

(سورة آل عمران: ١٣٤)   ﴿۱۳٤﴾

﴿...Those who repress anger, and who pardon people; verily, Allah loves the doers of good.﴾   *(Qur'an 3: 134)*

That is, first control your anger, then forgive the offender, then be good to the one who offended you; this is even better and more loved by Allah. This act of responding to evil by good actions purifies the heart and elevates your spirit to a higher level of wisdom and power, enabling you to take control of your life and overcome obstacles.

I remember when I first got married; I used to get very angry at every misunderstanding that arose between my husband and me. This stage of anger made me remember each and every mistake he had made since I first met him, and I would temporarily forget all the good things he had done. Then one day I read this hadith:

«The Prophet said: I saw Hellfire and I never saw a scene like today, and I saw that most of its people are women. They (the companions) asked: O Messenger of Allah. Why? He said: Because of their disbelief. They asked: Do they disbelieve in Allah? He replied: They are ungrateful to their companions (husbands) and for what they provide for them; if you were kind to one of them for ages, then she sees you make some mistake once, she says: I never saw any good from him.»[103]

O my God! I thought, *That is exactly what I have been doing!*

What is the solution then? The solution is mentioned in the hadith itself: «*saw any good from him*». Since that day, whenever I have a disagreement with my husband, I just sit quietly and think of all his good deeds towards me, my kids, and my family or even towards other friends and relatives. At the same time I also remind myself of this saying: 'Seek seventy excuses for your brother.'

Amazingly, these simple exercises, practiced for just few minutes, totally changed my emotional state from anger and resentment to peace and forgiveness. Anger cannot resolve problems, it blocks your ability for rational thinking, while on the contrary, tranquillity and serenity enable you to think clearly and to find a wise solution for your problems.

I read a story once about a little boy who had a bad temper:

His father gave him a bag of nails and told him that every time he lost his temper, he must hammer a nail into the back of the fence. The first day the boy had driven 43 nails into the fence Over the next few weeks, as he learned to control his anger, the number of nails hammered daily gradually dwindled down as the boy discovered that it was easier to hold his temper than to drive those nails into the fence. Finally a day came when the boy did not lose his temper at all.

He told his father about it, and the father suggested that the boy now pull out one nail for each day that he was able to control his anger. The days passed and the young boy was finally able to tell his father that all the nails were gone. The father took his son by the hand and led him to the fence. He said, "You have done well, my son, there are no nails in the fence anymore, but look at these holes. The fence will never be the same again!"

Remember, when you say things in anger, they leave a permanent scar![104]

13. Do not worry

Imam Adh-Dhahabi wrote: "Whoever worries too much sickens his body."[105]

Apprehension, anxiety, and woe are literally intoxicating our
bodies. When you worry and grieve, your body tends to secrete
more adrenalin neurotransmitter under the commands of the sympathetic nervous system; this is called the 'fight, flight and fright'
hormone. This hormone is secreted when facing danger to prepare
the body for self defence; it prepares the body to respond and cope
promptly and vigorously to life-threatening situations. Your body
does not differentiate between the nervousness and worry resulting from an attacking hungry leopard, or that caused by every day
life stresses. It responds by secreting the same type of hormones
that could prepare your body for a rapid flight from the approaching danger.[106] If a leopard was actually there, the energy and effort you would consume while running for your life would dissi-
pate the secreted hormones, and their levels in your blood would
eventually normalize again. But you are not running away from
a leopard, are you? You are just sitting on your living room sofa,
fretting.

When living under continuous stress and worry — working
overtime or without breaks, fussing about every event, and always
expecting the worst, your sympathetic nervous system is continuously generating its stress hormones. Any unused hormones are
then circulating in your system, generating a big mess: decreased
activity of the digestive tract, increased blood sugar level, increased rate and force of your heartbeat and elevated blood pressure, just to start with.

As mentioned in Chapter Three, another toxic effect of continuous worry and stress is the overproduction of certain steroidal hormones such as cortisol. These hormones are naturally secreted to help your body to reduce inflammation and resist long term stress. The constant high level of these hormones may lead to *hyperglycaemia* (a rise in blood sugar level), hypertension, the breakdown of body fats and proteins, weakening of the bones and suppression of the immune system. In addition, some studies have found that excess cortisol damages your brain by its destructive effect on the neuro-connectors or *dendrites* (the branches connecting brain cells together).[107]

The solution for worry and stress is taught to us repeatedly in the Qur'an and the Sunnah. Allah teaches us that fearing nothing and no one but Allah and detaching oneself from materialistic, worldly thoughts will free your mind by allowing you to remember that nothing in this life can last forever, that what may seem to you today to be an unsolvable problem will soon pass and fade away.

﴿ اعْلَمُوٓا أَنَّمَا الْحَيَوٰةُ الدُّنْيَا لَعِبٌ وَلَهْوٌ وَزِينَةٌ وَتَفَاخُرٌۢ بَيْنَكُمْ وَتَكَاثُرٌ فِى الْأَمْوَٰلِ وَالْأَوْلَٰدِ كَمَثَلِ غَيْثٍ أَعْجَبَ الْكُفَّارَ نَبَاتُهُۥ ثُمَّ يَهِيجُ فَتَرَىٰهُ مُصْفَرًّا ثُمَّ يَكُونُ حُطَٰمًا ... ﴾

(سورة الحديد: ٢٠)

﴾Know that the life of this world is only play and amusement, pomp and mutual boasting among you, and rivalry in respect of wealth and children, as the likeness of vegetation after rain, thereof the growth is pleasing to the tiller; afterwards it dries up and you see it turning yellow; then it becomes straw...﴿   *(Qur'an 57: 20)*

We have to concentrate on what is truly important, on our main goal in life: to attain Allah's pleasure and approval, to work for an eternal happiness in Paradise. Prophet Muhammad (ﷺ) said:

«Whoever's main concern is this worldly existence, Allah will bring his poverty between his eyes and disperse his union, and what will reach him from this world is only what is predestined for him. And whoever's main concern is the Hereafter, Allah will put wealth and prosperity into his heart and gather his union, and the world will be driven to him.»[108]

The Messenger of Allah (ﷺ) also said: «Whoever makes his concern only one (that of the Hereafter), Allah will make him content with (his share in this) worldly life; but whoever is surmounted by worries, Allah would not bother in which worldly valley he might perish.»[109]

The cure for sadness, worry and grief comes from true dependence on Allah, and from admitting that Allah is the Most Just, thus what comes about through His Will certainly holds a lesson, a mercy that although we might not see it at the present moment, will reveal itself in due course. The Qur'an should be our comfort, our relief and our true companion at all times, and especially in times of distress. Performing prayers, supplication and repentance to Allah are also potent cures that help us to discard worries.

Ibn al-Qayyim recommended, «Whenever sadness and grief intensify on someone, let him repeat often: There is neither power nor strength except from Allah.(*Lâ ḥawla wa lâ quwwata illâ billâh.*)» This is the supplication of those afflicted by distress: «O Allah, I seek Your Mercy. Do not make me reliant on my own self even for an instant, and lead all my affairs to success. There is none worthy of worship other than You. (*Allâhumma raḥmataka arjoo, fa lâ takalnee ilâ nafsee tarfata 'ayn, wa aṣliḥ lee sha'nee kullah, lâ ilâha illâ anta*).»[110]

He (ﷺ) also said:

«Whenever sadness or grief strikes someone he should say:
O Allah! I am your servant, the son of your servants. My
forelock is in Your grasp. Your decision about me will certainly come to pass. Your judgment on me is certainly just.
I ask you by every Name that is Yours and by which You
call Yourself, whether You revealed it in Your Book, taught
it to someone of Your creation or kept it in the Knowledge
of the Unseen that You have. Make the Qur'an the spring
of my heart, the light of my chest, the eliminator of my sadness and the end of my grief. (*Allâhumma innee 'abduka,
ibnu 'abdika, ibnu amatika. Nâṣiyatee bi yadika, mâḍin fiyya ḥukmuk, 'adlun fiyya qaḍâ'uk. As'aluka bi kulli ismin
huwa laka sammayta bihi nafsaka, aw anzaltahu fee kitâbi-
ka, aw 'allamtahu aḥadan min khalqika, aw ista'tharta bihi
fee 'ilm il-ghaybi 'indaka, an taj'al al-Qur'âna rabee'a
qalbee, wa noora ṣadree, wa jalâ'a ḥuznee wa dhahâba
hammee.*) Then Allah will remove his sadness and depression and will replace with joy.»[111]

In Chapter 70 of the Qur'an Allah describes human beings in
this way:

$$ ﴿ إِنَّ ٱلْإِنسَـٰنَ خُلِقَ هَلُوعًا ۝ إِذَا مَسَّهُ ٱلشَّرُّ جَزُوعًا ۝ وَإِذَا مَسَّهُ ٱلْخَيْرُ مَنُوعًا ۝ ﴾ $$

(سورة المعارج: ١٩-٢١)

❨Truly humans were created very impatient; fretful when evil
touches them; and grudging when good touches them.❩

(Qur'an 70: 19-21)

Allah makes an exception; in this same soorah He gives us a
Divine prescription for the treatment of impatience, anxiety and
worries:

Prayers:

﴿إِلَّا ٱلْمُصَلِّينَ ۞ ٱلَّذِينَ هُمْ عَلَىٰ صَلَاتِهِمْ دَآئِمُونَ ۞﴾ (سورة المعارج: ٢٢-٢٣)

﴿Not so those devoted to Prayer: those who remain constant in their prayers.﴾   *(Qur'an 70: 22-23)*

Charity:

﴿وَٱلَّذِينَ فِىٓ أَمْوَٰلِهِمْ حَقٌّ مَّعْلُومٌ ۞ لِّلسَّآئِلِ وَٱلْمَحْرُومِ ۞﴾ (سورة المعارج: ٢٤-٢٥)

﴿And those in whose wealth is a recognized right; for the [needy] who asks and him who is prevented [for some reason from asking].﴾   *(Qur'an 70: 24-25)*

Belief in the Hereafter:

﴿وَٱلَّذِينَ يُصَدِّقُونَ بِيَوْمِ ٱلدِّينِ ۞﴾   (سورة المعارج: ٢٦)

﴿And those who hold to the truth of the Day of Judgment.﴾
(Qur'an 70: 26)

Fear from and faith in Allah:

﴿وَٱلَّذِينَ هُم مِّنْ عَذَابِ رَبِّهِم مُّشْفِقُونَ ۞ إِنَّ عَذَابَ رَبِّهِمْ غَيْرُ مَأْمُونٍ ۞﴾
(سورة المعارج: ٢٧-٢٨)

﴿And those who fear the punishment of Allah, for Allah's punishment is not a thing to feel secure from.﴾   *(Qur'an 70: 27-28)*

Chastity:

﴿وَٱلَّذِينَ هُمْ لِفُرُوجِهِمْ حَٰفِظُونَ ۞ إِلَّا عَلَىٰٓ أَزْوَٰجِهِمْ أَوْ مَا مَلَكَتْ أَيْمَٰنُهُمْ فَإِنَّهُمْ غَيْرُ مَلُومِينَ ۞ فَمَنِ ٱبْتَغَىٰ وَرَآءَ ذَٰلِكَ فَأُوْلَٰٓئِكَ هُمُ ٱلْعَادُونَ ۞﴾ (سورة المعارج: ٢٩-٣١)

❨And those who guard their chastity, except with their wives and the [captives] whom their right hands possess, for [then] they are not to be blamed, but those who trespass beyond this are transgressors.❩   *(Qur'an 70: 29-31)*

Good manners and honesty:

﴿وَٱلَّذِينَ هُمْ لِأَمَـٰنَـٰتِهِمْ وَعَهْدِهِمْ رَٰعُونَ ۝ وَٱلَّذِينَ هُم بِشَهَـٰدَٰتِهِمْ قَآئِمُونَ ۝﴾

(سورة المعارج: ٣٢-٣٣)

❨And those who respect their trusts and covenants. And those who stand firm in their testimonies.❩   *(Qur'an 70: 32-33)*

Strong religious beliefs:

﴿إِلَّا ٱلْمُصَلِّينَ ۝﴾   (سورة المعارج: ٢٢)

❨And those who [strictly] guard their worship.❩   *(Qur'an 70: 34)*

These are indeed the seven characteristics that are guaranteed to bring success in this life as well as in the Hereafter.

14. Surrender to Allah's will

A friend of mine once sent me this story about a butterfly struggling for its life:

One day, a small opening appeared in a cocoon; a man sat and watched for the butterfly for several hours as it struggled to force its body through that little hole. Then, it seemed to stop making any progress. It appeared as if it had gotten as far as it could and it could not go any further; so the man decided to help the butterfly: he took a pair of scissors and opened the cocoon. The butterfly then emerged easily. But it had a withered body; it was tiny with shrivelled wings. The man continued to watch because he expected that, at any moment, the wings would open, enlarge and expand, to be able to support the butterfly's body, and become firm. Neither happened! In fact, the butterfly spent the rest of its life crawling around with a withered body and shrivelled wings. It was never able to fly. What the man in his kindness and his goodwill did not understand was that the restricting cocoon and the struggle required for the butterfly to get through the tiny opening, were Allah's way of forcing fluid from the body of the butterfly into its wings, so that it would be ready for flight once it achieved its freedom from the cocoon. Sometimes, struggles are exactly what we need in our life. If God allowed us to go through our life without any obstacles, it would cripple us. We would not be as strong as we could have been.[112]

Sometimes the little inconveniences and obstacles in our lives are Allah's lessons to give us strength and wisdom. Calamities and afflictions are part of our big life test; contained within them are valuable guidance and wisdom. Sickness and loss are favours from Allah that wipe away our sins, so that we revert to Him with a pure, loving heart. Sometimes, during our sorrows and frustrations, we mistakenly think that our prayers are not answered; we assume that we have nothing. No, think again: we have it all.

Reliance on Allah means to entrust your affairs to Him and to fully believe in Him, in His All-encompassing Power and Wisdom and in His Kindness and Mercy.

Allah (ﷻ) says:

﴿ قُل مَنۢ بِيَدِهِۦ مَلَكُوتُ كُلِّ شَيۡءٍ وَهُوَ يُجِيرُ وَلَا يُجَارُ عَلَيۡهِ إِن كُنتُمۡ تَعۡلَمُونَ ۝ ﴾

(سورة المؤمنون: ٨٨)

◆Say: In Whose Hand is the sovereignty of everything? And He proztects [all], while against Whom there is no protector, [if Allah saves anyone none can punish or harm him, and if Allah punishes or harms anyone none can save him], if you know.❯   *(Qur'an 23: 88)*

Some people think that depending on Allah means giving up work, earnings, actions and efforts. This is totally unlawful in Islamic sharia (law). Muslims ought to work, seek knowledge and adopt the most praiseworthy means of attaining a successful and prosperous life.

Ghazâli the Elder narrated this story of a man who went on a journey carrying only a loaf of bread. He was afraid to eat it and leave no food reserve for the rest of his voyage. He kept telling himself: "If I eat it, I will die."

Allah entrusted an angel to him, saying: "If he eats it, give him more provision." The man never ate his loaf; it lay there before him at the time of his death.[113]

This man planned his journey and thought out his means, but forgot to rely on his Allah. However endowed with knowledge and experience, we cannot predict our fate. A stage comes in life when all that is humanly possible has been done, yet the results cannot be anticipated. At that time, you leave everything to Allah and make your will conform to the Divine Will. Allah only knows what the final outcome is to be, and as He says in the Qur'an:

﴿ ... وَعَسَىٰٓ أَن تَكْرَهُواْ شَيْـًٔا وَهُوَ خَيْرٌ لَّكُمْ وَعَسَىٰٓ أَن تُحِبُّواْ شَيْـًٔا وَهُوَ شَرٌّ لَّكُمْ وَٱللَّهُ يَعْلَمُ وَأَنتُمْ لَا تَعْلَمُونَ ﴾ (٢١٦) (سورة البقرة: ٢١٦)

◆...And it may be that you dislike a thing which is good for you and that you like a thing which is bad for you. Allah knows but you do not know.❯   *(Qur'an 2: 216)*

This is what is sometimes called 'synchronicity';[114] that is, the willingness to believe in the Divine Power and Wisdom that supports and controls all creatures and all creation, allowing the whole universe to work in perfect harmony.

There is a supplication that Prophet Muhammad (ﷺ) taught us, it reminds us about the necessity of surrendering to Allah's will, to work and plan, but to let Allah show us the correct path:

«O Allah! I submit myself to You and entrust my affairs to You and I turn my face towards You and my hope and fear is of You. Verily, there is neither refuge nor safe haven from You except with You. I believe in Your Book which You have revealed and in Your Prophet whom You have sent. (*Allâhumma aslamtu nafsee ilayk, wa fawwaḍtu amree il-ayk, wa wajjahtu wajhee ilayk, wa alja'tu dhahree ilayk, raghbatan wa rahbatan ilayk, lâ malja'a wa lâ manjâ min-ka illâ ilayk, âmantu bikitâbika alladhee anzalta wa bina-biyyika alladhee arsalt*).»[115]

Prophet Muhammad (ﷺ) told us: «If you put your trust in Allah as properly as it should be, He would bestow upon you as He provides for the bird; they leave early in the morning with an empty stomach and return full.»[116]

Allah says in the Qur'an:

$$﴿ وَفِى ٱلسَّمَآءِ رِزْقُكُمْ وَمَا تُوعَدُونَ ۞ فَوَرَبِّ ٱلسَّمَآءِ وَٱلْأَرْضِ إِنَّهُ لَحَقٌّ مِّثْلَ مَآ أَنَّكُمْ تَنطِقُونَ ﴾$$

(سورة الذاريات: ٢٢-٢٣)

﴿And in the heaven is your provision, and that which you are promised. Then, by the Owner of the sky and the earth, it is the truth [i.e., what has been promised to you], just as it is the truth that you can speak.﴾   *(Qur'an 51: 22-23)*

I remember the story of a friend of mine who had just got divorced from an abusive husband. She was now a single mother with two little kids, in a foreign country with no house, no money, no job, nothing. A year earlier she had invested all her savings to buy an apartment in a project that had not even started yet. Her residence visa was expiring in few days' time while she was trying desperately to sell this apartment so that she could afford airfare back home to try to make a new start to a decent life. She was just running out of time, with no hope in sight, and she started to panic. I did not know how to help her; I gave her a copy of Shaykh 'Aaidh Qarni's book *Don't Be Sad*, a valuable practical guide on how to have an ultimately satisfying Islamic outlook on life and how to effectively deal with everyday trials and tribulations in our lives.[117]

The next morning she came to me announcing that she had booked her trip back home in a week's time. In the book, she said, Shaykh 'Aaidh advises that if you are struck with a calamity, sit down and analyse your situation wisely, then devise some plans: Plan A, an alternative Plan B and then C, and start implementing them right away. Do your best and leave the rest to Allah, do not think of the results, be sure that Allah knows the best and will help you out. My friend called all the real estate agents she knew, she started looking for housing and schools for her kids in her hometown through the Internet; she worked day and night and did all that was humanly possible. The week passed by with no incoming results. She came to my house on her last day in the country telling me that she was completely satisfied with what she had achieved: she knew that she tried her best and if the apartment was not sold, it was just not meant to be. She knew deep inside that Allah knows what is best for her. I was astonished by her total surrender, deep satisfaction and faith. Then, the telephone rang, it was the real es-

tate agent announcing that he had found a buyer for an unexpect-
edly high price; and another phone call followed from a friend of
hers announcing that she arranged for a good place to stay and
friends to help her in her new life start. All was solved in a blink
of an eye! *Subhan Allah*!

We all know the story of Prophet Ibrâheem when he was given
Allah's order to sacrifice his beloved young son Ismâ'eel, and
how Allah ransomed him with a momentous sacrifice, the ram.
We may not have noticed when this ransom was delivered to
them, however. Allah tells us:

﴿فَلَمَّآ أَسْلَمَا وَتَلَّهُۥ لِلْجَبِينِ ۝ وَنَدَيْنَٰهُ أَن يَـٰٓإِبْرَٰهِيمُ ۝ قَدْ صَدَّقْتَ ٱلرُّءْيَآ إِنَّا كَذَٰلِكَ

نَجْزِى ٱلْمُحْسِنِينَ ۝ إِنَّ هَٰذَا لَهُوَ ٱلْبَلَـٰٓؤُا۟ ٱلْمُبِينُ ۝ وَفَدَيْنَٰهُ بِذِبْحٍ عَظِيمٍ ۝﴾

(سورة الصافات: ١٠٣-١٠٧)

⟪Then, when they had both submitted themselves [to the Will of
Allah], and he had laid him prostrate on his forehead [or on the
side of his forehead for slaughtering]; We called out to him: O
Ibrâheem! You have fulfilled the dream [vision]! Verily! Thus do
We reward the doers of good. Verily, that indeed was a manifest
trial. And We ransomed him with a great sacrifice.⟫

(Qur'an 37: 103-107)

After they fulfilled Allah's order, they totally surrendered and
'submitted' to the will of Allah! This is the point to stress here:
Allah knows best, do what you can then totally surrender to His
Will.

Surrendering to Allah involves two important features:[118]

➢ Maintaining your patience and forbearance under all circumstances, without getting stressed, worried or deressed.

> Remaining content and satisfied with whatever is destined for you and making your will conform to the Divine Will with total acceptance, trust and faith.

True surrender to Allah's will is only achieved through strong belief in Allah. It helps to recognise and understand the meanings of His Names and Attributes.

Allah (ﷻ) says:

﴿ وَتَوَكَّلْ عَلَى ٱلْعَزِيزِ ٱلرَّحِيمِ ۝ ٱلَّذِى يَرَىٰكَ حِينَ تَقُومُ ۝ وَتَقَلُّبَكَ فِى ٱلسَّٰجِدِينَ ۝ إِنَّهُۥ هُوَ ٱلسَّمِيعُ ٱلْعَلِيمُ ۝ ﴾
(سورة الشعراء: ٢١٧-٢٢٠)

❨And put your trust in the All-Mighty, the Most Merciful, Who sees you [O Muhammad] when you stand up [alone at night for *tahajjud* prayers], and your movements among those who fall prostrate [along with you to Allah in the five compulsory congregational prayers]. Verily! He, only He, is the All-Hearer, the All-Knower.❩   *(Qur'an 26: 217-220)*

﴿ وَقَالَ مُوسَىٰ يَٰقَوْمِ إِن كُنتُمْ ءَامَنتُم بِٱللَّهِ فَعَلَيْهِ تَوَكَّلُوٓاْ إِن كُنتُم مُّسْلِمِينَ ۝ ﴾
(سورة يونس: ٨٤)

❨And Moosâ [Moses] said: O my people! If you have believed in Allah, then put your trust in Him if you are Muslims [those who submit to Allah's Will].❩   *(Qur'an 10: 84)*

Only with true reliance on Allah can you achieve peace of mind. By relying on Allah, we pass the stage of entrusting all our affairs to Him from a consideration of His Power and Compassion to reach a stage of complete dependence: relying on Him as the infant relies on its mother, knowing no one except her.[119]

Allah (ﷻ) says:

﴿ قُلِ ٱللَّهُمَّ مَٰلِكَ ٱلْمُلْكِ تُؤْتِى ٱلْمُلْكَ مَن تَشَآءُ وَتَنزِعُ ٱلْمُلْكَ مِمَّن تَشَآءُ وَتُعِزُّ مَن تَشَآءُ وَتُذِلُّ مَن تَشَآءُ بِيَدِكَ ٱلْخَيْرُ إِنَّكَ عَلَىٰ كُلِّ شَىْءٍ قَدِيرٌ ﴾ ٢٦

(سورة آل عمران: ٢٦)

﴿Say [O Muhammad]: O Allah! Possessor of the kingdom, You give the kingdom to whom You will, and You take the kingdom from whom You will, and You endue with honour whom You will, and You humiliate whom You will. In Your Hand is all good. Verily, You are Able to do all things.﴾ *(Qur'an 3: 26)*

﴿ قُلْ مَن يُنَجِّيكُم مِّن ظُلُمَٰتِ ٱلْبَرِّ وَٱلْبَحْرِ تَدْعُونَهُۥ تَضَرُّعًا وَخُفْيَةً لَّئِنْ أَنجَىٰنَا مِنْ هَٰذِهِۦ لَنَكُونَنَّ مِنَ ٱلشَّٰكِرِينَ ٦٣ قُلِ ٱللَّهُ يُنَجِّيكُم مِّنْهَا وَمِن كُلِّ كَرْبٍ ثُمَّ أَنتُمْ تُشْرِكُونَ ٦٤ ﴾

(سورة الأنعام: ٦٣-٦٤)

﴿Say [O Muhammad]: Who rescues you from the darkness of the land and the sea [dangers like storms], when you call upon Him in humility and in secret [saying]: If He [Allah] only saves us from this [danger], we shall truly be grateful. Say [O Muhammad]: Allah rescues you from it and from all [other] distresses, and yet you worship others besides Allah.﴾ *(Qur'an 6: 63-64)*

15. Be flexible

Prophet Muhammad (ﷺ) said: «The likeness of the believer is as a stalk of corn which the wind does not cease to blow down; even so trials do not cease to fall upon the believer. The likeness of a hypocrite is as a cypress tree which does not bend (or shake) unless it is felled.»[120]

In a similar hadith he (ﷺ) said: «The parable of the believer is that of an herb, the wind pushes it over and straightens it in turn, till it strengthens.»[121]

Then there is another analogy, as explained in *The Moral Vision*; the author looks at life's events as trains reaching their stations one by one. If you reach the platform.and find that you missed your train, be confident, there are always many trains coming next. It is up to you to choose which one to take Falling into despair and gloom will not bring your train back; it will only delay your chance of catching the next one. What you need to do is to assess your situation wisely, taking every possibility into account, and grab new opportunities to reach your destination even if this means you have to wait for a while. Think clearly and be ready to accept and appreciate God-given opportunities.[122]

First you have to accept your situation with all its unpleasant surprises; you have to adjust yourself to the Divine will; only then will you be able to assess your options wisely and be flexible in confronting life with tolerance and endurance.

There is an old tale (not of Islamic origin) about a wise worshipper who had tremendous faith and belief in his Creator. One day the village where this worshipper lived was flooded by a huge storm. People started fleeing their houses. Since this poor old worshipper had no means of transportation, he stood on the sidewalk in the middle of a highway praying for God's help. A man saw him and stopped to save him, but the old man refused, saying that he knew that only God would save him. The water rose higher and the wind blew stronger. Another man stopped to rescue the old worshipper, then a third one, then a fourth, and each time he stubbornly refused, insisting that only God would save him. The weather became worse, and the man was finally struck by lightening; he died while waiting for his imagined salvation. What that man did not realise was that God's help can come in any form. It may not be in the manner or shape that we expect to receive it. We have to be flexible enough to figure out the different 'deliverance options' sent to us by the Owner of the Universe.

Allah (ﷻ) says:

$$ \left\{ ... \text{ فَعَسَىٰٓ أَن تَكْرَهُوا۟ شَيْـًٔا وَيَجْعَلَ ٱللَّهُ فِيهِ خَيْرًا كَثِيرًا } \text{ ﴿١٩﴾} \right\} $$

(سورة النساء: ١٩)

❨...It may be that you dislike a thing and Allah brings through it a great deal of good.❩　　　　　　　　　　　　　*(Qur'an 4: 19)*

$$ \left\{ ... \text{ وَعَسَىٰٓ أَن تَكْرَهُوا۟ شَيْـًٔا وَهُوَ خَيْرٌ لَّكُمْ ۖ وَعَسَىٰٓ أَن تُحِبُّوا۟ شَيْـًٔا وَهُوَ شَرٌّ لَّكُمْ } \text{ وَٱللَّهُ يَعْلَمُ وَأَنتُمْ لَا تَعْلَمُونَ } \text{ ﴿٦٦﴾} \right\} $$

(سورة البقرة: ٢١٦)

❨...It may be that you dislike a thing which is good for you and that you like a thing which is bad for you. Allah knows but you do not know.❩　　　　　　　　　　　　　*(Qur'an 2: 216)*

I learned a great deal from the story of Steve Jobs, CEO of Apple Computer and of Pixar Animation Studios, as he told it during a speech he delivered at Stanford University.[123] Jobs started his career in his parent's garage and proceeded his way up to be, in ten years, the leader of Apple, a $2 billion company with thousands of employees. Then, against all odds, the board of directors decided to fire him. I can imagine someone in his place, who got fired from a company that he started, to be devastated, depressed and overwhelmed. This was not the case: Jobs decided to work his way up again, to turn his calamity into challenge, into an opportunity for growth and creativity. He started two new companies, NeXT and Pixar, the world's most successful animation studio which created the famous computer-animated feature film, *Toy*

Story. It was only a matter of time before Apple bought NeXT and Jobs returned to Apple.

This is a marvellous example of flexibility, a great way to perceive a devastating situation as a lesson and an occasion for growth and progress.

In neurolinguistic programming (see Chapter Three), an important concept is that your approach to any situation is mainly determined by your way of thinking — or rather, your perception of your situation (P) and your emotional state (E). For instance, if you have too much work to do, you may perceive your situation as stressful and overwhelming. But, if you are flexible enough to change one aspect of your approach, it will be easier for you to adapt. You could focus on the final rewards of your hard work, the appreciation that you expect to receive from your boss, a promotion, or maybe some time off at the end (P), or you could change your frustration into feelings of motivation and challenge (E). By changing any aspect of your inner world, you generate high quality options so that in the end you can change the results you come up with.[124]

In the book *Teach Yourself to Think*, Edward de Bono gives an example of two hawks: one of them has excellent eyesight, while the other is short-sighted.[125] Both of them love to eat frogs. From a great height, the hawk with excellent eyesight can see and recognize a frog; it immediately dives and eats it. On the other hand, the hawk with poor eyesight dives to catch any small thing that moves; this might be a frog, a lizard, a rat, or it might turn out, at other times, to be just a false alarm. Which of the two hawks would you consider the best? Probably, the hawk with good eyesight. According to de Bono, the second hawk is better, because it is the flexible one. If frogs suddenly become extinct, this hawk would be easily able to carry on with his life. In contrast, the

sharp-sighted hawk that has not learned to vary its diet would die
out with the frogs.

The point of this analogy is that you can turn virtually any disadvantage into an advantage, if you have the right attitude.

16. Remember death

You are probably asking yourself now: Is she serious? How is
remembering death going to make me any happier? Well, it will.
This is truly not an invitation for depression and grief, nor is it
gloomy, bleak advice favouring pessimism and passiveness. It is
just a reminder of an absolute fact, a fact that we all tend to forget
while immersed in this transient, falsely embellished world and
cheated by its charming coquetries. We are all one breath away
from death. We usually do not remember that and we do not like
to be reminded, either. Nevertheless, it is an inescapable fact.

Allah (ﷻ) says:

$$ ﴿ قُلۡ إِنَّ ٱلۡمَوۡتَ ٱلَّذِى تَفِرُّونَ مِنۡهُ فَإِنَّهُۥ مُلَٰقِيكُمۡ ثُمَّ تُرَدُّونَ إِلَىٰ عَٰلِمِ ٱلۡغَيۡبِ $$
$$ وَٱلشَّهَٰدَةِ فَيُنَبِّئُكُم بِمَا كُنتُمۡ تَعۡمَلُونَ ٨ ﴾ $$

(سورة الجمعة: ٨)

◉Say [to them]: Verily, the death from which you flee will surely
meet you, then you will be sent back to [Allah], the All-Knower of
the unseen and the seen, and He will tell you what you used to do.◉
(Qur'an 62: 8)

Ghazâli the Elder divided people into three classes:

1) those who are addicted to the world,

2) those who are repentant and

3) those who have surrendered to Allah.[126]

The people who are addicted to the world do not remember
death, and do not like to. Allah describes them, saying:

﴾ ۞ ... ﴿وَلَا يَتَمَنَّوْنَهُۥٓ أَبَدَۢا بِمَا قَدَّمَتْ أَيْدِيهِمْۚ﴾   (سورة الجمعة: ٧)

﴾But they will never long for it [death], because of what [deeds]
their hands have sent before them!...﴿   *(Qur'an 62: 7)*

Those who are repentant, on the other hand, remember death
and fear it. They do not like death, as they fear that they will die
before they repent from their sins and purify their souls from cor-
rupt deeds. He is just not prepared for death. The third type of
person is those who are dedicated to Allah: the ones who always
remember death because they would like to meet with the Beloved. Such a person is waiting to live in the neighbourhood of Allah.
Remembering death keeps them unattached to false worldly desires and urges them to work and perform good deeds in order to
prepare for the next (eternal) world. That is how remembering
death helps you in your journey towards detachment.

Prophet Muhammad (ﷺ) said: «Remember (death) often
— the terminator of pleasures.»[127]

«Ibn 'Umar said: I, along with ten other companions, was
near the Messenger of Allah (ﷺ). Then a man from the
Anṣâr asked him: O Prophet of Allah! Who are the wisest
and most honoured of people? The Prophet answered: They
die honoured (or honourably) in this world and they are also
honoured in the next life (for the way they lived and died
on earth).»[128]

Remembering death is not about denying the joy of living. On
the contrary, it is about enjoying the freedom of flowing with life,
knowing that it is a temporary residence.

«Ibn 'Umar related that the Prophet (ﷺ) took hold of his
shoulders and said: Be in the world as if you are a stranger
or a traveller. Ibn 'Umar used to say: When you arrive at
the evening do not expect to see the morning and when you

arrive at the morning do not expect to see the evening. During health prepare for illness and while you are alive prepare for death.»[129]

Going through life without attachment makes you happier and more content; and leaves you grateful and satisfied, whereas attaching yourself to life gives it the power to control you, to dominate your feelings and emotions.

17. Be content and satisfied

The voyage towards emotional and spiritual satisfaction is continuously interrupted by inevitable worries, perturbation, and deceptions along the way. These discomforts are lessons to teach us and guidelines to lead the way towards Allah's Straight Path. Trying to get every single factor in your life under your control is futile, as life constantly challenges us with new tests.[130]

Allah (ﷻ) says:

﴿ أَحَسِبَ ٱلنَّاسُ أَن يُتْرَكُوٓا أَن يَقُولُوٓا ءَامَنَّا وَهُمْ لَا يُفْتَنُونَ ۝ ﴾(سورة العنكبوت: ٢)

❨Do people think that they will be left alone because they say: We believe, and will not be tested?❩   *(Qur'an 29: 2)*

That is the law of existence and it is in your own interest to surrender to it. Appreciate your Divine blessings, focus on your gifts and blessings, adapt your needs to your earnings and possessions, and stop questioning the Divine arrangement of your life.[131] Prophet Muhammad (ﷺ) said:

«Donot impeach Allah about something He preordained for you.»[132]

A person's misery stems from the inability to achieve this balance in life. If you measure your happiness by your material achievements, you may be faced with many disappointments and frustrations since it is impossible to control your outside world. You only have control over your inner choices, your awareness, consciousness and feelings; and these are the factors that can change your whole world view. To fail to accept Allah's Will and conform to it is to deny yourself the opportunity to advance and prosper. Prophet Muhammad (ﷺ) said:

«If the son of Adam (that is, a human being) had two valleys full of gold, he would wish for three!»[133]

You have to look within your heart to find inner peace and contentment. Prophet Muhammad (ﷺ) said:

«If one wakes up in the morning in the full security of his heart, and his body free from harm, and having a day's provision, then it is as if the world, all of it, is driven to him.»[134]

When you are afflicted with a calamity, you can choose how to respond to it:[135] you can nurture hostility, anxiety, and disbelief, even complain and lose patience, but then you will be harming only yourself. Furthermore, you may become so overwhelmed and depressed that you abandon your obligations and neglect your commitments. Alternatively, you can be patient and wait for Allah's deliverance, or — even better — feel content and grateful, praising Allah for His precious lesson that is delivered to you in the form of a test. According to Ibn al-Qayyim, the cure for sorrow and distress lies in the acceptance and satisfaction experienced deep in your heart, knowing that all that matters is seeking Allah's pleasure and rewards. We should also be certain that afflictions will only affect us as much as we permit them to.[136] Being contented dissipates your worries and your fears for tomorrow. Ibn al-Qayyim also said: "Contentment is heaven on earth." Know that your share of life is there waiting for you and your

sustenance has been preordained even before the creation of humankind. Allah (ﷻ) says:

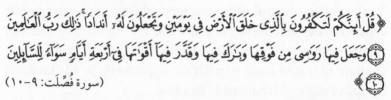

﴿قُلْ أَئِنَّكُمْ لَتَكْفُرُونَ بِالَّذِى خَلَقَ الْأَرْضَ فِى يَوْمَيْنِ وَتَجْعَلُونَ لَهُۥ أَندَادًا ذَٰلِكَ رَبُّ الْعَٰلَمِينَ ۝ وَجَعَلَ فِيهَا رَوَٰسِىَ مِن فَوْقِهَا وَبَٰرَكَ فِيهَا وَقَدَّرَ فِيهَآ أَقْوَٰتَهَا فِىٓ أَرْبَعَةِ أَيَّامٍ سَوَآءً لِّلسَّآئِلِينَ ۝﴾

(سورة فُصِّلَت: ٩-١٠)

﴿Say [O Muhammad]: Do you verily disbelieve in Him Who created the earth in two Days and you set up rivals [in worship] with
Him? That is the Creator and Owner of the Universe. He placed
therein firm mountains from above it, and He blessed it, and measured therein its sustenance [for its dwellers] in four Days equal
[i.e., all these four (days) were equal in length of time], for all
those who ask [about its creation].﴾   *(Qur'an 41: 9-10)*

We should look at affliction as merely a test for our patience,
acceptance and faith; they rid us of sins, strengthen our resolve
and purify our souls.

Prophet Muhammad (ﷺ) said: «The bigger the test is, the
greater the reward for it will be. When Allah loves people,
He tests them. If they are accept the affliction (cheerfully),
then they will achieve contentment (or Allah's pleasure);
and those who become enraged (or evade the affliction) will
only reap Allah's rage.»[137]

No matter how long you may complain or grieve, sooner or later
you will have to forgo the matter and get on with your life. A wise
man once said: "On the first day that a calamity strikes, the wise person behaves just like the ignorant person behaves days later."[138]

To help you in your journey towards satisfaction, adopt this
dhikr that Prophet Muhammad (ﷺ) taught us, to be said three
times in the morning after fajr prayer and three times in the evening after 'Aṣr prayer:

«O Allah, I am satisfied with Allah as my God, Islam as my religion and Muhammad (ﷺ) as my Prophet.

(*Allâhumma innee raḍeetu billâhi rabban wa bil Islâmi deenan wa bi Muḥammadin nabiyyâ*).[139]

Prophet Muhammad (ﷺ) said that if one says this dhikr at these specified times, it is mandatory that Allah will grant that person satisfaction and contentment.»[140]

Another help in your journey towards satisfaction is the adjustment of your will to the Divine Will, which can be achieved by a non-obligatory prayer called *istikhârah* (seeking what is good). Prophet Muhammad (ﷺ) taught us that whenever anyone intends to undertake a matter, s/he should first offer two non-obligatory units (raka'ah) of ṣalât and then supplicate to Allah seeking guidance to make the right decision or choose the proper course. This puts one in total agreement with Allah's choice and brings satisfaction into one's heart. Prophet Muhammad (ﷺ) said: «A source of a person's happiness is being content with Allah's will; while among the sources of misery are refraining from asking for Allah's guidance and feeling discontented with Allah's decree.»[141]

18. Be patient and steadfast

We are faced with lessons in patience every day of our lives. Spiritual enlightenment and contentment are hard tasks and long-term goals that are difficult to achieve. Since this is not an easy journey, patience is required at each step along the way. Patience is the driving power that will keep you going.[142]

Do you hate getting stuck in traffic jams? This is the easiest test to check your patience. If you do hate traffic, then you certainly need to work more on increasing your patience, because chances are — according to Cherie Carter-Scott — you will probably face more traffic jams than someone who has no problem with it: this is mainly because you will just focus on the bad traffic more than someone who does not mind it.[143] Remember this hadith:

«Suhayb reported that the Prophet (ﷺ) said: The believer's affair is amazing: it is all for the good, and that is not the case of anyone other than a believer. If good times come to him, he is thankful and thus it is good for him, and if bad times befall him, he is patient, and thus it is also good for him.»[144]

The Arabic word *ṣabr* in that hadith is often translated as 'patience', but in this and many other contexts the word 'steadfast' may be closer to the true meaning, because ṣabr carries the meaning of (constant), (firm) and (unwavering). In many verses in the Qur'an, Allah praises those who are patient. Allah also links good deeds and merits to patience:

﴿ وَجَعَلْنَا مِنْهُمْ أَئِمَّةً يَهْدُونَ بِأَمْرِنَا لَمَّا صَبَرُوا ... ۝ ﴾ (سورة السجدة: ٢٤)

❲And We made from among them [Children of Israel], leaders, giving guidance under Our Command, when they were patient...❳
(Qur'an 32: 24)

﴿ مَا عِندَكُمْ يَنفَدُ وَمَا عِندَ اللَّهِ بَاقٍ وَلَنَجْزِيَنَّ الَّذِينَ صَبَرُوا أَجْرَهُم بِأَحْسَنِ مَا كَانُوا يَعْمَلُونَ ۝ ﴾ (سورة النحل: ٩٦)

❲Whatever is with you, will be exhausted, and whatever with Allah [of good deeds] will remain. And those who are steadfast, We will certainly pay them a reward in proportion to the best of what they used to do.❳
(Qur'an 16: 96)

﴿ ... إِنَّمَا يُوَفَّى الصَّابِرُونَ أَجْرَهُم بِغَيْرِ حِسَابٍ ۝ ﴾ (سورة الزُّمَر: ١٠)

❲...Only those who are steadfast shall receive their rewards in full, without reckoning.❳
(Qur'an 39: 10)

﴿ ... وَٱللَّهُ مَعَ ٱلصَّٰبِرِينَ ﴾ ۝   (سورة البقرة: ٢٤٩)

﴿...And Allah is with the steadfast ones.﴾   *(Qur'an 2: 249)*

'Umar ibn Khattâb once wrote to Abu Moosâ Ash'ari saying:Observe patience. Know that patience is of two kinds; one is better than the other. It is good to have patience in disasters, but it is even better to keep yourself away from unlawful things. And know that patience is the gist of faith and this is because the fear of Allah is the best religious act and this is gained by patience.[145]

«Prophet Muhammad (ﷺ) observed: The best (aspects) of faith are patience and tolerance.»[146]

According to Ghazâli the Elder, there are three kinds of patience:[147]

1. Patience over things that we cannot control, like accidents and natural disasters, physical pain and diseases. The practice of this type of patience leads to the contentment of the soul. Prophet Muhammad (ﷺ) said: «Wondrous is the case of a believer; there is good for him in everything, and it is so for (the believer) only. If he experiences something agreeable, he is grateful to Allah and that is good for him; and if he experiences adversity, he is steadfast (patient) and that is good for him.»[148] Allah (ﷺ) says:

﴿ وَلَنَبْلُوَنَّكُم بِشَىْءٍ مِّنَ ٱلْخَوْفِ وَٱلْجُوعِ وَنَقْصٍ مِّنَ ٱلْأَمْوَٰلِ وَٱلْأَنفُسِ وَٱلثَّمَرَٰتِ وَبَشِّرِ ٱلصَّٰبِرِينَ ۝ ٱلَّذِينَ إِذَآ أَصَٰبَتْهُم مُّصِيبَةٌ قَالُوٓا۟ إِنَّا لِلَّهِ وَإِنَّآ إِلَيْهِ رَٰجِعُونَ ۝ أُو۟لَٰٓئِكَ عَلَيْهِمْ صَلَوَٰتٌ مِّن رَّبِّهِمْ وَرَحْمَةٌ وَأُو۟لَٰٓئِكَ هُمُ ٱلْمُهْتَدُونَ ﴾ ۝

(سورة البقرة: ١٥٥-١٥٧)

﴿And certainly, We shall test you with something of fear, hunger, loss of wealth, lives and crops, but give glad tidings to the steadfast ones. Who, when afflicted with calamity, say: Truly, to Allah we belong and truly, to Him we shall return. They are those on whom are the blessings [i.e., who are blessed and will be forgiven] from Allah, and [they are those who] receive His Mercy, and it is they who are the guided ones.❯   *(Qur'an 2: 155-157)*

2. Patience at the inclination of evil and this includes self-control, forbearance by containing one's anger and the acceptance of one's situation. If bad habits are added to desire or passion, things can really get out of control. To restrain oneself from sinful deeds, a person really needs to practice patience. Prophet Muhammad (ﷺ) said: «A *mujâhid* (one who strives in Allah's cause) is one who engages in jihad against his own self in obeying Allah, and a *muhâjir* (immigrant) is one who migrates from all crimes and sins.»[149]

This type of patience includes patience in the face of people's offences, forgiveness and forbearance. Prophet Muhammad (ﷺ) said:

«Join the tie with one who severs it from you, give charity to the one who deprives you and forgive the one who oppresses you.»[150]

This is a high degree of patience that needs a lot of training and self-control, but it is true nourishment for the soul and a way to enlightenment and self-purification.

3. Patience (forbearance) in experiencing pleasure and happiness. When people feel very comfortable enjoying physical health, safety, property, wealth and the admiration of others; they can throw themselves into these worldly comforts and possessions without control and fail to remember either the source of their blessings or the ultimate purpose of their creation. According to Muslim scholars, this kind of patience is more difficult to practice than the other two types.

Allah (ﷻ) says:

﴿ إِنَّمَآ أَمْوَٰلُكُمْ وَأَوْلَٰدُكُمْ فِتْنَةٌ ۚ وَٱللَّهُ عِندَهُۥٓ أَجْرٌ عَظِيمٌ ﴾ ﴿١٥﴾ (سورة التغابن: ١٥)

❝Your wealth and your children are only a trial, whereas Allah! With Him is a great reward [Paradise].❞   *(Qur'an 64: 15)*

These material things are tests that require us to exercise patience in order to prevent them from controlling our lives, and to keep us from becoming enslaved by our desires. Again we are reminded of the importance of detachment. Patience is an essential requirement to keep us detached from worldly passions. Enjoy your youth, your wealth and your children, but do not get too attached to any of them: do not let them distract you from your true mission in life.

Practice patience

Once 'Ali ibn Abi Ṭâlib (ﷺ) had some guests in his house; he called his servant several times to ask him for some water, but the servant did not answer. After a few minutes, 'Ali got up himself to fetch the water. To his surprise, he found the boy lying on the kitchen floor, chanting. 'Ali asked him: Didn't you hear me calling for you? The boy answered: Yes I did; so 'Ali asked: Then why didn't you answer me? The boy replied: Because I know that you wouldn't do me any harm. 'Ali laughed and went back to his friends and told them what had happened. Of course they advised him to fire this servant. 'Ali said: No, I practice my patience on him.[151]

There are many ways to practice patience through Islamic teachings; Ramadan fasting is an important one. Prophet Muhammad (ﷺ) said: «Fasting is half of patience.»[152] Fasting is an exercise of patience. People who fast regularly learn to control their desire for sex and food, and also learn to control their tempers.

Our Prophet also taught us a du'â' to help us in different situations throughout our lives: «If a servant is inflicted with adversity let him supplicate: We belong to Allah and to Him we shall return. O Allah, give me blessing in this adversity, and follow it with what is better for me. (*Innâ lillâhi wa innâ ilayhi râji'oon. Allâhumma ajurnee fee muṣeebatee wakh-luf lee khayran minhâ*). And Allah will answer his request.»[153]

The belief in predestination (Allah's decree) is one of the pillars of faith, and it is a prerequisite for patience. This means that the Muslim should believe that what has befallen him or her was not going to miss them and what has missed them was not meant to befall them. This attitude is an excellent way to learn to tolerate calamities and difficulties in life. It also helps to know what Prophet Muhammad (ﷺ) said: «No fatigue, no disease, no sorrow, no sadness, no hurt, no distress befalls a Muslim, even if it was the prick he received from a thorn, but that Allah expiates some of his sins for it.»[154]

19. Time for yourself

When I get overwhelmed by too many things to do, when I am running out of time and my energy seems to be leaking out of me, I remember 'the mayonnaise jar and the coffee':[155]

A professor stood before his Philosophy class and picked up a very large and empty mayonnaise jar and proceeded to fill it with golf balls. He then asked the students if the jar was full. They agreed that it was. The professor then picked up a box of pebbles and poured them into the jar. He shook the jar lightly. The pebbles rolled into the open areas between the golf balls. He then asked the students again if the jar was full. They agreed it was. The professor next picked up a box of sand and poured it into the jar. Of course, the sand filled up everything else. He asked once more if

the jar was full. The students responded with a unanimous, «Yes!»
The professor then poured the content of two cups of coffee into
the jar; this effectively filled the empty space between the sand.
The students laughed.

'Now,' said the professor, as the laughter subsided, "I want you
to recognize that this jar represents your life, the golf balls are the
important things — God, family, your children, your health and
your close friends and relatives — things that if everything else
was lost and only they remained, your life would still be worthwhile. The pebbles are the other things that matter like your job,
your house, and your car; the sand is everything else-the small
stuff." "If you put the sand into the jar first," he continued, "there
will be no room for the pebbles or the golf balls. The same goes
for life: if you spend all your time and energy on the small stuff,
you will never have room for the things that are important to you.
Pay attention to the things that are critical to your happiness: say
your prayers, play with your children, take time to get medical
checkups, take your partner out to dinner. There will always be
time to clean the house and fix the disposal. Take care of the golf
balls first, the things that really matter. Set your priorities. The rest
is just sand."

One of the students raised her hand and inquired what the coffee represented.

The professor smiled, "I'm glad you asked. It just goes to show
you that no matter how full your life may seem, there is always
room for a cup of coffee with a friend."

«It was reported that Salmân once said to Abu Dardâ': Allah
has a right over you, your own self has a right over you and
your partner has a right over you; so give everyone his due
right. When the Prophet (ﷺ) was informed of what he had
said, he replied: Salmân has spoken the truth.»[156]

When I graduated at the top of my class, I was immediately hired as a teaching assistant in the same university. I loved my job, but it took most of my time and energy. After I got married, my husband's job kept him out most of the day, so I got even more involved and dedicated to my work. Then, after I had my first son, I had to take maternity leave, then my daughter came along, and I was now too busy doing housework and parenting to find any time for my academic work. I loved my kids, and I enjoyed playing with them and reading them stories. I also loved cooking, so it was still fun preparing food for the family and creating new recipes. My husband was a fine, caring man — responsible and supportive. Strangely, though, I was feeling depressed; I was crying almost every day, I did not know what was wrong with me, until I read a book that turned my life around: *Nurturing Yourself and Others*.[157] In her book, Lee Schnebly explained how she was suffering from the same symptoms when, like me, she had every reason to be happy in her life. Her counsellor Bill McCartin put it for her in a simple, beautiful way. He advised her to think of herself as 'an apple barrel'. The apple barrel is only useful if it actually holds some apples. If we keep distributing our apples to our kids, relatives, family, and friends, we will soon run out of apples and feel worthless. To restore our function in life we have to replenish our supply of apples.[158]

You have to find the source of your apples: what makes you really relaxed, and replenishes your depleted energy? For you,

it might be reading a book, memorizing the Qur'an, spending some time with a friend, or meditating in front of the wide open sea. Think, and make your own list. Refer back to this list whenever you feel down or depressed — whenever you

are out of apples — and do one of those things for yourself, so
that your 'apple barrel' fills up again!

20. Seek Allah's forgiveness

Seeking Allah's forgiveness brings happiness, peace of mind
and well-being. Allah (ﷻ) says in His Book:

﴿ وَأَنِ ٱسْتَغْفِرُوا۟ رَبَّكُمْ ثُمَّ تُوبُوٓا۟ إِلَيْهِ يُمَتِّعْكُم مَّتَٰعًا حَسَنًا إِلَىٰٓ أَجَلٍ مُّسَمًّى وَيُؤْتِ كُلَّ ذِى
فَضْلٍ فَضْلَهُۥ ... ۝ ﴾   (سورة هود: ٣)

❨And [commanding you]: Seek the forgiveness of Allah, and turn
to Him in repentance, that He may grant you good enjoyment, for
a term appointed, and bestow His abounding Grace to every gracious one [i.e., those who help and serve the needy and deserving,
physically and with their wealth, and even with good words]...❩

(Qur'an 11: 3)

Prophet Muhammad (ﷺ) said: «By Allah, I seek Allah's
forgiveness and repent to Him (saying: *Astaghfir Allâh wa
atoobu ilayhi*) more than seventy times each day.»[159]

A man once came to Imam Hassan Baṣri,[160] complaining that
the amount of rainfall was insufficient; the Imam told him, "Ask
Allah's forgiveness." Another man came complaining from poverty; the Imam said once again, "Ask Allah's forgiveness." A third
man complained to the Imam of infertility; the advice was the
same: "Ask Allah's forgiveness." Eventually, a fourth man came
to complain that his garden did not yield fine produce, and for
the fourth time the Imam suggested: "Ask Allah's forgiveness."
A man who had been sitting next to the Imam asked in surprise,
"O Imam, how can you prescribe the same solution for these four
different cases?" The Imam replied, "I remembered the verse in
Allah's Book that says:

﴿ فَقُلْتُ ٱسْتَغْفِرُوا رَبَّكُمْ إِنَّهُۥ كَانَ غَفَّارًا ۝ يُرْسِلِ ٱلسَّمَآءَ عَلَيْكُم مِّدْرَارًا ۝ وَيُمْدِدْكُم بِأَمْوَٰلٍ وَبَنِينَ وَيَجْعَل لَّكُمْ جَنَّٰتٍ وَيَجْعَل لَّكُمْ أَنْهَٰرًا ۝ ﴾   (سورة نوح: ١٠-١٢)

﴿I said [to them]: Ask forgiveness from Allah; Verily, He is Oft-Forgiving; He will send rain to you in abundance; and give you increase in wealth and children, and bestow on you gardens and bestow on you rivers.﴾   *(Qur'an 71: 10-12)*"

Seeking Allah's forgiveness repels afflictions, temptations and distress. Allah says in His Holy Book:

﴿ وَمَا كَانَ ٱللَّهُ لِيُعَذِّبَهُمْ وَأَنتَ فِيهِمْ وَمَا كَانَ ٱللَّهُ مُعَذِّبَهُمْ وَهُمْ يَسْتَغْفِرُونَ ۝ ﴾
(سورة الأنفال: ٣٣)

﴿And Allah would not punish them while you [Muhammad] are amongst them, nor will He punish them while they seek [Allah's] Forgiveness.﴾   *(Qur'an 8: 33)*

Allah promises that He will forgive us our sins and grant us His unlimited benefaction:

﴿ ...وَٱدْخُلُوا ٱلْبَابَ سُجَّدًا وَقُولُوا حِطَّةٌ نَّغْفِرْ لَكُمْ خَطَٰيَٰكُمْ وَسَنَزِيدُ ٱلْمُحْسِنِينَ ۝ ﴾
(سورة البقرة: ٥٨)

﴿...And enter the gate in prostration [or bowing with humility] and say: 'Forgive us', and We shall forgive you your sins and shall increase [reward] for those who do good.﴾   *(Qur'an 2: 58)*

Repentance is a higher step in seeking Allah's forgiveness. It is a return to Allah after committing a sin; it is a beginning of a new life, a new hope. According to Ghazâli, repentance is the key that guides us to the Straight Path and it is the instrument that will purify our souls, to bring us closer to Allah.[161]

It is normal to make mistakes, even to commit sins. Our father Adam was the first to introduce the concept of repentance; he was taught by Allah to ask forgiveness for the sin he had committed:

$$﴿فَتَلَقَّىٰٓ ءَادَمُ مِن رَّبِّهِۦ كَلِمَٰتٍ فَتَابَ عَلَيْهِۚ إِنَّهُۥ هُوَ ٱلتَّوَّابُ ٱلرَّحِيمُ ۝﴾ (سورة البقرة: ٣٧)$$

❨Then Adam received from Allah Words. And Allah pardoned him [accepted his repentance]. Verily, He is the One Who forgives [accepts repentance], the Most Merciful.❩   *(Qur'an 2: 37)*

It is necessary for everyone to return to Allah, this is the way for our salvation. Allah (ﷻ) says:

$$﴿ ... وَتُوبُوٓا۟ إِلَى ٱللَّهِ جَمِيعًا أَيُّهَ ٱلْمُؤْمِنُونَ لَعَلَّكُمْ تُفْلِحُونَ ۝﴾$$
$$(سورة النور: ٣١)$$

❨...And all of you repent to Allah, O believers, that you may be successful.❩   *(Qur'an 24: 31)*

He (ﷻ) also informs us:

$$﴿ٱلتَّٰٓئِبُونَ ٱلْعَٰبِدُونَ ٱلْحَٰمِدُونَ ٱلسَّٰٓئِحُونَ ٱلرَّٰكِعُونَ ٱلسَّٰجِدُونَ ٱلْءَامِرُونَ بِٱلْمَعْرُوفِ وَٱلنَّاهُونَ عَنِ ٱلْمُنكَرِ وَٱلْحَٰفِظُونَ لِحُدُودِ ٱللَّهِۗ وَبَشِّرِ ٱلْمُؤْمِنِينَ ۝﴾ (سورة التوبة: ١١٢)$$

❨[The believers whose lives Allah has purchased are] those who repent to Allah [from polytheism and hypocrisy, etc.], who worship Him, who praise Him, who fast [or go out in Allah's Cause], who bow down [in prayer], who prostrate themselves [in prayer], who enjoin doing good [all that Islam ordains] and forbid [people] from evil [all that Islam has forbidden], and who observe the limits set by Allah [do all that Allah has ordained and abstain from evil deeds which Allah has forbidden]. And give glad tidings to the believers.❩   *(Qur'an 9: 112)*

The Prophet (ﷺ) once told his companions: «A man went to a vast field with a camel loaded with food and fuel. He fell asleep, and when he awoke, he did not find his camel. He began to search for it, running to and fro, and after the sun and his hunger had exhausted him, he said: I will go to my former place to sleep such a sleep that it may cause my death. Then, he placed his head upon his hands and slept there waiting for his death. When he awoke, he found his camel standing before him with the food and water. His joy then knew no bounds. Allah becomes more pleased with the repentance of a believer than this man's joy.»[162]

Social life

*I*n 360 CE, Plato started talking about the ideal socio-political state which he called the 'Republic'[163], and over the centuries people have tried to find or establish this perfect society without success. Although most people never realized it, this ideal society really existed; it was there in the social system built by Prophet Muhammad (ﷺ) in Madinah, a system that operated according to Allah's guidance and Islamic teachings. This righteous system survived after the death of the Prophet (ﷺ) and throughout the period of influence of his four wise and rightly-guided followers as Caliphs (*al-Kulafâ' ar-Râshidoon*): Abu Bakr, 'Umar, 'Uthmân and 'Ali — may Allah be pleased with them all.

When Abu Bakr was Caliph (*Khaleefah*), he appointed 'Umar ibn Khaṭṭâb as a judge. Months used to pass by with no one coming to 'Umar with any complaint.[164] Finally, 'Umar came to the Caliph to — according to our present days terms — present his resignation, saying: "I have nothing to do; you hired me as a judge over people who knew their duties and accomplished them, and who knew their rights and didn't transgress them."

How would you feel if you lived in such a society? You wake up every morning knowing that justice prevails, love and care surround you and mercy is your society's main slogan.

Psychological research points to the necessity of a stable social life for the emotional, psychological and even physical health and welfare of individuals. There is a specialized branch in psychology known as 'social psychology' which studies the human social system, including people's modes of living, thinking, mutual relations and interactions.

Human beings cannot live in isolation; people need each others' support, love, friendship, intimacy, and interaction. To build a healthy community, we need parents, teachers, workers, friends and families; we need the strong and the weak, the rich and the poor, the wise and the average. Our spirits are interconnected, and we are empowered by one another. Dr. Andrew Weil notes in his book, *Eight Weeks for Optimum Health*, that healthy human relationships are the 'most powerful healers' which are able of buffering many discomforts and stresses of daily life.[165]

Allah (ﷻ) says in His Holy Book:

﴿ يَٰٓأَيُّهَا ٱلنَّاسُ إِنَّا خَلَقْنَٰكُم مِّن ذَكَرٍ وَأُنثَىٰ وَجَعَلْنَٰكُمْ شُعُوبًا وَقَبَآئِلَ لِتَعَارَفُوٓاْ ... ﴿١٣﴾

(سورة الحُجُرات: ١٣)

﴾O humankind! We have created you from a male and a female, and made you into nations and tribes, that you may know one another...﴿
(Qur'an 49: 13)

We cannot isolate ourselves from society; it influences every aspect of our lives: thoughts, emotions, decision-making — everything. First let me ask you: What is your social identity? How do you first identify yourself to a stranger? Is it by your ethnic group, your country, your region, where you received your education, your job title, or by your religion? Are you proud of being a Muslim?

To have a social identity means to share common features with other members of the same group.[166] We are constantly trying to boost our self-worth through both our personal and social identities. This does not mean that Islam favours discrimination. On the contrary, discrimination is totally rejected by Islamic law. Any unjustified negative or harmful action towards any member of the society simply because s/he belongs to another ethnic or religious group is unacceptable. In some Western societies, civil rights legislation has made it illegal to discriminate between different ethnic groups; despite this many forms of racism still exist, and usually involve negative feelings towards those of a different ethnic, religious or cultural background.[167]

Our Prophet (ﷺ) said: «All humankind is from Adam and Eve, an Arab has no superiority over a non-Arab nor a non-Arab has any superiority over an Arab; also a white has no superiority over a black nor a black has any superiority over white except by piety and good action.»[168]

This echoes what Allah (ﷻ) says in the Qur'an:

﴿ ... إِنَّ أَكْرَمَكُمْ عِندَ اللَّهِ أَنقَىٰكُمْ إِنَّ اللَّهَ عَلِيمٌ خَبِيرٌ ۝ ﴾   (سورة الحُجُرات: ١٣)

﴿...Verily, the most honourable of you with Allah is that [believer] who has God-consciousness [piety]. Verily, Allah is All-Knowing, All-Aware.﴾   *(Qur'an 49: 13)*

«Abu Dharr related that the Prophet (ﷺ) said: Abu Dharr, when you prepare broth put plenty of water in it and take careof your neighbours.»[169]

When I was a little girl, I lived with my grandmother. I used to see her cook in surprisingly large pots; she always told me, "When you cook, the aroma of your food reaches your neighbours — that is why they should taste from it." After she finished cooking, she used to send me to deliver small plates to our neighbours so they could share our food. It made no difference if these neighbours were Muslims or Christians, they were all our neighbours, so we had to share with them, and everyone had to take his share — even the servants. Through this regular action, I was taught that the meaning of family in Islam expands to accommodate not just parents and children, not even just relatives and friends, but it includes neighbours, colleagues, co-workers, servants and the whole society. Islamic teachings ensure a fair and just social life, which in turn provides individuals with emotional stability and a happy environment. Psychologist John Santrock devised some ways to improve social interconnection.[170] We apply these same guidelines on our Islamic community by referring to our precious Qur'anic and Prophetic teachings.

Contact

It was narrated that some noble men from the dominant tribe of Quraysh told the Prophet (ﷺ) that if he wanted them to follow his faith and become Muslims, he must no longer allow poor believers and slaves to attend the same meetings with them. The Prophet (ﷺ), in his desire for them to believe in the new religion, briefly considered their demand, but Allah sent down these verses to announce the true values of Islamic nation:

﴿وَٱصۡبِرۡ نَفۡسَكَ مَعَ ٱلَّذِينَ يَدۡعُونَ رَبَّهُم بِٱلۡغَدَوٰةِ وَٱلۡعَشِيِّ يُرِيدُونَ وَجۡهَهُۥۖ وَلَا تَعۡدُ عَيۡنَاكَ عَنۡهُمۡ تُرِيدُ زِينَةَ ٱلۡحَيَوٰةِ ٱلدُّنۡيَاۖ وَلَا تُطِعۡ مَنۡ أَغۡفَلۡنَا قَلۡبَهُۥ عَن ذِكۡرِنَا وَٱتَّبَعَ هَوَىٰهُ وَكَانَ أَمۡرُهُۥ فُرُطًا ٢٨﴾ (سورة الكهف: ٢٨)

❨And keep yourself [O Muhammad] patiently with those who call on Allah [i.e., your companions who remember their Creator with glorification, praising in prayers and other righteous deeds] morning and afternoon, seeking His Face, and do not let your eyes overlook them, desiring the pomp and glitter of the life of the world; and do not obey him whose heart We have made heedless of Our Remembrance, one who follows his own lusts and whose affair [in the form of deeds] has been lost.❩   *(Qur'an 18: 28)*

Contact between various members of a society is essential to build strong feelings of love and commitment. Contact within the same mosques and other places of worship, schools, public libraries, parks, workplaces and other places where people go about their business enables people to get to know each other better, to understand or share in their ideas, beliefs, sorrows and joys. This contact involves all members, whether they are rich or poor, Arabs or non-Arabs, Muslims or non-Muslims.

Allah (﷾) says:

﴿ لَّا يَنْهَىٰكُمُ ٱللَّهُ عَنِ ٱلَّذِينَ لَمْ يُقَٰتِلُوكُمْ فِى ٱلدِّينِ وَلَمْ يُخْرِجُوكُم مِّن دِيَٰرِكُمْ أَن تَبَرُّوهُمْ وَتُقْسِطُوٓا۟ إِلَيْهِمْ إِنَّ ٱللَّهَ يُحِبُّ ٱلْمُقْسِطِينَ ﴾   (سورة الممتحنة: ٨)

❨Allah does not forbid you to deal justly and kindly with those who have not fought against you on account of religion and did not drive you out of your homes. Verily, Allah loves those who deal with equity.❩   *(Qur'an 60: 8)*

Contacts do not stop at a superficial limit like simply sharing the same schools or working in the same company, but it involves more intimate levels like sharing and empathizing with others' problems, concerns, happiness, grief, hopes, expectations and disappointments; helping the needy; taking care of orphans; and feeling responsible for the welfare of the whole society.

Respecting others' rights

You may wonder, *How can respecting other's rights help if I live in an unfriendly environment that does not respect my rights?* Well, start with yourself and your close family and friends, and you will be amazed how fast these feelings will spread.

Allah (﷾) says:

﴿ ... اَدْفَعْ بِالَّتِى هِىَ أَحْسَنُ فَإِذَا الَّذِى بَيْنَكَ وَبَيْنَهُ عَدَاوَةٌ كَأَنَّهُ وَلِىٌّ حَمِيمٌ ۝ ﴾

(سورة فُصِّلَت: ٣٤)

﴾...Repel [evil] with that which is better [i.e., Allah orders the faithful believers to be patient at the time of anger, and to excuse those who treat them badly], then verily, the one who between you and him there was enmity, [will become] as though he were a close friend.﴿
(Qur'an 41: 34)

«Ibn Mas'ood (﷦) related that the Messenger of Allah (ﷺ) said: After I am gone you will experience discrimination and will observe things that you will disapprove. Someone asked: O Messenger of Allah, what do you command us we should do then? He (ﷺ) said: Discharge your obligations and supplicate Allah for your rights.[171] A man once told Abu Bakr (may Allah be pleased with him): I will insult you such an insult that will enter to your grave with you. Abu Bakr replied: It will enter the grave with you — not with me!»[172]

Ken Keyes, in his book *The Hundredth Monkey*, described a very strange phenomenon. It started in 1952, on the Japanese island of Koshima where scientists studying a monkey colony provided the animals with dirty sweet potatoes. The monkeys liked the taste regardless of the unpleasant feeling of dirt. One day, an 18-month-old female monkey started washing her sweet potato in a nearby stream and taught her mother and playmates the trick. Soon, this innovation was picked up by other members of the colony. By 1958, all young monkeys had learned to wash their sweet potatoes before eating them. Of the adults, only those who were humble enough to accept the change introduced by a young female monkey learned this 'social improvement', while the others kept eating dirty sweet potatoes. Then, when the number of Koshima monkeys washing their sweet potatoes reached a given mass — the exact number is unknown — almost every member of the tribe was now washing their sweet potatoes before eating them. Moreover, at that exact moment, the most surprising thing happened: the phenomenon spread overseas. Colonies of monkeys on other islands began washing their sweet potatoes! This phenomenon explains what scientists call the 'critical mass.' When this critical number is reached — it is symbolised here by the hundredth monkey — a powerful awareness level is achieved that can be spread from mind to mind and can be easily picked up by others.[173]

Whether this is a true story or just a theory, I think the message that the author is trying to introduce is very important. It teaches that when enough people believe in something and behave accordingly, they create an expanding energy field that can spread their awareness to other members of their society or maybe to the whole world. Do not ever assume that you cannot make a difference, that there is no hope in changing our communities and our world for the better; even one person can make a difference, and this person could be you: you could be 'the hundredth human!'

Remember our Prophet's (ﷺ) hadith: «Remake the bond with one who severs it from you, give charity to the one who deprives you and forgive the one who oppresses you.»[174]

Muslims' rights

«Prophet Muhammad (ﷺ) said: The most beloved of you all to me is the one who has the best manners,»[175] and «The Muslim has six rights that other Muslims must fulfil: if you meet him, salute him (with the greeting of peace); if he calls for you, answer his call; if he asks for advice, give him your advice; if he sneezes and thanks Allah, ask Allah to bless him; if he is sick, visit him; and when he dies, attend his funeral.» He (ﷺ) also said: «Those who convey gossip from one person to another will not enter paradise.»[176]

Allah (ﷻ) says:

﴿ إِنَّمَا ٱلۡمُؤۡمِنُونَ إِخۡوَةٌ فَأَصۡلِحُواْ بَيۡنَ أَخَوَيۡكُمۡ وَٱتَّقُواْ ٱللَّهَ لَعَلَّكُمۡ تُرۡحَمُونَ ۝ يَٰٓأَيُّهَا ٱلَّذِينَ ءَامَنُواْ لَا يَسۡخَرۡ قَوۡمٌ مِّن قَوۡمٍ عَسَىٰٓ أَن يَكُونُواْ خَيۡرًا مِّنۡهُمۡ وَلَا نِسَآءٌ مِّن نِّسَآءٍ عَسَىٰٓ أَن يَكُنَّ خَيۡرًا مِّنۡهُنَّ وَلَا تَلۡمِزُوٓاْ أَنفُسَكُمۡ وَلَا تَنَابَزُواْ بِٱلۡأَلۡقَٰبِ بِئۡسَ ٱلِٱسۡمُ ٱلۡفُسُوقُ بَعۡدَ ٱلۡإِيمَٰنِ وَمَن لَّمۡ يَتُبۡ فَأُوْلَٰٓئِكَ هُمُ ٱلظَّٰلِمُونَ ۝ يَٰٓأَيُّهَا ٱلَّذِينَ ءَامَنُواْ ٱجۡتَنِبُواْ كَثِيرًا مِّنَ ٱلظَّنِّ إِنَّ بَعۡضَ ٱلظَّنِّ إِثۡمٌ وَلَا تَجَسَّسُواْ وَلَا يَغۡتَب بَّعۡضُكُم بَعۡضًا أَيُحِبُّ أَحَدُكُمۡ أَن يَأۡكُلَ لَحۡمَ أَخِيهِ مَيۡتًا فَكَرِهۡتُمُوهُ وَٱتَّقُواْ ٱللَّهَ إِنَّ ٱللَّهَ تَوَّابٌ رَّحِيمٌ ۝ ﴾

(سورة الحُجُرات: ١٠-١٢)

❴The believers are nothing else than brothers [in Islamic religion]. So make reconciliation between your brothers, and fear Allah, that you may receive mercy. O you who believe! Let not a group scoff at another group, it may be that the latter are better than the former; nor let [some] women scoff at other women, it may be that the latter are better than the former, nor defame one another, nor insult one another by nicknames. How bad it is, to insult one's brother after having Faith [i.e., to call your Muslim brother (a faithful believer) a sinner, or wicked, etc.]. And whosoever does not repent, then such are indeed wrong-doers. O you who believe! Avoid much suspicion, indeed some suspicions are sins. And do not spy, nor backbite one another. Would one of you like to eat the flesh of his dead brother? You would hate it [so hate backbiting]. And fear Allah. Verily, Allah is the One Who accepts repentance, Most Merciful.❯   *(Qur'an 49:10-12)*

Prophet Muhammad (ﷺ) also taught us:

«It is not lawful for anyone to abandon his brother in Islam for more than three nights, that when they meet they ignore one another, and the best of them is the one who greets the other first.»[177] He (ﷺ) also said: «Do not hate each other, do not be jealous of each other, do not abandon each other, and, O worshippers of Allah, be brotherly, for it is not permissible for any Muslim to abandon his brother for more than three days.»[178]

Our Prophet (ﷺ) also said: «Smiling at your brother (fellow Muslim or another human being) is (a form of) charity.»[179]

Robert Winston, the author of *The Human Mind,* wrote that human beings are inclined to copy each other. The role of the 'mirror neurons' in our brain is to respond to the actions of other people we encounter, generating the proper reaction to their feelings as well as to their facial expressions.[180]

In other words, smiling is contagious! Try to smile at everyone you meet, especially the poor and unfortunate, at whom nobody smiles; you will be surprised at the instant response you get: people are usually friendly, they tend to respond to good feelings with warmth, and it spreads rapidly. A caution: do not expect all of them to smile back. Unfortunately, the nature of our modern life, especially in the West, makes people sometimes feel threatened by any unexplained behaviour coming from a stranger. A further caution: among Muslims around the world it is also considered inappropriate for a person to smile at a stranger who is of the opposite sex.

Neighbours' rights

Allah (ﷻ) says in His Holy Book:

﴿وَٱعْبُدُوا۟ ٱللَّهَ وَلَا تُشْرِكُوا۟ بِهِۦ شَيْـًٔا ۖ وَبِٱلْوَٰلِدَيْنِ إِحْسَـٰنًا وَبِذِى ٱلْقُرْبَىٰ وَٱلْيَتَـٰمَىٰ وَٱلْمَسَـٰكِينِ وَٱلْجَارِ ذِى ٱلْقُرْبَىٰ وَٱلْجَارِ ٱلْجُنُبِ وَٱلصَّاحِبِ بِٱلْجَنۢبِ وَٱبْنِ ٱلسَّبِيلِ وَمَا مَلَكَتْ أَيْمَـٰنُكُمْ ۗ إِنَّ ٱللَّهَ لَا يُحِبُّ مَن كَانَ مُخْتَالًا فَخُورًا ﴾ ۝

(سورة النساء: ٣٦)

❰Worship Allah and join none with Him in worship, and do good to parents, kinsfolk, orphans, the poor, the neighbour who is near of kin, the neighbour who is a stranger, the companion by your side, the wayfarer [you meet], and those [slaves] whom your right hands possess. Verily, Allah does not like those who are proud and boastful.❱   *(Qur'an 4: 36)*

> Prophet Muhammad (ﷺ) said: «Gabriel continued to enjoin upon me the duty of neighbours towards one another, until I thought that Allah would make neighbours the heirs of the deceased.»[181]

> He (ﷺ) also said:

> «Whoever believes in Allah and the Last Day should treat his neighbour generously.»[182]

Relatives' rights

> Our Prophet (ﷺ) said: «The word *rahm* (womb) is derived from the Name *ar-Rahmân* (Most Gracious, One of Allah's Names) and Allah has said: I will keep good relations with the one who keeps good relations with you (the womb,

meaning here kith and kin) and sever relations with him who severs relations with you.»[183]

He (ﷺ) also said:

«Whoever desires an increase in their sustenance and age, should keep good relations with their kith and kin.»[184]

In yet another hadith,

«One who connects with his blood relatives' is not the one who keeps in contact only with those (relatives) who have kept in contact with him, and who does not re-establish contact with those who have severed contact with him. (On the contrary,) it is he who, when his relatives have severed contact with him, (nevertheless) maintains contact with them.»[185]

Parents' rights

In many verses of the Qur'an, Allah commands us to be dutiful to our parents:

﴿وَٱعْبُدُوا۟ ٱللَّهَ وَلَا تُشْرِكُوا۟ بِهِۦ شَيْـًٔا ۖ وَبِٱلْوَٰلِدَيْنِ إِحْسَٰنًا ...﴾ (سورة النساء: ٣٦)

❁Worship Allah and join none with Him in worship, and do good to parents...❁
(Qur'an 4: 36)

﴿ وَقَضَىٰ رَبُّكَ أَلَّا تَعْبُدُوٓا۟ إِلَّآ إِيَّاهُ وَبِٱلْوَٰلِدَيْنِ إِحْسَٰنًا ۚ إِمَّا يَبْلُغَنَّ عِندَكَ ٱلْكِبَرَ أَحَدُهُمَآ أَوْ كِلَاهُمَا فَلَا تَقُل لَّهُمَآ أُفٍّ وَلَا تَنْهَرْهُمَا وَقُل لَّهُمَا قَوْلًا كَرِيمًا ۝ وَٱخْفِضْ لَهُمَا جَنَاحَ ٱلذُّلِّ مِنَ ٱلرَّحْمَةِ وَقُل رَّبِّ ٱرْحَمْهُمَا كَمَا رَبَّيَانِى صَغِيرًا ۝ ﴾

(سورة الإسراء: ٢٣-٢٤)

❁And Allah has decreed that you worship none but Him. And that you be dutiful to your parents. If one of them or both of them attain old age in your life, say to them no word of disrespect, nor shout at them, but address them in terms of honour. And lower unto them the wing of submission and humility through mercy, and say: O Allah, Bestow on them Your Mercy as they did bring me up when I was small.》 *(Qur'an 17: 23 -24)*

﴿ وَوَصَّيْنَا ٱلْإِنسَـٰنَ بِوَٰلِدَيْهِ حَمَلَتْهُ أُمُّهُۥ وَهْنًا عَلَىٰ وَهْنٍ وَفِصَـٰلُهُۥ فِي عَامَيْنِ أَنِ ٱشْكُرْ لِي وَلِوَٰلِدَيْكَ إِلَىَّ ٱلْمَصِيرُ ﴿١٤﴾ ﴾ (سورة لقمان: ١٤)

《And We have enjoined on the human [to be dutiful and good] to his parents. His mother bore him in weakness and hardship upon weakness and hardship, and his weaning is in two years. Give thanks to Me and to your parents, unto Me is the final destination.》 *(Qur'an 31: 14)*

«Abu Hurayrah related that a man came to the Prophet (ﷺ) and asked: O Messenger of Allah, which of all the people is best entitled to kind treatment and good companionship from me? He (ﷺ) answered: Your mother. The man asked: And after her? He said: Your mother. (The man asked:) And after her? He said: Your mother. (The man asked:) And after her? (The Prophet (ﷺ) answered:) Your father.»[186]

In another hadith, Abu Hurayrah again related that the Messenger of Allah (ﷺ) said:

«May his nose be rubbed in dust, may his nose be rubbed in dust, may his nose be rubbed in dust who found his parents, one or both, approaching old age and he did not enter Paradise through serving them.»[187]

Spouse and family rights

The family is the nucleus of society and it is the key for a stable, fulfilled life.

﴿ وَٱللَّهُ جَعَلَ لَكُم مِّنۡ أَنفُسِكُمۡ أَزۡوَٰجٗا وَجَعَلَ لَكُم مِّنۡ أَزۡوَٰجِكُم بَنِينَ وَحَفَدَةٗ وَرَزَقَكُم مِّنَ ٱلطَّيِّبَٰتِ ... ﴿٧٢﴾ ﴾   (سورة النحل: ٧٢)

﴾And Allah has made for you spouses of your own kind, and has made for you, from your spouses, children and grandchildren, and has bestowed on you good provision...﴿   *(Qur'an (16: 72)*

﴿ وَمِنۡ ءَايَٰتِهِۦٓ أَنۡ خَلَقَ لَكُم مِّنۡ أَنفُسِكُمۡ أَزۡوَٰجٗا لِّتَسۡكُنُوٓاْ إِلَيۡهَا وَجَعَلَ بَيۡنَكُم مَّوَدَّةٗ وَرَحۡمَةًۚ إِنَّ فِي ذَٰلِكَ لَأٓيَٰتٖ لِّقَوۡمٖ يَتَفَكَّرُونَ ﴿٢١﴾ ﴾   (سورة الروم: ٢١)

﴾And among His Signs is this, that He created for you spouses from among yourselves, that you may find repose in them, and He has put between you affection and mercy. Verily, in that are indeed signs for a people who reflect.﴿   *(Qur'an 30: 21)*

The relationship between spouses should be built on mutual love, mercy and respect. They should build a stable and warm environment for their children to grow in; they are also responsible for their children's education (in the fullest sense of the word — not just formal schooling), and they have to provide them with love, care and continuous advice.

Even if living together becomes impossible for a couple and they decide upon divorce, Allah asks them to fear Him and treat each other well. This is especially incumbent upon the husband, who might otherwise be tempted to wield his financial, physical and emotional power over his wife while they are in the process of divorce.

﴿ ... فَأَمۡسِكُوهُنَّ بِمَعۡرُوفٍ أَوۡ فَارِقُوهُنَّ بِمَعۡرُوفٖ ... ﴿٢﴾ ﴾   (سورة الطلاق: ٢)

﴾...Either take them back in a good manner or part with them in a good manner...﴿   *(Qur'an 65: 2)*

Servants' rights

It was related in Bukhâri that Anas ibn Mâlik, the Prophet's (ﷺ) servant, said:

«The Prophet (ﷺ) was not one who used to insult another or speak obscenities, or curse, and when he wished to admonish any one of us he simply used to say: What is the matter with him, may his forehead be rubbed in dust.»

Anas also said:

«I served the Prophet for ten years and he never told me, Uff! Nor did he ever scold me by saying: Why did you do such a thing or why did you not do such a thing?»[188]

'Goal-oriented' cooperation[189]

Sharing one goal and working together to achieve it is the best way to break down social and psychological barriers between individuals and get them closer together.

Allah (ﷺ) says:

$$﴿ وَٱلْمُؤْمِنُونَ وَٱلْمُؤْمِنَٰتُ بَعْضُهُمْ أَوْلِيَآءُ بَعْضٍ ۚ يَأْمُرُونَ بِٱلْمَعْرُوفِ وَيَنْهَوْنَ عَنِ ٱلْمُنكَرِ وَيُقِيمُونَ ٱلصَّلَوٰةَ وَيُؤْتُونَ ٱلزَّكَوٰةَ وَيُطِيعُونَ ٱللَّهَ وَرَسُولَهُۥٓ ۚ أُوْلَٰٓئِكَ سَيَرْحَمُهُمُ ٱللَّهُ ۗ إِنَّ ٱللَّهَ عَزِيزٌ حَكِيمٌ ﴾$$

(سورة التوبة: ٧١)

❨The believers, men and women, are friends and protectors of one another, they enjoin [on the people] good [all that Islam orders one to do], and forbid [people] from evil [all that Islam has forbidden]; they perform Salât and give the Zakât, and obey Allah and His Messenger. Allah will have Mercy on them. Surely Allah is All-Mighty, Most Wise.❩   *(Qur'an 9: 71)*

Cooperation creates positive relationships; teamwork should be encouraged and taught in schools to build a youth capable of

connecting together to form a strong unified nation. Prophet Muhammad (ﷺ) said:

> «The believers in their friendliness, compassion and affec-
> tion are like the body, if one organ complains, all other or-
> gans become dilapidated with insomnia and fever.»[190]

The best example of goal-oriented cooperation was the social
status in Madinah after the *Hijrah* (migration of the Prophet from
Makkah to Madinah); there were the *Muhâjireen* (emigrants) who
had given up their homes, money and possessions in order to mi-
grate to Madinah where they would be able to practice their religion freely. They came from a desert environment where the
economy was based mainly on trading, and the women were not
very involved in community work or social life. On the other side
there were the *Anşâr*, the citizens of Yathrib or Madinah, whose
economy was based on agriculture; the Ansâri women were more
active in the society. The primary goal was to build a strong, faithful Islamic nation, able to face the opposing challenges (and defend itself against enemies) and to spread the message of Islam
worldwide. The success of this mission depended on unification
of purpose and cooperation, and on the efforts of all members of
the society, thus dissolving their differences and creating feelings
of brotherhood, love and mutual understanding between them.
This was the primary goal to be achieved before anything else,
and this was the main concern of the Prophet (ﷺ) upon his ar-
rival in his new home. Studies have shown that cooperative work
is associated with increased sense of self-worth, productivity and
accomplishments, improved relationships among members and
even enhanced *interethnic perceptions*.[191] This is because people
of different ethnic backgrounds who share goals and work together to achieve those aims will tend to lose their old prejudices and
have more positive attitudes towards (or become more apprecia-
tive of) each other's differences.

Altruism

Altruism is the unselfish act of helping others without expecting any personal gain from it. Muslims should seek only Allah's reward in all their acts. Islam encourages volunteer work such as caring for the homeless, the elderly, orphans, the poor and needy, and even for animals. In psychology, there is a concept known as 'reciprocity', which encourages us to 'do unto others as we would have them do unto us'.[192] The same concept is taught by our Prophet (ﷺ) when he said:

«None of you truly believes until he wishes for his brother (fellow human being) what he wishes for himself.»[193]

The practice of this concept of reciprocity creates mutual trust within the society. According to a contemporary psychologist, to achieve a successful social system, it is not enough just to work towards your own personal achievements, but it is equally necessary to have a strong sense of commitment to your society.[194] We see a clear example of this altruistic behaviour in the behaviour of bees.[195] Worker bees, which lack the ability to reproduce, spend their entire lives with complete self-denial serving their community, helping around the hive, collecting the nectar, producing the honey and taking care of their queen's young bees. Their goal is unified: the wellbeing of their community; and by promoting the welfare of the offspring, they are achieving their desired goal.

CHAPTER 5

SPIRITUAL BODY

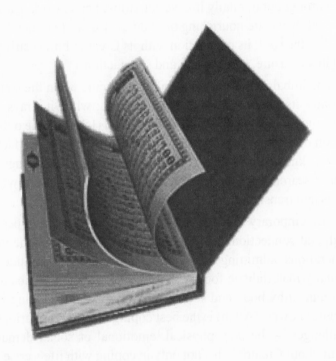

$\mathcal{W}$e definitely cannot have healthy lives without a strong, positive connection with our Almighty Creator, Allah. This fact has been honoured by all civilizations — ancient and modern — though they have disagreed on the nature of the One and Only Creator.

Allah created human beings with both a body and a soul; the body was created from clay and the soul was a breath from the Spirit of the Almighty. Allah says in His Holy Book:

﴿ فَإِذَا سَوَّيْتُهُۥ وَنَفَخْتُ فِيهِ مِن رُّوحِى فَقَعُواْ لَهُۥ سَٰجِدِينَ ۝ ﴾   (سورة الحجر: ٢٩)

﴾When I have fashioned him [in due proportion] and breathed into him of My spirit, then prostrate in obeisance unto him.﴿

(Qur'an 15: 29)

Throughout our daily life we eat, drink, bathe, work, learn and rest; while we are nourishing our bodies, we rarely remember the food of the soul: its connection with its Creator, how it strives for Allah's pleasure, compassion and satisfaction.

The imbalance of the spiritual body occurs when the soul dissociates itself and disconnects from Allah; when it strays away from the Straight Path. Submission to God (Islam) is the only salvation of the soul: it is the only spiritual healer. This is a fact that is well known but intentionally ignored by human beings who vainly search for their happiness and peace of mind in worldly gains and transient trivial pursuit.

Contemporary societies are now struggling to rebuild people's faith and connections with their Creator, especially in the young generations, admitting finally that a closed-minded attitude with a totally materialistic focus can only end up with an imbalanced and unhealthy body and soul. Studies show that believing in the 'Higher Power' (Allah) is the best coping strategy for various life challenges — be they physical, emotional or social demands.[1] Faith in our Creator helps not only in coping with life's crises and serious calamities, but also in handling everyday minor hassles and discomforts.

Science and the Spiritual Quest program (SSQ) was an international event organized by the Centre for Theology and the Natural Sciences of UNESCO (United Nations Educational, Scientific and

Cultural Organization) from 1996 to 2003. SSQ was a quest for ethical and spiritual meanings in the different scientific fields.[2] The program questioned the role of the human being in the world, the true meaning and purpose of human life and work and the moral basis of human actions. This unique program represented a world-wide awakening to the need for integration of the spiritual dimension into our everyday activities, even the most scientific ones.

Desperately seeking a way out of the meaninglessness of their hectic daily lives, many people are now resorting to yoga, practicing Buddhist meditation or considering certain forms of spiritual retreat. These techniques are often confused with the true meaning of a spiritual life, although they do help one to reach a temporary balance between unlimited pleasure and the total denial of passions and worldly desires.

In contrast, says Muslim philosopher Tariq Ramadan, Islamic spirituality is not a half-hour routine, neither is it achieved through one's separation from the external world, nor is it deprivation from life's pleasures and enjoyments. It is instead a perpetually liberating process, a purification and nourishment for the soul.[3] Islam spirituality increases our awareness of the true meaning behind our creation; it is a constant reminder of our true goal and mission in life so that we stay focused on the right path, satisfied and content with whatever life hands.

If religion is the rituals, the officially recognized and applied system of faith and worship, then spirituality is the essence of these practices. We cannot disconnect religion and spirituality; we cannot practice one without the other. We cannot pray without feeling love, submissiveness and connectedness to Allah; there is no point in giving charity without seeking Allah's forgiveness and feeling compassion and supportiveness for others. Religion and spirituality are not synonymous, they are complementary.[4]

Your spirituality represents your own interpretation of life; it is a unique and distinctive concept that belongs only to you. It is an inner feeling that generates your interests and actions. Spirituality helps you to understand why you are here on earth and what your values, goals and purposes are. It makes you adjust your priorities and it supplies the driving force and stamina required to fulfil your mission.[5] Most importantly, it connects you to the Greatest Power of all, to your Creator, Allah, the Creator of the heavens and the earth.

Allah has put into each and every one of us an original breath, a natural craving, an instinct that leads the way to Him:

﴿ ... فِطْرَتَ ٱللَّهِ ٱلَّتِى فَطَرَ ٱلنَّاسَ عَلَيْهَا ۚ لَا تَبْدِيلَ لِخَلْقِ ٱللَّهِ ۚ ذَٰلِكَ ٱلدِّينُ ٱلْقَيِّمُ وَلَٰكِنَّ أَكْثَرَ ٱلنَّاسِ لَا يَعْلَمُونَ ﴿٣٠﴾ ﴾   (سورة الروم: ٣٠)

﴿...Allah's fiṭrah [Allah's Islamic monotheism], with which He has created humankind. No change let there be in Allah's Creation [the Religion of Allah], that is the straight religion, but most people do not know.﴾   *(Qur'an 30: 30)*

Tariq Ramadan in his book *Western Muslims and the Future of Islam* further explains that spirituality is your way to know and worship Allah; it is your liberation from the worldly idols and your transcendence to a higher level of being where your soul is only longing for its Creator and seeking His pleasure in each and every action. This liberation process, he adds, is far from easy. It requires a continuous struggle to avoid being consumed by worldly passions.[6] Nevertheless, it is a road worth travelling, as it is the only way for true satisfaction and bliss in both this mortal life and the eternal Paradise.

This is the true meaning of *jihad*: struggle against one's own self, the work needed to overcome internal conflict, to liberate one's soul and to live in peace with oneself and the rest of the universe. This inner peace is the aim of each and every one of us. Whatever our level of education, fame or wealth, we need this inner peace, this feeling of harmony with ourselves and with the rest of the world.[7] This inner Jihad is a daily requirement in every Muslim's life and it is actuated by the acts of worship that were clearly taught and demonstrated by our dear Prophet, Muhammad. Again, Muslims' acts of worship are not weekly or monthly requirements; they are perfectly spread over our daily, weekly, and annual schedules as constant and continuous reminders of our spiritual dimension. Our five daily prayers evenly distributed throughout our waking hours, the Jumu'ah (Friday) congregational prayer and gathering with fellow Muslims, our acts of charity, be it obligatory or an optional act of soul purification, our Ramadan fasting, Qur'an reading, remembrance of Allah, and pilgrimage to the two holy places, all these acts enhance our spiritual connection and adjust our intention and sincerity all along our path through life.[8]

These practices are the restorative of one's exhausted soul; they are the curative prescription for modern society's ailments like misery, depression, stress and loneliness; they are our bridge to Allah.

Ṣalât (Prayer)

While we are always interested in our body's needs, we tend to ignore the needs of our souls. That is an important reason why Muslims are ordered to pray five times a day: to keep renewing their connection with Allah throughout the day, adjusting any minor deviation or unintentional straying away from the Straight Path, and thus to supply their souls with an infinite source of energy.

«It was related that Abu Hurayrah said: I heard the messenger of Allah say: If there was a river at the door of anyone of you and you bathed in it five times daily, would you see any dirt on yourselves? They (his Companions) answered: No trace of dirt would remain. He (ﷺ) added: That is the similitude of the five prayers with which Allah blots out evil deeds.»[9]

Early Muslims sought the prayer time like a slave seeking his freedom; that is the true freedom of the soul from all earthly connections, boundaries and limitations. Prophet Muhammad (ﷺ) used to say to Bilâl, his Companion who was responsible for the call to prayer:

«O Bilâl, give the call to prayer, and bring comfort to my heart.»[10]

Prayer energises the soul and helps us transcend to a higher level of awareness. Nick Williams gave the analogy of an airplane pilot following his usual path, but when he encounters any rough weather, he needs to shift to a higher altitude to acquire a clearer view.[11] As Muslims, we should not even wait for turbulence to resort to higher altitudes: we constantly seek these higher connections to transcend our situations and adjust our priorities.

Prophet Muhammad taught us: «You are in prayer for as long as you are waiting for it.»[12] Studies show that engaging in regular ritual activities helps us relax, which in turn adjusts our blood pressure and heart rate, and harmonizes our breathing.[13] Relaxation reduces the over-secretion of adrenaline resulting from the constant stresses of life. By reducing stress, as we learnt in the previous chapter, one empowers the immune system, protects the heart and adjusts one's blood pressure and circulation. This regular act not only harmonizes the soul, but also heals our physical ailments and helps us cope with the tensions of everyday life. Many studies now show the evidence of reduced rates of depression, melancholy, sorrow, and pessimism among individuals who perform their prayers regularly.

The books on the Prophet's life show how the Prophet (ﷺ) resorted to prayer when he had any worries or problems. Allah says in His Noble Book:

﴿وَٱسْتَعِينُواْ بِٱلصَّبْرِ وَٱلصَّلَوٰةِ وَإِنَّهَا لَكَبِيرَةٌ إِلَّا عَلَى ٱلْخَٰشِعِينَ ۝﴾ (سورة البقرة: ٤٥)

﴾And seek help in patience and prayer, and truly it is extremely heavy and hard except for those who have true humility [those who obey Allah with full submission, fear His Punishment, and believe in His Promise [Paradise] and in His Warnings [Hell].﴿

(Qur'an 2: 45)

Allah (ﷻ) also says:

﴿ يَٰٓأَيُّهَا ٱلَّذِينَ ءَامَنُواْ ٱسْتَعِينُواْ بِٱلصَّبْرِ وَٱلصَّلَوٰةِ إِنَّ ٱللَّهَ مَعَ ٱلصَّٰبِرِينَ ۝ ﴾

(سورة البقرة: ١٥٣)

﴾O you who believe! Seek help in patience and prayer. Truly Allah is with the patient ones.﴿   *(Qur'an 2: 153)*

In order to acquire the full benefits of prayer, one should approach it after ablution, which aims first at cleaning any physical dirt on the body and clothing.

﴿يَٰٓأَيُّهَا ٱلَّذِينَ ءَامَنُوٓاْ إِذَا قُمْتُمْ إِلَى ٱلصَّلَوٰةِ فَٱغْسِلُواْ وُجُوهَكُمْ وَأَيْدِيَكُمْ إِلَى ٱلْمَرَافِقِ وَٱمْسَحُواْ بِرُءُوسِكُمْ وَأَرْجُلَكُمْ إِلَى ٱلْكَعْبَيْنِ ... ۝ ﴾

(سورة المائدة: ٦)

﴾O you who believe! When you intend to offer the prayer, wash your faces and your hands [forearms] up to the elbows, rub [by passing wet hands over] your heads, and [wash] your feet up to the ankles...﴿   *(Qur'an 5: 6)*

Ablution is not a mere physical act; it is a sign of the purification of the soul, driving away evil thoughts, clearing the mind and preparing one to concentrate only on the glorification and worship of Allah. Prophet Muhammad (ﷺ) taught us that ablution washes away sins, purifying and cleansing the soul:

«If the Muslim performs ablution and washes his face, any offence he overlooked with his eyes will come out with the water; and when he washes his hands, any assault he committed with his hands will come out with the water; and when he washes his feet any misdeed to which he walked with his feet will come out with the water, till he concludes (the ablution) free from sins.»[14]

After ablution, one should perform prayer with a complete sense of humility and submissiveness to Allah. Put all worldly thoughts behind you; in prayer you are directly addressing Allah. You should try to sense the meanings of each word and verse you are reciting; contemplate these meanings as deeply and sincerely as you can to keep you away from any mental distractions. According to scholars of the Sunnah, it is disliked to close the eyes during prayer, but if this is necessary to help you concentrate, you can do it. I cannot even try to explain the marvellous effects of a true prayer. One who practices it will soon feel and learn for himself; it is enough to say that Prophet Muhammad (ﷺ) told us:

«If one prays two rak‘ah with full concentration, Allah forgives that person for whatever sins were committed before.»[15]

Timings of the five prayers are adjusted according to the daylight and nighttime calculations; this helps us to maintain our connection with Allah all our waking hours, and organizes our eating, working, resting, and sleeping pattern.[16] To be able to pray fajr (dawn prayer), we have to go to sleep early and wake up early, thus we eat our supper early and sleep soon after ‘ishâ’ (evening prayer), to allow the body to rest. This gives the brain the chance to synthesize and secrete the neurotransmitter dopamine, a chemical responsible for giving us energy, motivation and increased interest and focus.

Early in the morning, Prophet Muhammad (ﷺ) used to wake up, drink a cup of warm water with one teaspoonful of honey dissolved in it, and then pray. After fajr prayer, he rested for meditation and morning dhikr Allah (remembrance of Allah) till sunrise, when he prayed *ḍuḥâ'* prayer (a non-obligatory prayer in the forenoon). This habit is very beneficial for increasing concentration and mood elevation throughout the whole day. Waking up early and drinking a honey tonic enables the brain to secrete enough serotonin to boost one's mood for the rest of the day. The two hours after sunrise are the peak production time of serotonin, the hormone responsible for a feeling of wellbeing and for uplifting the mood.[17] After ḍuḥâ' prayer, it is time to start work till noon, when we take another short break to recharge our souls with an extra boost of energy while praying the midday prayer (*dhuhr*), after which it is usually time for lunch, then we resume work till *'aṣr* (afternoon prayer) time, about which we are specifically ordered by Allah to respect its timing:

﴿حَٰفِظُوا۟ عَلَى ٱلصَّلَوَٰتِ وَٱلصَّلَوٰةِ ٱلۡوُسۡطَىٰ وَقُومُوا۟ لِلَّهِ قَٰنِتِينَ ﴾ ۞

(سورة البقرة: ٢٣٨)

﴿Guard strictly the [five obligatory] prayers, especially the middle Salât [i.e. the best prayer 'aṣr]. And stand before Allah with obedience [and do not speak to others during the prayers].﴾

(Qur'an 2: 238)

The middle prayers are believed to be fajr and 'aṣr prayers. Prophet Muhammad (ﷺ) said:

«The angels descend to you in succession by night and by day, but they all gather together with you at the dawn and afternoon prayers. Those who have passed the night with you ascend to Heaven and Allah asks them, although He is well aware: How did you leave my servants? The angels reply: They were praying when we left them and when we arrived we found them praying.»[18]

In order to respect 'aṣr prayer timing, people should not sleep after lunchtime.[19] This is beneficial to health, as sleeping directly after eating slows down digestion and weakens the body. After 'aṣr, Prophet Muhammad (ﷺ) used to take another few minutes for meditation and evening dhikr Allah. After this little rest, the body is fully reenergized for resuming work till sunset (*maghrib*) prayer, after which comes dinnertime, followed by some gentle physical exercises such as walking, which aids digestion, benefits the metabolism, strengthens the heart and boosts blood circulation — as previously discussed. At the end of the day it is time for the evening prayer ('ishâ'), then a early to bed for a good night's sleep, interrupted for some extra night prayers (*tahajjud*) for more energy supply and food for hungry souls.

Night prayer

Night prayer is not obligatory for Muslims, yet it offers many spiritual and physical benefits. In the Qur'an, Allah stresses the importance of this sacred prayer:

﴿ قُمِ ٱلَّيۡلَ إِلَّا قَلِيلًا ۝ نِّصۡفَهُۥٓ أَوِ ٱنقُصۡ مِنۡهُ قَلِيلًا ۝ أَوۡ زِدۡ عَلَيۡهِ وَرَتِّلِ ٱلۡقُرۡءَانَ تَرۡتِيلًا ۝ إِنَّا سَنُلۡقِى عَلَيۡكَ قَوۡلًا ثَقِيلًا ۝ إِنَّ نَاشِئَةَ ٱلَّيۡلِ هِىَ أَشَدُّ وَطۡـًٔا وَأَقۡوَمُ قِيلًا ۝ ﴾

(سورة المُزَّمل: ٢-٦)

﴿Stand [to pray] all night, except a little, half of it, or a little less than that, or a little more; and recite the Qur'an [aloud] in a slow, pleasant tone and style. Verily, We shall send down to you a weighty Word [obligations and legal laws]. Verily, the rising by night [for tahajjud prayer] is very hard and most potent and good for governing [the soul], and most suitable for [understanding] the Word [of Allah].❭   *(Qur'an 73: 26)*

Some researchers advise patients suffering from various physical or mental ailments or distress to get out of their beds at night, freshen themselves up with some water, massage their hands and feet and perform some gentle breathing exercises and physical postures. We can see that this practically describes waking up at night for ablution and night prayer. Prophet Muhammad (ﷺ) said:

«Perform night prayer, as it is the habit of the righteous people before you. It brings you closer to Allah, prevents you from wrongdoing, expiates your sins and drives away illnesses from your body.»[20]

Pilgrimage

ℋajj is one of the five pillars of Islam and it is the only pillar that has a chapter in the Qur'an that bears its name. Hajj is obligatory once in one's lifetime, for all Muslims who are physically and financially capable of performing it.

﴿ ... وَلِلَّهِ عَلَى ٱلنَّاسِ حِجُّ ٱلْبَيْتِ مَنِ ٱسْتَطَاعَ إِلَيْهِ سَبِيلًا ... ﴾ ﴿٩٧﴾

(سورة آل عمران: ٩٧)

❬...And Hajj [pilgrimage to Makkah] to the House [Ka'bah] is a duty that people owe to Allah, those who can afford the expenses [for their conveyance, provision and residence]...❭ *(Qur'an 3: 97)*

Our journey to Allah's House has to start with complete detachment, total freedom from any earthly bonds, and complete devotion to Allah[21]. A Muslim sets out on the hajj with a clear, unoccupied mind; nothing should distract him or her. That is why Muslims should pay all their debts, finalize their business deals, leave enough provision for their children and dependents, forgive any past transgressions, and purify their hearts and souls before heading towards Makkah.

During the pilgrimage, Muslims gather on a specific day in Makkah to perform the specified rites; this is the largest annual gathering for all Muslims, who go there seeking only Allah's forgiveness and mercy. Prophet Muhammad (ﷺ) said:

«Whoever performs the pilgrimage and does not commit obscenity or wickedness, will return as (pure and free of sin as) on the day that his mother gave birth to him.»[22]

He (ﷺ) also said:

«People performing hajj or 'umrah (the minor pilgrimage) are Allah's guests, if they supplicate to Him, He will respond to their demands, if they ask something of Him, He will give them and if they ask for His forgiveness, He will forgive them.»[23]

Whoever goes to Makkah and visits the Kaaba can definitely tell how distinguished this place is. Makkah is the centre of earth, it is the first house ever built by our father Adam and was reconstructed by Prophet Ibrâheem and his son Ismâ'eel, to be the spiritual centre of Islam. Just being there relieves the heart and boosts the spirit; it gives the feeling of closeness to Allah when one remembers that in this same spot many of Allah's prophets stood and worshipped.[24]

This place offers an immense uplifting energy; it gives the feeling of dominant peace and serenity through the enormous demonstration of humanitarian bonding and universal brotherhood.[25]

Hajj is a course of spiritual enlightenment, devotion and human-ity. The first lesson learnt in this course is shown in the first verse of the chapter known as 'The Hajj', where Allah (ﷻ) says:

$$﴿يَٰٓأَيُّهَا ٱلنَّاسُ ٱتَّقُواْ رَبَّكُمْ إِنَّ زَلْزَلَةَ ٱلسَّاعَةِ شَىْءٌ عَظِيمٌ ١﴾$$

(سورة الحج: ١)

﴿O people! Fear Allah and be dutiful to Him! Verily, the earth-quake of the Hour [of Judgment] is a terrible thing!﴾

(Qur'an 22: 1)

The rites of pilgrimage are a clear and stern reminder of the Day of Resurrection, when all humankind will be gathered. The crowds, the seemingly unending waiting under the blazing sun, the sound of millions of voices raised in supplication and prayers everywhere, all these are striking reminders to us all of how we will await our final fate on the Day of Judgment.[26] The simple white garment of hajj (ihrâm), resembling a shroud, is a reminder of the end of this life, when we will all be gathered waiting for Allah's final decree regarding our ultimate destiny — heaven or hell.[27] The hajj is a reminder of our equality before Allah: no su-periority of race, wealth or origin. It is a lesson in detachment and self-denial. It is an invitation to think of the next life, to perform more good deeds, to detach ourselves from the material aspects of life and seek only Allah's satisfaction and approval.

$$﴿وَأَنَّ ٱلسَّاعَةَ ءَاتِيَةٌ لَّا رَيْبَ فِيهَا وَأَنَّ ٱللَّهَ يَبْعَثُ مَن فِى ٱلْقُبُورِ ٧﴾$$ (سورة الحج: ٧)

﴿And surely, the Hour is coming, there is no doubt about it, and certainly, Allah will resurrect those who are in the graves.﴾

(Qur'an 22: 7)

Hajj is a confirmation of our obedience and submission to Allah, a promise to fulfil His orders and avoid the deeds that He has forbidden. It is a source of faith, strength and devotion. It is training the soul for the complete and unconditional surrender (Islam) to Allah. As we hurry between ṣafâ and Marwah, and drink water from the spring of Zamzam, we remember when Prophet Ibrâheem, on Allah's orders, left his infant son Ismâ'eel and his wife Hâjar in Makkah, which was back then totally uninhabited. We acknowledge the strength and faith of that mother submitting to Allah's will. Hâjar stayed in Makkah for some days before her food and water supply ran out. She then ran in all directions trying to seek help for herself and her infant. She hurried between the two hills of ṣafâ and Marwah seven times before the water of Zamzam spurted out in the middle of the desert at the feet of her baby boy.

Throwing the pebbles at the three stone pillars allows us to relive the historical moment when Prophet Ibrâheem was ordered to slaughter his son Ismâ'eel as the ultimate sacrifice to Allah. The pebbles they threw at Satan when he tried to prevent them from obeying Allah symbolised complete submissiveness, devotion and servitude to Allah; this is the true meaning of Islam.

﴿فَلَمَّآ أَسْلَمَا وَتَلَّهُ لِلْجَبِينِ ۝ وَنَٰدَيْنَٰهُ أَن يَٰٓإِبْرَٰهِيمُ ۝ قَدْ صَدَّقْتَ ٱلرُّءْيَآ إِنَّا كَذَٰلِكَ نَجْزِى ٱلْمُحْسِنِينَ ۝ إِنَّ هَٰذَا لَهُوَ ٱلْبَلَٰٓؤُاْ ٱلْمُبِينُ ۝ وَفَدَيْنَٰهُ بِذِبْحٍ عَظِيمٍ ۝﴾

(سورة الصافات:١٠٣-١٠٧)

﴿Then, when they had both submitted themselves [to the Will of Allah], and he had laid him prostrate on his forehead [or on the side of his forehead for slaughtering]; and We called out to him: O Ibrâheem! You have indeed fulfilled the vision! Thus do We reward the doers of good. Verily, that was a manifest trial, and We ransomed him with a great sacrifice.﴾   *(Qur'an 37: 103 - 107)*

This lesson is clear in the 32nd verse of Soorat al-Hajj:[28]

﴿ ... وَمَن يُعَظِّمْ شَعَٰٓئِرَ ٱللَّهِ فَإِنَّهَا مِن تَقْوَى ٱلْقُلُوبِ ۝ ﴾   (سورة الحج: ٣٢)

❮...And whosoever honours the Symbols of Allah, then it is truly from the piety of the heart.❯   *(Qur'an 22: 32)*

That is total obedience, submissiveness and surrender! Allah says in the 77th verse of the same chapter:

﴿يَٰٓأَيُّهَا ٱلَّذِينَ ءَامَنُواْ ٱرۡكَعُواْ وَٱسۡجُدُواْ وَٱعۡبُدُواْ رَبَّكُمۡ وَٱفۡعَلُواْ ٱلۡخَيۡرَ لَعَلَّكُمۡ تُفۡلِحُونَ ۩ ⟨۷۷⟩﴾

(سورة الحج: ۷۷)

❮O you who believe! Bow down, and prostrate yourselves, and worship Allah and do good that you may be successful.❯

(Qur'an 22: 77)

Hajj is a strong confirmation of the importance of the unity and brotherhood of Muslims.[29] All Muslims assemble in response to Allah's call. The men are all dressed in the same way, and the women wear simple, plain clothing without adornment, so that there is no indication of rank or superiority. All must follow the same regulations, perform the same prayers and supplications and observe the same rituals in the same way, time and place. It is a reminder that they all worship the One and Only Allah, and honour the same religion, so they should follow the same path in order to promote their mutual welfare. We are ordered to face the Ka'bah in all our prayers; Muslims from all over the world are facing the same direction everyday, at every prayer, but still, this universal symbol of unity is not clear to us. Here in front of the Ka'bah, it is crystal clear. All Muslims are directed to one and the same central point. The view of the large concentric circles of worshippers around the Ka'bah is a sound reminder of the unity of our goal, purpose and view in life — if we take the time to reflect upon it.

The next lesson one learns from Hajj is how precious time is — the one currency that you can never return! We only have few days in this holy place; we should take advantage of each and every second. Time is so precious; there is not a moment to lose. You will discover that you can do a lot more with your time than you think. The more efficient you are with it, the more fruitful it will be.

Meditation and dhikr Allah

$\mathcal{M}$editation is the safest way for true knowledge and spiritual transcendence, the right path to get closer to Allah,[30] to free the mind from superstitions, doubts and any thoughts that lead to sin, and fill it instead with certainty, love, compassion, and purity. The beauty of the universe is a continuous reminder of Allah's Power, Wisdom and Mercy. It is a clear manifestation of Allah's Names and attributes: The First and The Last, The Manifest and The Hidden, The Sublime, The Most High, The Transcendent, The Most great, The All-Hearing, All-Seeing and the Knower of All.

Reflecting on Allah's creations gives us a feeling of serenity and peace; it fills the soul with relief and surrender to its Omnipotent, Ever-Mighty, and Omniscient Creator. Pondering assures you that you are in safe hands; you are well taken care of and well protected. Meditation and deep thinking is a valuable source of spiritual enlightenment; it is your way to humility and pure wisdom. It is an incessant source of peace, gratefulness and appreciation for all Allah's gifts and blessings. It teaches patience, surrender and love for our Most Holy, Most Beneficent Creator. It is a great way to detach yourself from daily struggles and worldly distractions, giving your mind a chance to relax and recharge, and allowing you to reconsider your priorities.[31] Besides these immense spiritual benefits, meditation is a powerful relaxation tool that heals your physical body and enhances your intellectual performance, as mentioned in previous chapters.

Some Muslim scholars consider meditation as a sign of worship and devotion to Almighty Allah, as it brings us closer to Him through His wonderful creations. Al-Hassan (may Allah be pleased with him) said: "Deep thinking for an hour is better than one night of standing in prayer."[32]

'Umar ibn 'Abd al-Aziz once said: "Meditation about Allah's benefactions is one of the greatest acts of worship."[33]

In the Qur'an, many verses urge us to think and meditate; they even give us clues as to what we should think about:

﴿أَفَلَا يَنظُرُونَ إِلَى ٱلْإِبِلِ كَيْفَ خُلِقَتْ ۝ وَإِلَى ٱلسَّمَاءِ كَيْفَ رُفِعَتْ ۝ وَإِلَى ٱلْجِبَالِ كَيْفَ نُصِبَتْ ۝ وَإِلَى ٱلْأَرْضِ كَيْفَ سُطِحَتْ ۝﴾   (سورة الغاشية:١٧-٢٠)

《Do they not look at the she-camels, how they are created? And at the heaven, how it is raised? And at the mountains, how they are rooted and fixed firm? And at the earth, how it is spread out?》

(Qur'an 88: 17-20)

﴿إِنَّ فِى ٱلسَّمَوَٰتِ وَٱلْأَرْضِ لَءَايَٰتٍ لِّلْمُؤْمِنِينَ ۝ وَفِى خَلْقِكُمْ وَمَا يَبُثُّ مِن دَآبَّةٍ ءَايَٰتٌ لِّقَوْمٍ يُوقِنُونَ ۝ وَٱخْتِلَٰفِ ٱلَّيْلِ وَٱلنَّهَارِ وَمَا أَنزَلَ ٱللَّهُ مِنَ ٱلسَّمَاءِ مِن رِّزْقٍ فَأَحْيَا بِهِ ٱلْأَرْضَ بَعْدَ مَوْتِهَا وَتَصْرِيفِ ٱلرِّيَٰحِ ءَايَٰتٌ لِّقَوْمٍ يَعْقِلُونَ ۝﴾   (سورة الجاثية: ٣-٥)

《Verily, in the heavens and the earth are signs for the believers. And in your creation, and what He scattered [through the earth] of moving [living] creatures are signs for people who have Faith with certainty. And in the alternation of night and day, and the provision [rain] that Allah sends down from the sky, and revives therewith the earth after its death, and in the turning about of the winds [sometimes towards the east or north, and sometimes towards the south or west, sometimes bringing glad tidings of rain, and sometimes bringing the torment], are signs for a people who understand.》

(Qur'an 45: 3-5)

﴿ قُل سِيرُوا فِى ٱلْأَرْضِ فَٱنظُرُوا كَيْفَ بَدَأَ ٱلْخَلْقَ ثُمَّ ٱللَّهُ يُنشِئُ ٱلنَّشْأَةَ ٱلْأَخِرَةَ إِنَّ

ٱللَّهَ عَلَىٰ كُلِّ شَىْءٍ قَدِيرٌ ۝ ﴾   (سورة العنكبوت: ٢٠)

﴿Say: Travel in the land and see how [Allah] originated creation, and then Allah will bring forth [resurrect] the creation of the
Hereafter [resurrection after death]. Verily, Allah is Able to do all
things.﴾   *(Qur'an 29: 20)*

When we adopt the habit of meditation and reflect on Allah's
signs all around us, we feel the submission to our Creator and
reach a state of humility, gratefulness and detachment from our
worldly possessions: neither grieving over our losses and calamities nor over rejoicing in our wealth or fame.[34] Allah (ﷻ) says:

﴿ لِّكَيْلَا تَأْسَوْا عَلَىٰ مَا فَاتَكُمْ وَلَا تَفْرَحُوا بِمَآ ءَاتَىٰكُمْ وَٱللَّهُ لَا يُحِبُّ كُلَّ

مُخْتَالٍ فَخُورٍ ۝ ﴾   (سورة الحديد: ٢٣)

﴿In order that you may not be sad over matters that you fail to
get, nor rejoice because of that which has been given to you. And
Allah does not like prideful boasters.﴾   *(Qur'an 57: 23)*

Studies show that the regular practice of meditation not only
helps to control our feelings and reactions, it also regulates and
harmonizes our internal body functions.[35] The effect of meditation extends from relaxing the mind and voluntary muscles to the
relaxation of involuntary body structures like the digestive, cardiovascular and pulmonary systems. Meditation leads to physical
wellbeing in addition to spiritual transcendence.[36]

Physiologically, meditation can be considered a transient state
between sleep and wakefulness. Research has found that meditation induces positive physiological changes; it regulates breathing, harmonizes the heart beat, improves blood circulation and
relaxes the mind.[37] Meditation is a powerful tool in stress management: it is an essential part of self-improvement and healing

programs, helping individuals take control of their emotional responses as well as of their thoughts and actions.

Passive meditation

The simplest form of meditation is to focus on your breathing. This type of meditation acts by clearing and relaxing the mind from its preoccupation with problems — whether at work or in daily life. You may find thoughts intruding preventing you from total concentration on your breathing, this is perfectly normal. Just return to your breathing: feel your lungs filling and emptying; do not try to control their movements, just follow their pattern in peace and tranquillity. Prophet Muhammad (ﷺ) used to meditate for hours in the cave of Hirâ' before being selected as Allah's Messenger to humanity.

This type of meditation has to be performed in a quiet place. You can practice it in your room by closing your eyes and visualizing whatever brings you peace and serenity. You may also choose to look at a pretty sight like a flower or a plant. Or, you could perform this kind of meditation in the open air looking at beautiful scenery around you like the seashore, waterfalls, or green hills. Practicing this meditation regularly focuses the consciousness on one's inner quietude, retreating for a while from all worldly interests and striving to overcome all tensions, distractions and negative emotions. It helps you to see the world in a different way, free of any selfish thoughts, and increases spiritual awareness of the beauty and perfection of the creation and the Creator. It teaches you to simply let go and just be.

Start with five minutes of total calm, focus on your breathing, slowly inhale, then exhale and be aware of the air entering and leaving your body. Do not control your breathing, do not force it or try to adjust its rhythm; relax and let it harmonize on its own. Gradually, you will find yourself able to increase your meditative time. Through regular practice, you will also be able to reach a clearer mental state more rapidly.

Dhikr Allah

This is another type of meditation; it works by increasing your concentration. Choose a word or a small phrase that makes you feel good when you say it, like one of the Names of Almighty Allah for example, or a dhikr: «There is no one worthy of worship other than Allah (*Lâ ilâha illâ Allah*).» This meditation can either be passive, just helping you to relax and clear your mind, or it can be active: using the resulting relaxed state of mind to solve your day-to-day problems or direct your concentration to some new meaning you want to add to your life (you will find many remembrances that give one hope by asking Allah for guidance, health or provision).

Sit in a relaxed position, keep your eyes closed, breathe freely and regularly through your nostrils; and each time you exhale repeat your word or phrase, try to send away any intruding thoughts and concentrate only on your chosen dhikr. You can use prayer beads to help you focus, but it is better to use the fingers of your right hand as our Prophet (ﷺ) used to do. A man once came to Prophet Muhammad (ﷺ) asking him to specify an important Islamic ritual for him to cling to; the Prophet (ﷺ) said:

«Keep your tongue moist from (repeating) dhikr Allah.»[38]

In the Qur'an, Allah (ﷻ) says:

﴿ وَاذْكُر رَّبَّكَ فِي نَفْسِكَ تَضَرُّعًا وَخِيفَةً وَدُونَ ٱلْجَهْرِ مِنَ ٱلْقَوْلِ بِٱلْغُدُوِّ وَٱلْآصَالِ
وَلَا تَكُن مِّنَ ٱلْغَفِلِينَ ﴿٢٠٥﴾ ﴾   (سورة الأعراف: ٢٠٥)

﴿And remember Allah by your tongue and within yourself, humbly and with fear, without loudness in words, in the mornings and in the afternoons, and do not be of those who are neglectful.﴾

(Qur'an 7: 205)

Allah urges us to find time during our busy day for this sacred act of worship:

﴿ يَٰٓأَيُّهَا ٱلَّذِينَ ءَامَنُوا لَا تُلْهِكُمْ أَمْوَٰلُكُمْ وَلَآ أَوْلَٰدُكُمْ عَن ذِكْرِ ٱللَّهِ ۚ وَمَن
يَفْعَلْ ذَٰلِكَ فَأُوْلَٰٓئِكَ هُمُ ٱلْخَٰسِرُونَ ﴿٩﴾ ﴾   (سورة المنافقون: ٩)

﴿O you who believe! Let neither your property nor your children divert you from the remembrance of Allah. And whosoever does that, then they are the losers.﴾   *(Qur'an 63: 9)*

Chanting your dhikr aloud or repeating it silently both offer great benefits to your heart and soul. Just focus on your words as deeply and profoundly as you can, feel the meanings behind each word you are saying and recognize what they carry of energy and sacredness. Enjoy their holy rhythm and shut your five senses to the outer world. Stay in your calm and serene place concentrating on one thing: your dhikr. Let go and relax! The body absorbs the energy generated from these holy words; through their frequencies, your whole system is relaxed until it reaches a stage of serenity and peace, releasing suppressed anger, fear or resentment and reducing stress.

The ability to record our brain waves and frequencies using EEG (electroencephalograms) has taught us a great deal about our amazing intellectual abilities. When you are awake your brain frequency (in beta waves) ranges from 14 to 60 waves per sec-

ond (Hz). At this level, your brain is
fully alert and active. On the
other hand, during your sleeping pattern your brain waves
(delta) slow down to about 3 Hz;
at this level we are fully unaware of our surroundings. Between
these two extremes there are two other known frequencies: theta
and alpha. The theta frequency is a near-sleep level of awareness
when we practically 'fall' into sleep. Alpha waves, ranging from
7.5 to 13 Hz, are the ones that interest most researchers nowadays. Those are the meditative levels of brain activity: an extremely relaxed rhythm, yet a fully conscious level of awareness
reached by the regular practice of deep meditation and reflection
techniques.[39] Scientists believe that at this state of awareness, the
mind is at its optimum creativity and inspirational potential. At
this level, the mind is ready to accept, assimilate, analyse and
memorize new ideas, information and suggestions; it is in its best
learning state. At this level, we are gradually getting into the habit
of engaging our right brain hemisphere in our regular intellectual
activities. As we learned in Chapter Three, this part of the brain
processes our emotions and feelings; it is involved in visualisa-
tion and creativity. At this level of awareness you can best deal
with your stresses and negative emotions, relax and reprogram
your mindset.[40]

Dhikr Allah does not need a specific time or place. It is one of
the easiest acts of worship, though it should fulfil three very important conditions. First, it should be performed with the intention of drawing closer to Allah. Second, it should be performed in
abundance. Allah says in the Qur'an:

﴿ ... وَاذْكُرُوا اللَّهَ كَثِيرًا لَّعَلَّكُمْ تُفْلِحُونَ ﴾   (سورة الأنفال: ٤٥)

❨...And remember the Name of Allah much [both with tongue and mind], so that you may be successful.❩   *(Qur'an 8: 45)*

﴿يَـٰٓأَيُّهَا ٱلَّذِينَ ءَامَنُوا۟ ٱذْكُرُوا۟ ٱللَّهَ ذِكْرًا كَثِيرًا ۝﴾   (سورة الأحزاب: ٤١)

❨O you who believe! Remember Allah often and much.❩
(Qur'an 33: 41)

From the phrase 'Divine Remembrance', we can understand the reason behind this condition. Divine remembrances help you not to forget...but, forget what? No one can forget Allah! That is true, but you can grow inattentive, you can lose focus, stray away from the main purpose of your creation. The human being, by nature, is inclined to forget, neglect or get distracted. This sacred practice, these few minutes you reserve from your time each day, help you restore your balance, remember your true goal, reorient your life and set your priorities straight. Divine remembrances, like any kind of meditation, need total concentration and absorption, so that they let you take charge of your thoughts and restore control over your life.

The third condition for effective dhikr Allah is that you should feel the words with your heart as well as murmur them with your tongue. It is sometimes difficult for a beginner to fully feel the meanings deep within his or her heart and soul. If other thoughts keep distracting you from your concentration, do not worry, just do not give up; repeat the dhikr as often as you can and with persistence and perseverance your heart will feel them and finally surrender to the Creator.

Saying your daily remembrances allows you to enjoy many benefits:[41]

➤ It takes you closer to Allah, and He responds to your calls. Allah (ﷻ) says:

﴿... فَٱذْكُرُونِىٓ أَذْكُرْكُمْ ۝﴾   (سورة البقرة: ١٥٢)

❨Therefore remember Me [through prayer and glorification]. I will remember you...❩   *(Qur'an 2: 152)*

➢ Dhikr Allah dissipates distress and grief, relieves the anguished heart and brings you joy, happiness, tranquillity and serenity:

(سورة الرعد: ٢٨)   ﴾ ... أَلَا بِذِكْرِ ٱللَّهِ تَطْمَئِنُّ ٱلْقُلُوبُ ۝ ﴿

❨...Verily, in the remembrance of Allah do hearts find rest.❩
(Qur'an 13: 28)

➢ It repels evil and enlightens the heart, showing this light as beauty and a glow on your face.

➢ It strengthens the body by diverting the mind from the source of anxiety, thus giving the body the chance to heal.

➢ Dhikr Allah revives the heart. Imam Ibn Taymiyyah said: "Remembrance is like water to the fish: imagine how the fish will be if they leave the water?" Prophet Muhammad (ﷺ) said: "The example of the one who remembers Allah and the one who does not is like the living one and the dead."[42] Remembrance of Allah is nourishment for the heart and soul and a remedy for cruelty and mercilessness. "A man came to Imam Al-Hassan complaining about his own hard heart. Al-Hassan replied: Soften it with dhikr Allah."[43]

Prophet Muhammad (ﷺ) said: «Do not talk too much without remembering Allah, as too much useless talk without Divine remembrances hardens the heart; and those with hard, cruel hearts are the farthest away from Allah.»[44]

Fasting

$\mathcal{F}$asting is an ancient practice long known as a healthful treatment for the body and soul. It is a common ritual in many cultures and various religions, and has been since the beginning of documented history. In Islam, fasting literally means voluntary refraining from food, drink and sexual intercourse before the break of dawn till sunset during the entire holy month of Ramadan.[45] The true purpose of fasting goes way beyond that, however. Apart from its physical requirements, the teachings of the Qur'an and the Sunnah about Ramadan fasting carry valuable spiritual lessons, intellectual insights, social and humanitarian aims, and educational and moral values.[46]

Ramadan fasting is one of the five pillars of Islam; it has been obligatory since the second Hijri year, that is, two years after the Prophet's migration to Madinah. Allah says in Soorat al-Baqarah:

﴿ يَـٰٓأَيُّهَا ٱلَّذِينَ ءَامَنُواْ كُتِبَ عَلَيۡكُمُ ٱلصِّيَامُ كَمَا كُتِبَ عَلَى ٱلَّذِينَ مِن قَبۡلِكُمۡ لَعَلَّكُمۡ تَتَّقُونَ ۝ ﴾

(سورة البقرة: ١٨٣)

﴿O you who believe! Fasting is prescribed for you as it was prescribed for those before you, that you may attain piety [God-consciousness].﴾   *(Qur'an 2: 183)*

From these verses we can clearly see the main purpose of fasting: piety. Fasting is thus a remedy for the suffering of the soul: a time to draw closer to Allah so as to purify our souls from sins, while purifying our bodies from toxins, so as to find our way back to our Creator — Almighty Allah.

Fasting and spiritual benefits

The spiritual lessons learnt through fasting in Ramadan are countless. Ramadan teaches us sincere, true love for Allah, as we perform this act only for Him. Allah says in this hadith qudsi:

«All human deeds are for themselves, except fasting: it is for Me and I will reward them for it.»[47]

Fasting is a lesson in patience and self-control; it disciplines the body by giving the mind control over physical desires and temptations, building strong willpower and effective devotion. Fasting frees the soul from the slavery of earthly cravings, from whatever it takes as essential in life to restore its command over the body, regaining dignity, freedom and total peace with its Creator, with itself and with the whole universe.

Dr. Hammudah Abd al-Ati, in his book *Islam in Focus*, points out further spiritual features of fasting as it is performed by Muslims:[48] During the Ramadan daytime, no one — except Allah — can see us if we sneak to the kitchen and grab a bite of our favourite dessert, but we never do it; even young children who start practicing the fast at an early age never do it. This is a test and a training lesson for our conscious mind and our willpower, our self-respect and moral dignity. Ramadan fasting improves our economic skills, teaching us adaptability, patience and forbearance. During Ramadan we learn to alter our eating schedule to only two meals per day, in which we consume less food and consequently spend less time, effort and money on the purchase and preparation of food — or at least, this is what we are supposed to do!

Fasting is also a lesson in self-denial, evoking in us feelings of compassion for the poor and others less fortunate than we. It strengthens family ties and instils a sense of social belonging. In Ramadan, people are urged to preserve family ties by gathering the whole family for *iftâr* (breaking the fast); this extends to distant family members, friends and even neighbours, as it is highly encouraged to invite others to break the fast with you, and if this is not feasible, to send iftâr meals to neighbours and the poor. In this way, fasting is a reminder of Allah's countless blessings, prompting us to be always humble, grateful and content. «Zaid ibn Khâlid Juhni related that Prophet Muhammad (ﷺ) said: "He who provides for the breaking of the fast (*iftâr*) of another will acquire the same reward as the fasting person without diminishing in any way the latter's reward."»[49]

Fasting in Islam is never practiced in isolation from society and life. Muslims should keep their normal daily routine — including work, exercise, exams and appointments. However, extra time should be taken for the purification of the soul through Qur'an reading and dhikr Allah, and more effort should be made to increase and strengthen social ties, developing a real spirit of unity and brotherhood. In Ramadan, we are urged to search out the needy and to give extra charity.

«Ibn 'Abbâs related that the Prophet (ﷺ) was the most generous of people, and he was even more generous during Ramadan when Gabriel visited him every night and recited the Qur'an with him. During this period the bounty of the Prophet became faster than the rain-bearing wind.»[50]

The Islamic method of fasting is a true lesson in morality and ethics; it spreads the spirit of forgiveness. The peace you make with your Creator and your soul extends as it were to the whole universe, increasing your feelings of tolerance, and giving you a sense of harmony and peaceful coexistence. Prophet Muhammad's (ﷺ) teachings of Ramadan ethics also stressed the importance of guarding our senses: restraining the eyes from looking at any sinful act or event, the ears from listening to and the tongue from uttering any gossip or bad language. At the same time we must guard all our body parts: restraining our hands from wrongdoing, our limbs from taking us towards any sinful act or event and above all, he (ﷺ) urged us to control our tempers.

«Abu Hurayrah related that Prophet Muhammad (ﷺ) said: "If a person does not give up falsehood and false conduct, Allah has no need that he should abstain from food and drink."[51] He also said: "Some people who fast gain nothing beyond hunger and thirst."»[52]

Prophet Muhammad (ﷺ) also taught us: «Satan flows through a human being like blood in his veins, so restrain his paths with hunger.»[53]

By emptying the stomach, we relax the whole body which of course helps to clear the mind and invigorates the soul. Abstaining from eating when one is hungry is not easy, but practicing it frees the mind and aids in developing concentration and wisdom, by providing time to focus on spiritual matters — the food of the soul: prayers, supplication, dhikr Allah, and reading and reciting the Qur'an.

Fasting and physical benefits

Besides the various spiritual benefits of fasting, recent research has shown its valuable effects on physical health. According to Adh-Dhahabi in his *Medicine of the Prophet*, it was thought that the stomach was "the seat of disease".[54] The Prophet (ﷺ) told his people: «Fasting is a (form of) protection,»[55] and this can be interpreted as indicating both the immediate and long-term benefits of abstaining from food, drink and sexual activity.

Allah (ﷺ) says in the Qur'an:

﴿ ... وَأَن تَصُومُوا۟ خَيْرٌ لَّكُمْ إِن كُنتُمْ تَعْلَمُونَ ۝ ﴾   (سورة البقرة: ١٨٤)

❨...And if you fast, it is better for you, if only you knew.❩

(Qur'an 2: 184)

Fasting gives the digestive system a rest and makes the body feel lighter. The energy usually consumed in digestion and food metabolism will be directed towards body detoxification, tissue repair and system healing.

Leon Chaitow recommended fasting in his book *Natural Alternatives to Antibiotics* as an effective way to 'supercharge' the immune system.[56] He states that fasting boosts the activity of essential parts of the body's natural defence mechanism. During fasting the ability of the lymphocytes and other blood cells to encounter any bacterial attack is much improved, and since the level of free radicals in the body is reduced by reducing food intake, the activity of the antioxidants is retained for better cell protection. From this we can see the wisdom in the Prophet's (ﷺ) advice:

«Do not force your patients to eat or drink, as Allah feeds them and gives them what they need of water.»[57]

In addition, fasting gives a chance for the stomach and intestines to regenerate their mucous cell lining, as digestive secretions are reduced during the day. Fasting also boosts the detoxification powers of the hepatic (liver) cells, cleans the kidneys and colon and purifies the blood. Furthermore, it helps overcome obesity, aids in ridding the body of any excess water, and clears the blood from extra fats, which in turn frees the tissues from stored fat-soluble toxins such as pesticides or drug metabolites.

The Most Gracious and Merciful Allah adapted the human body to withstand this difficult yet very beneficial fasting process. Dr. Ḥâmed Muhammad, in his book *Journey of Faith through the Human Body*,[58] explains the natural changes occurring in the body to accommodate the daily fasting in Ramadan. These changes include a reduction in the activity of the *thyroxin* hormone, thus the energy needed by the fasting Muslim to perform his or her daily functions is reduced, making him or her less susceptible to fatigue. In addition, the blood sugar level has been found to remain constant during the fasting hours and insulin secretion is kept under control, which is crucial to keep the brain supplied with glucose for mental concentration and optimum brain performance.

Sami Mosuli, in his book *Islam, the Physician of Modern Diseases,* demonstrated the role of autosuggestion and inspiration, gained through faith, devotion and Divine love, in changing body physiology, thus reducing in the fasting Muslim the feelings of thirst and hunger. This autosuggestion can be even more powerful than the neurotransmitter messages sent by the hypothalamus in the brain to the stomach for it to feel the hunger and start asking for food. Instead, the body refers to its stored glycogen and fat deposits for energy supply.[59]

Healthy habits in Ramadan

Prophet Muhammad (ﷺ) recommended breaking the fast immediately after sunset. He said:

«"My people will adhere to good as long as they hurry to break their fast."[60] He also said: "If anyone of you is fasting, let him break his fast with dates. In case he does not have them, then with water. Verily water is a purifier."»[61]

Next, Muslims should perform the sunset prayer in the mosque — for men this is obligatory — to reinforce social connections, then go back home to eat their iftâr, which should be a light one. Remember this basic rule:

﴿ ... وَكُلُواْ وَٱشْرَبُواْ وَلَا تُسْرِفُوٓاْ إِنَّهُۥ لَا يُحِبُّ ٱلْمُسْرِفِينَ ﴾ ٣١ (سورة الأعراف: ٣١)

❨...And eat and drink but do not waste by extravagance, certainly He [Allah] does not like those who waste by extravagance.❩

(Qur'an 7: 31)

Remember that fasting detoxifies and cleanses your body; you do not want to destroy all those benefits from your efforts in one meal. The whole purpose here is to have a lighter body in order to free the soul and focus on more important spiritual matters. Ghazâli wrote that satiety results in laziness and sluggishness of the heart: it slows down perception and awareness, while hunger clears the mind and purifies the heart.[62]

The Prophet (ﷺ) also strongly advised people not to skip *suhoor*, the meal before dawn:

«"Eat suhoor, as there is a blessing in it."[63] He recommended eating this light meal as close to dawn as we can, to be able to keep our full strength during the day. "Resort to the pre-dawn meal to help you fast during the day, and resort to a midday nap to help you in your night prayers (qiyâm)."»[64] A short nap also helps the fasting person to recharge in the middle of the day. This is especially important for pregnant or breastfeeding women if they have chosen to fast in Ramadan.

What's for iftâr?

After a long day of fasting it is wise to break the fast with a light, healthy meal. Start with dates if possible. Dates contain a high percentage of simple sugars that are easily and quickly absorbed by the body, giving an immediate boost of energy and restoring normal blood sugar levels (BSL) after a long fasting day.

Dates also provide the energy necessary for food digestion, assimilation and absorption, thus preventing the sluggishness often felt after the if̣ṭâr. This tradition is still applied in many Arab and Muslim countries, where Muslims break their fast on dates pre-soaked in milk before performing their sunset prayer. The combination of dates and milk is very healthy. Dates are rich in vitamins A and B, in addition to magnesium, potassium and phosphorus. In addition to simple, easily absorbed sugars, they contain fibre, which relieves constipation, aids in cholesterol reduction, fights colon cancer and rapidly gives a feeling of satiety. Milk is rich in proteins, calcium, vitamin B_2 and fat soluble vitamins. The high glycemic index[65] of dates is counteracted by milk. The fatty nature of milk slows down the absorption of the sugars in dates, preventing a sudden rush of insulin.

Some if̣ṭâr tips

1. Start with a bowl of soup — preferably a homemade, fat free one — and if you plan to have meat with your meal do not add meat to the soup. Here are some suggestions:

   ➢ Vegetable soups are very nutritious, rich in vitamins, fibres and phytonutrients. You can add any vegetable that you fancy; you can also blend it to make it smooth and creamy or just leave it naturally textured.

   ➢ Lentil and bean soups (like *hareerah*, the traditional Moroccan soup) are rich in proteins, minerals, vitamins and fibre. They are also quite filling, so if you are watching your weight, this is a good way to stop eating early!

> ➢ Mushroom soups are another good choice: healthy, nutritious and above all delicious!

> ➢ Tomato soup is my favourite; its high content of the anticancerous phytonutrient lycopene makes it an excellent nutritious dish.

2. Eat lots of fresh salad, it is both healthy and filling, but avoid the ready made dressings. You can prepare your own healthy dressing from olive oil, apple vinegar, thyme, basil and oregano. Include lots of fresh green leaves in your salad: the darker the green colour of the leaves, the more nutrients they hold. Green leaves provide vitamin C, folic acid (an essential B vitamin), beta carotene antioxidants, and lots of fibre, which helps the colon in its detoxification and cleansing process.

3. Avoid fats and fried food as much as you can. Frying food creates unnatural fats called *trans-fatty acids* [trans fats] which studies have shown to be involved in many heart and circulatory disorders. Also, frying carbohydrates at high temperatures generates a toxic by-product called *acrolin* which is believed to have a carcinogenic effect. Above all, there is the simple fact: 'fats make you fat.'

4. Do not consume lots of meat. Most of us consume more than enough protein in our diet, it is found — as noted in previous chapters — in meat, eggs, milk and beans. To reiterate, eating too much meat, the richest source of protein, results in painful gout symptoms in the joints. In addition, meat contains a considerable amount of fat and cholesterol.

5. Try to replace empty-calorie desserts with fresh or dried fruits. There is a healthy traditional Egyptian dessert made simply by

placing dried fruits [apricots, prunes, figs, sultanas or other raisins] in just enough water to cover and leaving them to soak for 8 to 12 hours; this is then topped with ground nuts and served.

6. Drink lots of fluids: fresh juices with no sugar added, herbal teas, milk and buttermilk. This does not compensate for your body's requirement of pure water, however. Drink as much as you can — at least 1.5 litres each night.

Do not sleep after ifṭâr, be active, and take a walk even for just a few minutes to help your body digest the food. Be aware that if you fast properly (no overeating), you may experience some natural symptoms of detoxification as the toxins are slowly withdrawn from your body, especially in the first few days. These symptoms can be anything from fatigue to headache and maybe bad breath. These are totally safe and natural symptoms which you will soon overcome (as long as you are getting enough fluids). Always remember the hadith of the Prophet (ﷺ):

«By Him in whose Hands is the life of Muhammad, the odour of the breath of one who is fasting is more pleasant to Allah than the fragrance of musk.»[66]

And what's for suhoor?

The pre-dawn meal is a Sunnah; the Prophet (ﷺ) said:

«There is a blessing in eating suhoor, so do not skip it. At least drink a sip of water, for Allah and his angels give their blessings to the people who eat their meal before the break of dawn.»[67]

So, we have to wake up even to drink some water or a cup of milk. The best food for suhoor is a light meal of bread and cheese, (low-fat ricotta cheese — known as *labnah* in Arabic — is a good choice) or buttermilk. You can also eat some salad, fresh veggies, dried fruits, or bananas and muesli with some yogurt.

Our basic rule applies here too: 'Do not overdo it,' and remember that the purpose of fasting in this holy month is to empty the stomach and lighten the body to free the soul.

Zakât (charity)

Zakât is one of the five pillars of Islam. It is a fixed percentage of Muslims' wealth that they should distribute annually to certain categories of beneficiaries as stated in the Qur'an. Zakât, in its real meaning, is not a mere act of charity, nor is it a tax or donation, nor is it just an expression of kindness. Zakât carries within its teachings valuable spiritual lessons;[68] it is a continuous act of devotion aiming at purifying one's soul. Allah says in the Qur'an:

(سورة التوبة: ١٠٣)   ﴾ ... ﴿ خُذْ مِنْ أَمْوَالِهِمْ صَدَقَةً تُطَهِّرُهُمْ وَتُزَكِّيهِم بِهَا

﴾Take alms from their wealth in order to purify them and sanctify them with it...﴿   *(Qur'an 9: 103)*

Islam allows us to acknowledge the fact that possession is a natural human instinct. Islam is nevertheless the religion of moderation, thus a fascination with money and possessions is highly discouraged, as it can weave itself into one's life and become its main driving force.

(سورة التغابن: ١٥)   ﴾ إِنَّمَا أَمْوَالُكُمْ وَأَوْلَادُكُمْ فِتْنَةٌ وَاللَّهُ عِندَهُ أَجْرٌ عَظِيمٌ ﴿

❨Your wealth and your children are only a trial, whereas Allah! With Him is a great reward [Paradise].❩   *(Qur'an 64: 15)*

Attachment to money wealth and material goods gives them an unacceptable power over our emotions, and this affects us physically as well. Who has not heard of someone who suffered a heart attack when they lost their fortune or their job? Their sudden loss of money or income source generated a major 'leak' in their body energy, dangerously draining their power and vitality.[69]

The aim of zakât is to achieve a level of consciousness in which money and fortune is no longer a purpose in life, no longer an obsession or fascination; these feelings are replaced by contentment. It is good to be rich and wealthy, but your soul will accept any changes in your financial state, your feelings are detached, not enslaved by money. Faith in Allah is our priority; wealth and possessions are simply tools in our work as 'vicegerents on earth,' to put things to right on earth according to Allah's law, and wealth and possessions should never be in control of our actions and emotions.

Literally, the word zakât in Arabic means 'purification'. Zakât purifies the donor's heart from selfishness, avarice and greed, Allah (﷾) says in the Qur'an:

$$ \text{﴿ ٱلشَّيْطَٰنُ يَعِدُكُمُ ٱلْفَقْرَ وَيَأْمُرُكُم بِٱلْفَحْشَآءِ ۖ وَٱللَّهُ يَعِدُكُم مَّغْفِرَةً مِّنْهُ وَفَضْلًا ۗ وَٱللَّهُ وَٰسِعٌ عَلِيمٌ ۝ ﴾} $$

(سورة البقرة: ٢٦٨)

❨Satan threatens you with poverty and orders you to commit sins; whereas Allah promises you Forgiveness from Himself and Bounty, and Allah is All-Sufficient for His creatures' needs, All-Knower.❩   *(Qur'an 2: 268)*

Zakât also purifies the recipient's heart from envy, hostility, rancour and hatred. It converts these destructive feelings into good wishes for the wealthy, contentment and hope that Allah will expand their fortunes for them to contribute more in the wellbeing of the society as a whole.[70]

Zakât also purifies one's money from any doubtful shares which could have been mistakenly added to it, as pure and honest wealth are prerequisites for permanent prosperity and are an important condition for one's prayers and supplications to be accepted by Allah. It is mentioned by Adh-Dhahabi that the Prophet (ﷺ) said:

«Allah only prescribed zakât to purify the remainder of their money.»[71]

So, as we can see, this simple yet meaningful act aims at purifying individuals and inculcates in them the spirit of cooperation, love and mutual assistance. It cleanses the Muslim Ummah from corruption and dissociation.

Zakât is an act of kindness, consolation and comfort for the less fortunate, without encouraging in them laziness or dependence on others for their subsistence. Prophet Muhammad (ﷺ) said:

«"The hand that gives is better than the hand that receives."[72] He also said: "If one refrains from asking others for money, Allah will forgive him, and Allah will provide for him and spare him the need to ask."[73] In yet another hadith, he (ﷺ) said: "By Him in whose Hand is my soul, it is better for any of you to fetch a rope, cut and collect wood and carry it upon his back and sell it, rather than asking someone for something and that person may give it to him or he may not."»[74]

Zakât encourages all the members of society to work harder, to earn more and feel the inner satisfaction that comes from contributing to the wellbeing and happiness of others. It builds the spirit of social responsibility, commitment and interaction, and increases feelings of safety and security among members of the community.[75]

Moral motives are an essential condition for zakât. Muslims should perform this act only for Allah's sake. When giving this money in charity, we should not feel pride or tell too many people about our good deeds. While performing this religious duty, we should avoid hypocrisy, which nullifies all good deeds. We should remain humble and sincere. Allah warns us against arrogance and hypocrisy in His Noble Book:

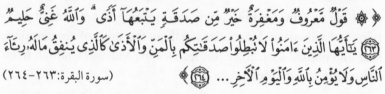

﴿ ۞ قَوْلٌ مَّعْرُوفٌ وَمَغْفِرَةٌ خَيْرٌ مِّن صَدَقَةٍ يَتْبَعُهَآ أَذًى ۗ وَٱللَّهُ غَنِيٌّ حَلِيمٌ ۝ يَـٰٓأَيُّهَا ٱلَّذِينَ ءَامَنُوا۟ لَا تُبْطِلُوا۟ صَدَقَـٰتِكُم بِٱلْمَنِّ وَٱلْأَذَىٰ كَٱلَّذِى يُنفِقُ مَالَهُۥ رِئَآءَ ٱلنَّاسِ وَلَا يُؤْمِنُ بِٱللَّهِ وَٱلْيَوْمِ ٱلْأَخِرِ ... ۝ ﴾   (سورة البقرة:٢٦٣-٢٦٤)

❨Kind words and forgiving of faults are better than charity followed by injury. And Allah is Rich [Free of all needs] and He is Most-Forbearing. O you who believe, Do not render in vain your charity by reminders of your generosity or by injury, like him who spends his wealth to be seen of people, and he does not believe in Allah, nor in the Last Day...❩   *(Qur'an 2: 263 -264)*

﴿ إِن تُبْدُوا۟ ٱلصَّدَقَـٰتِ فَنِعِمَّا هِىَ ۖ وَإِن تُخْفُوهَا وَتُؤْتُوهَا ٱلْفُقَرَآءَ فَهُوَ خَيْرٌ لَّكُمْ ۚ وَيُكَفِّرُ عَنكُم مِّن سَيِّـَٔاتِكُمْ ۗ وَٱللَّهُ بِمَا تَعْمَلُونَ خَبِيرٌ ۝ ﴾

(سورة البقرة: ٢٧١)

❨If you disclose your charity, it is well, but if you conceal it, and give it to the poor, that is better for you. [Allah] will forgive you some of your sins. And Allah is Well-Acquainted with what you do.❩   *(Qur'an 2: 271)*

Supplication (Du'â')

$\mathcal{S}$upplication is a beautiful type of worship. Prophet Muhammad (ﷺ) said: «Supplication is worship.»[76] The word '*ibâdah* in Arabic is derived from '*uboodiyyah*, which means servitude or slavery. We are all slaves and servants of Allah; we all need Him and can never do without His guidance and mercy. Allah says in His Holy Book:

﴿وَقَالَ رَبُّكُمُ ٱدْعُونِىٓ أَسْتَجِبْ لَكُمْ إِنَّ ٱلَّذِينَ يَسْتَكْبِرُونَ عَنْ عِبَادَتِى سَيَدْخُلُونَ جَهَنَّمَ دَاخِرِينَ ۝﴾ (سورة غافر: ٦٠)

❴And your Master and Creator said: Invoke Me, [i.e. believe in My Oneness and ask Me for anything], I will respond to you. Verily, those who scorn My worship [i.e. do not invoke Me, and do not believe in My Oneness] will surely enter Hell in humiliation!❵

(Qur'an 40: 60)

Supplication is a direct connection between you and Allah. It fills your heart with humility and devotion, love and longing. It relieves sadness and strengthens the faith. Allah (ﷻ) says:

﴿يَٰٓأَيُّهَا ٱلنَّاسُ أَنتُمُ ٱلْفُقَرَآءُ إِلَى ٱللَّهِ وَٱللَّهُ هُوَ ٱلْغَنِىُّ ٱلْحَمِيدُ ۝﴾ (سورة فاطر: ١٥)

❴O people! It is you who stand in need of Allah, but Allah is Rich [Free of all wants and needs], Worthy of all praise.❵

(Qur'an 35: 15)

Is there anyone who does not need God? Even the most powerful people on earth, the rulers and tycoons, all need Allah.

A hadith states: «There is nothing as dear to Allah as supplication (by His worshippers).»[77]

Supplication is so important that the first chapter in the Qur'an is actually a supplication: *Soorat al-Fâtiḥa*, which we must recite in each unit (raka'ah) of our prayers. The verses in this chapter are structured so as to show us how to supplicate: first, start with Allah's Name,

(۱ :سورة الفاتحة)

❨In the Name of Allah, the Most Beneficent, the Most Merciful.❩

(Qur'an 1: 1)

(*Bismillâh ir-Raḥmân ir-Raḥeem*)

— then, thank Allah for all His blessings,

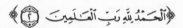

(۲ :سورة الفاتحة)

❨All praise and thanks be to Allah, the Creator and Master of the Universe [all that exists].❩   *(Qur'an 1: 2)*

(*alḥamdu lillâhi rabbil 'alameen*)

— and praise Him,

(٤-۳ :سورة الفاتحة)

❨The Most Beneficent, the Most Merciful; the Only Owner [and the Only Ruling Judge] of the Day of Recompense [i.e. the Day of Resurrection].❩   *(Qur'an 1: 3-4)*

(*ar-Raḥmân ir-Raḥeem, Mâliki yawm id-deen*)

— and admit your need and total submissiveness to Him;

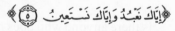

(٥ :سورة الفاتحة)

❨You [Alone] we worship, and You [Alone] we ask for help [for each and every thing].❩   *(Qur'an 1: 5)*

(*iyyâka na'budu wa iyyâka nasta'een*)

— Then, ask what you wish:

﴾ أَهْدِنَا ٱلصِّرَٰطَ ٱلْمُسْتَقِيمَ ۝ ﴿   (سورة الفاتحة: ٦)

﴾Guide us to the Straight Way﴿   *(Qur'an 1: 6)*

(ihdinaṣ-ṣirâṭal mustaqeem)

An important component of any supplication that we make should be to ask Allah to send His blessings and peace on Prophet Muhammad (ﷺ), as this hadith explains:

«Ibn 'Ubaid related that the Messenger of Allah heard someone supplicate in his prayer without glorification of Allah and without invoking blessings upon the Prophet. Concerning him, the Prophet (ﷺ) observed: That one was in a hurry; then he called him and said to him (or to someone beside him): When one of you is supplicating he should begin with praise of Allah and glorification of Him and then invoke blessings on the Prophet and then supplicate as he may wish.»[78]

A man came to the Prophet Muhammad (ﷺ) one day and asked him:

«Is Allah far away, so we call out to Him, or is He close by, so we should whisper to Him?»

Allah Himself answered the man's question;[79] a verse of the Qur'an was revealed that says:

﴾ وَإِذَا سَأَلَكَ عِبَادِى عَنِّى فَإِنِّى قَرِيبٌ ۖ أُجِيبُ دَعْوَةَ ٱلدَّاعِ إِذَا دَعَانِ ۖ فَلْيَسْتَجِيبُوا۟ لِى وَلْيُؤْمِنُوا۟ بِى لَعَلَّهُمْ يَرْشُدُونَ ۝ ﴿   (سورة البقرة: ١٨٦)

﴾And when My slaves ask you [O Muhammad] concerning Me, then [answer them], I am indeed near [to them by My Knowledge]. I respond to the invocations of the supplicant when he calls on Me [without any mediator or intercessor]. So let them obey Me and believe in Me, so that they may be led aright.﴿ *(Qur'an 2: 186)*

The answer came straight from Allah; this is a clear proof of His closeness and of how much He cares.

Do not be afraid that your invocation might not be granted, for Prophet Muhammad (ﷺ) said:

«No Muslim invokes with a supplication, but Allah answers it in one of the following three ways: He promptly answers his supplication, or delays it for him until the Hereafter, or keeps him away from an equivalent evil.»[80]

Pray and be sure that Allah is always there for you. Prophet Muhammad (ﷺ) said: «Allah is ever Generous and if a servant raises his hands to Him (in supplication), He hates to return them empty.»[81] Do not be impatient for the answer, for the Messenger of Allah said: «One's supplication will be granted if he is not impatient.»[82] Have complete faith in Allah and believe that He wills only what is best for you; He will eventually answer your prayers and grant your wishes: «Supplicate to Allah and be certain that it will be answered.»[83] Show awe, submissiveness and humility to your Creator, as the Messenger of Allah (ﷺ) said: «Know that Allah does not accept supplication from a negligent, inattentive heart.»[84]

Supplicate not only for yourself, but also for your family, relatives and for all Muslims around the globe; our Prophet (ﷺ) said:

«The supplication of a Muslim on behalf of his brother is granted; there is an assigned angel at his head, each time he invokes for his brother, the assigned angel says: Amen and the same goes for you.»[85]

This is a beautiful way to strengthen connections and the spirit of brotherhood among Muslims.

Finally, we must mention here the conditions for one's supplication to be accepted: Allah accepts our prayers and supplications only if our earnings are halal (from a legitimate source). Prophet Muhammad (ﷺ) said:

«"Allah is good, and accepts only what is good."[86] Another hadith promises: "Earn your provision lawfully and Allah will respond to your supplication."»[87]

Know that you are poor and Allah is Self-Sufficient, you are weak and Allah is Almighty, All-Powerful, you are needy and your Creator is the Sustainer of Life, the Most Generous and the Most Great.

The Qur'an

Allah (ﷺ) says:

$$﴿ لَوْ أَنزَلْنَا هَذَا ٱلْقُرْءَانَ عَلَىٰ جَبَلٍ لَّرَأَيْتَهُۥ خَـٰشِعًا مُّتَصَدِّعًا مِّنْ خَشْيَةِ ٱللَّهِ وَتِلْكَ ٱلْأَمْثَـٰلُ نَضْرِبُهَا لِلنَّاسِ لَعَلَّهُمْ يَتَفَكَّرُونَ ۝ ﴾ (سورة الحشر: ٢١)$$

❮Had We sent down this Qur'an on a mountain, you would surely have seen it humbling itself and being torn asunder by the fear of Allah. Such are the parables which We put forward to humankind that they may reflect.❯ *(Qur'an 59: 21)*

The Qur'an is a unique construction. Look at the way the words generate their own rhythm, a wonderful rhythm that arises not only from the letters, words and verses; but also from the meanings: a moving rhythm that leads to total peace, awe and submissiveness to Allah the moment we start listening and pondering over the meanings. Allah says in His Holy Book:

﴾أَلَمۡ يَأۡنِ لِلَّذِينَ ءَامَنُوٓاْ أَن تَخۡشَعَ قُلُوبُهُمۡ لِذِكۡرِ ٱللَّهِ وَمَا نَزَلَ مِنَ ٱلۡحَقِّ ... ۝ ﴿

(سورة الحديد: ١٦)

﴾Has not the time come for the hearts of those who believe [in the Oneness of Allah] to be affected by Allah's Reminder [this Qur'an], and that which has been revealed of the truth?...﴿

(Qur'an 57: 16)

Then Allah compares the believers who feel the power of and reflect on the Qur'an's verses with total awe and humility, to the earth that starts producing green life after it had been dry and barren. This is a pure blessing from Allah:

﴾ٱعۡلَمُوٓاْ أَنَّ ٱللَّهَ يُحۡيِ ٱلۡأَرۡضَ بَعۡدَ مَوۡتِهَا قَدۡ بَيَّنَّا لَكُمُ ٱلۡأَيَـٰتِ لَعَلَّكُمۡ تَعۡقِلُونَ ۝ ﴿

(سورة الحديد: ١٧)

﴾Know that Allah gives life to the earth after its death! Indeed We have made clear the Âyât [proofs, evidences, verses, lessons, signs and revelations] to you, so that you may understand.﴿

(Qur'an 57: 17)

If you dig further into the meanings, you will find treasures of information and knowledge beyond all expectation. The Qur'an is the Word of Allah, the last Message from Him to all humankind. Allah describes it this way:

﴾ ... كِتَـٰبٌ أُحۡكِمَتۡ ءَايَـٰتُهُۥ ثُمَّ فُصِّلَتۡ مِن لَّدُنۡ حَكِيمٍ خَبِيرٍ ۝ ﴿ (سورة هود: ١)

﴾...[This is] a Book, the Verses of which are perfected [in every sphere of knowledge], and then explained in detail from One [Allah], Who is Most Wise and Well-Acquainted [with all things].﴿   *(Qur'an 11: 1)*

It combines guidance, compassion and healing to enlighten your path, your life and your soul:

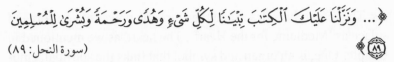

﴿ ... وَنَزَّلْنَا عَلَيْكَ ٱلْكِتَٰبَ تِبْيَٰنًا لِّكُلِّ شَىْءٍ وَهُدًى وَرَحْمَةً وَبُشْرَىٰ لِلْمُسْلِمِينَ ﴿٨٩﴾

(سورة النحل: ٨٩)

﴾...And We have sent down to you the Book [the Qur'an] as an
exposition of everything, a guidance, a mercy, and glad tidings
for those who have submitted themselves [to Allah as Muslims].﴿

(Qur'an 16: 89)

﴿ ... قُلْ هُوَ لِلَّذِينَ ءَامَنُواْ هُدًى وَشِفَآءٌ ﴿٤٤﴾ ... ﴾ (سورة فُصِّلَت: ٤٤)

﴾...Say: It is — for those who believe — a guide and a healing...﴿

(Qur'an 41: 44)

Note that the healing of the Qur'an is always linked with the
believers, you can only benefit from this tremendous spiritual energy, if you are a real believer. If your soul is filled with faith and
your heart is saturated with awe and humility, you will surely get
all the benefits intended for you. Allah says in the Qur'an:

﴿ وَنُنَزِّلُ مِنَ ٱلْقُرْءَانِ مَا هُوَ شِفَآءٌ وَرَحْمَةٌ لِّلْمُؤْمِنِينَ وَلَا يَزِيدُ ٱلظَّٰلِمِينَ إِلَّا خَسَارًا ﴿٨٢﴾

(سورة الإسراء: ٨٢)

﴾And We send down from the Qur'an that which is a healing and
a mercy to those who believe [in Islamic monotheism and act on
it], and it increases the oppressors and wrong-doers in nothing but
loss.﴿ *(Qur'an 17: 82)*

So to start your journey to a prosperous life, healthier body and
enlightened soul; the Qur'an is the first and most important step.
A study was performed in Morocco as a preliminary examination
of how, in everyday life, faith enhances the feeling of well-being.
The study found that the recitation of verses of the Qur'an offered
homemakers a way to deal with stress and to manage the emotions that caused them anguish and disturbed their hearts and bod-

ies. The researchers described the Qur'anic power of comfort and solace as 'Medicine for the Heart'. The heart, as we mentioned in Chapter One, is an organ and symbol that links the spiritual, emotional, and physical planes of existence. Hence the recitation of the Qur'an has been proved to generate a wholesome feeling of relief and wellbeing that is evident in the satisfaction and healing experienced by those who practice it.[88]

I once read a story about an old man who lived on a farm in the mountains with his young grandson.[89] Each morning Grandpa was up early sitting at the kitchen table reading his Qur'an. His grandson wanted to be just like him and tried to imitate him in every way he could. One day the grandson asked: "Grandpa, I try to read the Qur'an just like you but I don't understand it, and what I do understand I forget as soon as I close the book. What good does reading the Qur'an do?" The Grandfather quietly turned from putting coal in the stove and replied, "Take this coal basket down to the river and bring me back a basket of water." The boy did as he was told, but all the water leaked out before he got back to the house. The grandfather laughed and said, "You'll have to move a little faster next time," and sent him back to the river with the basket to try again. This time the boy ran faster, but again the basket was empty before he returned home. Out of breath, he told his grandfather that it was impossible to carry water in a basket, and he went to get a bucket instead. The old man said, "I don't want a bucket of water; I want a basket of water. You're just not trying hard enough," and he went out the door to watch the boy try again. At this point, the boy knew it was impossible, but he wanted to show his grandfather that even if he ran as fast as he could, the water would leak out before he got back to the house. The boy again dipped the basket into river and ran hard, but when he reached his grandfather the basket was again empty. Out of breath, he said,

"See Grandpa, it's useless!" "So, you think it is useless?" The old man said, "Look at the basket." The boy looked at the basket and for the first time realized that the basket was different. It had been transformed from a dirty old coal basket and was now clean, inside and out. "Son, that's what happens when you read the Qur'an. You might not understand or remember everything from the first time, but when you read it, you will be changed, inside and out. That is the work of Allah in our lives."

EPILOGUE

I want to end with a little story that happened long ago when the Muslim army was fighting against the Persian Empire.[1] The Muslims were defeated in the first few rounds of the battle, so their commander, Saʿd ibn Abi Waqqâṣ (ﷺ) gathered his men to re-evaluate their resources and position. All seemed under control: the Muslim army had a great number of fighters and good resources; so what was the problem then? Saʿd concluded that this defeat must be a punishment from Allah for their sins, so he ordered each of them to repent and ask Allah forgiveness and check for any misdeed that he had committed or any acts of worship that he had forgotten to perform. All the men were good Muslims, with sincere intentions and the true will and power to fight the enemies. Still, he insisted, they must have neglected some of Allah or His Prophet's orders. They went through the obligatory and the non-obligatory acts of worship, and then through the entire Sunnah of the Prophet to find their weak point. Finally, Saʿd realised that they had been neglecting the Sunnah of siwâk. They were not using siwâk as our Prophet used to do before prayer. How strange it seems: men at the battlefront who thought that their weak point was that they were not brushing their teeth five times a day!

Saʿd ordered for the siwâk sticks to be distributed to each Muslim in the army and asked them all to follow our Prophet's Sunnah. No one argued, no one questioned his commander's reasoning; no one asked what siwâk had to do with winning or loosing the battle against the strongest army on the face of the earth.

Meanwhile, the Persian army had sent spies to check on the Muslims' camp. The Persians at that time looked upon the Arabs as a primitive, uncivilized nation, so when the spies reached the Arabs' camp and saw them rubbing their teeth with sticks, they failed to understand what was going on, until one of them shouted: "They are sharpening their teeth to eat us alive; they are cannibals!"

The Persian spies ran back to their camp and the news spread like wildfire. The whole army panicked, and most of the Persian fortresses were abandoned and fell easily into the Muslims' hands.

Do you see the moral of the story? Do not underestimate even seemingly insignificant orders from Allah and His Messenger (ﷺ) (the Qur'an and the Sunnah), even if you do not understand the wisdom behind it. Until recently, scientists had not discovered enough to confirm most of the information present in this book, yet Islamic teachings were followed, grasped and regularly practiced by Muslims for years. They did not need to know that homosexuality causes the spread of fatal diseases; or that pork is a potential host for viral mutation; or that alcoholic beverages intoxicate the blood and nerves; they did not need to know that ablution boosts immunity, that regular prayers, supplications, and meditation reduce hypertension and relax the nerves; or that anger, hate, envy and severing family ties all disturb your biological functions; yet they were certain deep in their hearts that since the orders came from Allah, then they must hold tremendous benefits and great wisdom.

Do not get me wrong, though; we should still try to search for the wisdom and the meanings behind everything we do. We are required to learn, explore and experience, we should seek scientific knowledge in all fields and apply this knowledge in our everyday life. Even if we do not find an answer we should still believe that our Islamic teachings are the best source of health and happiness for our body and soul; and we should be certain that the meanings we grasp and the knowledge we attain can never encompass all the wisdom behind these precious teachings. Learning is a life-long process, Allah (ﷻ) says:

﴿ ... وَمَآ أُوتِيتُم مِّنَ ٱلۡعِلۡمِ إِلَّا قَلِيلٗا ۝ ﴾   (سورة الإسراء: ٨٥)

﴿...And of knowledge, you [humans] have been given only a little.﴾   *(Qur'an 17: 85)*

Our glory and success is a direct result of following the Qur'an and the Sunnah; these are our ultimate sources of enlightenment. Always ask yourself: what am I doing? What is my real goal and mission in life? What is the true purpose of my creation? Am I following the Right Path? Evaluate your intention, check your sincerity and adjust your will to the Divine Will. Know that this world is transient and our final reward is waiting for us. Plant your seeds in this life to reap your fine produce in the next eternal life.

The information I have shared with you in this book is practical self-help advice that can be easily implemented and integrated in your everyday life. Change is always hard and needs a strong will, time and effort; but if you take one step at a time, you will be able to gradually achieve a healthy and happy lifestyle that (most importantly) conforms to Islamic teachings. Do not push yourself too hard and always remember to adjust your intention and enjoy the present moment.

At the same time, do not procrastinate — start now. Get a notebook and write down your goals, make your statements as clear and specific as possible, then devise your plan to implement these goals. You should have short and long-term goals and some daily, weekly and yearly plans to implement. Always remember your irreplaceable Ultimate goal: To attain Allah's pleasure!

Think of yourself as a whole being, and work on the improvement of your five 'bodies': physical health, biochemical health (nutrition and environment), intellectual health (conscious and subconscious mind), psychological health (emotional and social planes) and last but not least your spiritual health (food for your soul).

Amira Ayad

*Always
Check your
intention*

Notes

Introduction

[1] Ibn Mâjah, Abu Dâwood, Ahmed and Mâlik in his *Muwaṭṭâ* (graded as sound by Albâni)

[2] Lindlahr, 2005

[3] the migration from Makkah to Madinah by Prophet Muhammad (ﷺ) and his Companions that marks the start of the Islamic calendar

[4] National Library of Medicine, n.d.

[5] Wood, 2005

[6] Mannion, 2002

[7] American Medical Association, 2007, June 1

[8] *Allopathy* is the treatment of disease using drugs that have opposite effects to the symptoms

[9] Lindlahr, 2005

[10] Nagamia, 1998

[11] Cited in Nagamia, 1998

[12] Nagamia, 1998

[13] Abouleish, n.d.

[14] Nagamia, 1998

[15] Marvin, 2000

[16] Hakam, 1999

[17] Hourani, 1991, p. 202

[18] Hakam, 1999

[19] Abouleish, n.d.

[20] (National Library of Medicine, 1998)

[21] Abouleish, n.d.

[22] Dhahabi, S. 2004 (أبي عبد الله شمس الدين بن عثمان الذهبي)

[23] Jauziyah, 2003

[24] Jauziyah, 2003

[25] Nagamia, 1998

[26] Note here the difference between mind and brain, the latter being a mere physical organ.

[27] Abu Dâwood

[28] Jauziyah, 2003

[29] Jauziyah, 2003

[30] Jauziyah, 2003

[31] 'Ulwân. 2003

[32] Ghazâli the Younger, (محمد الغزالي) 2003a

[33] 'Ulwân, 2003

[34] An agreed-upon hadith

[35] 'Ulwân, 2003

[36] Qardawi, 1995

[37] The translation of the meanings of the Qur'an used for the majority of the verses quoted in this book is taken from *The Noble Qur'an*, translation of the meanings by *Dr. Muhammad Taqi-ud-Din al-Hilali, Ph.D. and Dr. Muhammad Muhsin Khan*: http://www.al-sunnah.com/call_to_islam/quran/index.html *For some verses, The Holy Qur'an (Al-Qur'an al-Kareem)* Arabic text with English translation of the meanings by Abdullah Yusuf Ali, Revised edition 2004, by Muhammad Abdul Haleem Eliasi, Islamic Book Service.

Chapter 1
Physical Body

[1] Muslim

[2] Muslim

[3] Tirmidhi, Nasâ'i and Ibn Mâjah (a sound hadith)

[4] Abu Nâ'eem Dhahabi, *Prophetic Medicine*

[5] Ibn Mâjah and Imams Mâlik and Ahmed (Albâni graded it as 'good')

[6] Colome et al., 1994

[7] Cilia are tiny hair -like projections lining the inside of the lungs which act continuously to clear pulmonary mucous along with dirt, bacteria, and other irritants up into the throat, thus preventing them from affecting the respiratory system.

[8] Kleinman & Messina-Kleinman, 2001

[9] Moreno et al., 1991

[10] American Academy of Otolaryngology – Head and Neck Surgery. 2007

[11] Ibrahim, A. S. 2004 (أحمد شوقي ابراهيم)

[12] Ahmed and Abu Dâwood

[13] Bukhâri

[14] McManners, 2004

[15] Bâr, M. A. (محمد علي البار) 2000

[16] Muslim

[17] Tirmidhi and Ibn Mâjah (with a sound chain of narration), and Ahmed and Abu Dâwood from Ibn 'Umar in a traceable form

[18] Ibn Mâjah (Ibn Taymiyyah said its chain of narration was sound)

[19] Muslim

[20] Muslim

[21] Abu Dâwood, Tirmidhi and Ibn Mâjah (Tirmidhi graded it as 'good but strange', because at one point in its chain there is a single narrator.)

[22] Ahmed, Abu Dâwood and Tirmidhi (a good hadith)

[23] A sound hadith according to Albâni

[24] My thanks to my colleague, Jamila Hakam, for contributing the information on the wisdom behind ritual bathing and ablution.

[25] Muslim

[26] Jauziyah, 2003

[27] Duyff, 2002

[28] Bukhâri, Muslim, Abu Dâwood, Tirmidhi, Nasâ'i, Ibn Mâjah and Ahmed

[29] Bukhâri, Nasâ'i,, Ibn Mâjah and Ahmed

[30] Musṭeehy, M. R., Jâssem, A. A., Yâseen, I. A., Jandi, A. R., and Shukri, L. (n.d.)

[31] Bukhâri and Muslim

[32] Ahmed, Tirmidhi and Ibn Mâjah (sound according to Albâni)

[33] Weil, 1997

[34] Hale, 2001

[35] Dhahabi, S. (أبي عبد الله شمس الدين بن عثمان الذهبي) (2004)

[36] Bukhâri and Muslim

[37] Marieb, 2003

[38] Qardawi, Y. (يوسف القرضاوئ) 2002c.

[39] Jauziyah. 2003

[40] Marieb, 2003

[41] Marieb, 2003

[42] That means it has no blood supply of its own.

[43] Marieb, 2003

[44] Abu Dâwood and Ahmed (sound according to Albâni)

[45] Ibn Mâjah (sound according to Albâni)

[46] Budiyanto. 2000, Nov

[47] You can find more natural home remedies and recipes in Janice Cox's book, *Natural Beauty at Home* and Ambika Manchanda's books: *Naturally Beautiful Your Hair* and *Naturally Beautiful Your Skin.*

[48] Jauziyah, 2003

[49] Cox, 2002, p.35

[50] Colostrom is the clear yellowish fluid secreted from the breasts for two to four days after delivery.

[51] Duyff, 2002

[52] Jauziyah, 2003

[53] Marieb, 2003

[54] These are beneficial bacteria living in the body.

[55] Jauziyah, 2003

[56] The lymphatic organs include lymph nodes, spleen, thymus, tonsils and peyer's patches in the intestines.

[57] Marieb, 2003

[58] Marieb, 2003

[59] Arteriosclerosis is the loss of elasticity and thickening of the walls of the arteries that happens especially in old age.

[60] Hensrud, 2006

[61] McManners, 2004

[62] Jauziyah, 2003

[63] Qardawi, Y. (يوسف القرضاوي) 2002c

[64] Dhahabi, S. (أبي عبد الله شمس الدين بن عثمان الذهبي) 2004

[65] BMR is the amount of calories burnt by the body at rest for digestion, blood circulation, respiration and so on.

[66] This process is called aerobic metabolism.

[67] Smolin & Grosvenor, 1994

[68] McManners, 2004

[69] Jauziyah, 2003

[70] Smolin & Grosvenor, 1994

[71] 'Brittle bone disease', in which the bones are depleted of calcium and/or vitamin D, making them fragile

[72] Kenton, 1999

[73] Kenton, 1999

[74] Bukhâri, Muslim and Nasâ'i

[75] Ahmed and Abu Dâwood (sound according to Albâni)

[76] Bukhâri

[77] Abd Al-Ati, 2003

[78] Bukhâri

[79] A sound hadith agreed upon by the scholars

[80] Ghazâli,. M. (the Younger) (أبي حامد محمد الغزالي) 2004

[81] Ahmed (a sound hadith); and Tabarani narrated it from Ibn Mas'ood, while Mundhiri said that he knew of nothing wrong in it

[82] The degeneration of the arteries due to the build-up of fatty deposits

[83] Rashidy, 2000

[84] Bukhâri

[85] Ibn Mâjah

[86] Ahmed

[87] Qardawi, 1997

[88] Ibrahim, A. S. (أحمد شوقي ابراهيم) 2004

[89] Ibrahim, A. S. (أحمد شوقي ابراهيم) 2004

[90] Muslim

[91] Muslim

[92] Muslim

Chapter 2
Biochemical Body

[1] Abouleish, n.d

[2] Tirmidhi (sound according to Albâni)

[3] Bukhâri, Muslim and Tirmidhi

[4] Holford, 2005a

[5] This saying is commonly related to the Prophet but there is no certain proof that it actually is a hadith.

[6] Jauziyah, 2003

[7] Dhahabi, S. (أبي عبد الله شمس الدين بن عثمان الذهبي). 2004

[8] Bukhâri and Muslim

[9] Muslim

¹⁰ From a sound hadith recorded by Ahmed and Ibn Mâjah

¹¹ Greger, 2003, Dec 24

¹² A hadith graded as 'good, but at one point in its chain there is a single narrator'

¹³ Najjâr, Z. (زغلول النجار), 2003b.

¹⁴ Greger, 2003, Dec 24

¹⁵ Revill, 2005

¹⁶ Ahmed and Ibn Mâjah

¹⁷ Ibrahim, A. S., 2004

¹⁸ Ibrahim, A. S. (أحمد شوقي ابراهيم), 2004

¹⁹ Gajdusek, 1976, Dec.13

²⁰ Greger, 2003, Dec 24

²¹ Revill, 2005

²² Revill, 2005

²³ The information in this section had been written before the emergence of Swine flu virus and, *subhân Allâh*, it all came true. In 2009, the viral crossover occurred between bird flu and human flu viruses to yield the deadly new viral species. Pigs, as expected, had been the incubation vessel that enabled this crossover to occur.

²⁴ Beneficial nutrients of plant origin

²⁵ Holford, 2005a

²⁶ Duyff, 2002

²⁷ Note that the Arabic word حب 'Habb' is commonly translated as corn, although the word in Arabic includes all grains.

²⁸ What is an antioxidant? Antioxidants protect the body against 'free radicals' and other hazardous substances which are released in the body as a result of oxidative reactions. Oxygen is a vital nutrient needed by every cell in our body every second of our life to produce the energy necessary to sustain all vital processes. During normal biochemical reactions, oxygen may become unstable by losing one of its electrons; to regain stability, oxygen seeks to retrieve this missing electron from neighbouring cells and tissues converting them into what are called free radicals. Free radicals may be also generated by any other combustion process like smoking, exposure to radiation, deep-frying or barbecuing. The resulting free radicals are in their turn unstable molecules, they also try to reach stability by attacking other cells thus initiating a chain reaction that can set havoc to our whole system.

²⁹ These are beneficial nutrients from plant origin.

[30] Bukhâri

[31] Smolin & Grosvenor, 1994

[32] Duyff, 2002

[33] Prostaglandins are hormone -like substances controlling, among other things, the process of inflammation, blood clotting and allergic reactions.

[34] See the large body of hadiths on this topic in the collections of Bukhâri and Muslim

[35] Ṭabarâni in his *Mu'jam al-Kabeer* and Tirmidhi in *Ash-Shama'il al-Muhammadiyyah*

[36] Tirmidhi and Ahmed

[37] A light soup that has a soft milky consistency and hence its name 'talbeenah' from 'laban' which in Arabic means milk. It is made from whole barley flour.

[38] Bukhâri, Muslim and Ahmed

[39] Amino acids are the 'building blocks' of the protein molecules.

[40] The amino acid tyrosine is part of the adrenaline, noradrenaline and dopamine molecules; tryptophan is part of serotonin; and histidine is part of the histamine molecule.

[41] Ahmed and others

[42] The length of time food waste lingers in the intestine before it is excreted.

[43] Brown, 1991

[44] Gluten is the protein responsible for bread leavening and it is one of the most common food *allergens* (i.e. it causes allergic reaction).

[45] Note that the Arabic word حب الحصيد is translated as *grain for harvests*, although, in a more specified way, it particularly refers to wheat grains.

[46] Haemorrhoids: painful swelling of veins near the anus.

[47] Diverticulosis is the presence of tiny sacs formed when the intestinal wall becomes weakened, which can get infected and become very painful.

[48] Brown, 1991

[49] Ursell, 2000

[50] Brown, 1991

[51] Smolin & Grosvenor, 1994

[52] Brown, 1991

[53] Rutin is very effective in strengthening the fine blood capillaries, thus relieving many circulatory problems; it is also a treatment for glaucoma.

[54] Brown, 1991

[55] Holford, 2005a

[56] Brown, 1991

[57] Brown, 1991

[58] Langley, 2004

[59] Marsili, Calzuola, Gianfranceschi, 2004, July

[60] Langley, 2004

[61] *Hydrolytic* means that they react with water and eventually decompose.

[62] Lipschutz-Robinson, 1996-2005

[63] Kenton, 1999

[64] Chlorophyll is the green plant pigment responsible for absorbing energy from the sun and transporting it to the cells.

[65] Langley, 2004

[66] The acid waste is usually resulting from hot dry environment, low water consumption, and acid-forming food such as meat and processed sugars.

[67] Langley, 2004

[68] The essential amino acid s are protein building blocks which the human body is unable to synthesize, and instead must be provided from food.

[69] Lipschutz-Robinson, 1996-2005

[70] The word ثمرات in Arabic is translated as *fruits*, but also in a wider sense, it refers to various produce.

[71] Langley, 2004

[72] Divisi, et. al., 2006, and Simonich, et al., 2007

[73] Stansbry, 1999

[74] Stansbry, 1999

[75] Bukhâri, Muslim, Abu Dâwood and Ibn Mâjah

[76] Holford, 2005a

[77] Sayyid, A. (عبد الباسط السيد) 2002

[78] Ursell, 2000

[79] Holford, 2005a

[80] Duyff, 2002

[81] Duyff, 2002

[82] Ursell, 2000

[83] The ethylene gas causes the rapid ripening of fruits and vegetables and makes carrots taste bitter.

[84] Alkire, 1998

[85] Katzer, 2005

[86] Katzer, 2005

[87] Dhahabi, S. (أبي عبد الله شمس الدين بن عثمان الذهبي), 2004

[88] Bukhâri

[89] Jauziyah, 2003

[90] Ingram, 2002

[91] Berberoglu, 2003

[92] Lindgren, 1997

[93] Epicenter, 2003

[94] Epicenter, 2003

[95] Bukhâri, Muslim, Abu Dâwood, Nasâ'i and Ahmed

[96] Jauziyah, 2003

[97] Epicenter, 2003

[98] Ibn Mâjah, Abu Dâwood, and Tirmidhi, who graded it 'good, but at one point in its chain there is a single narrator'.

[99] Chard, n.d.

[100] Chard, n.d.

[101] Ursell, 2000

[102] Ursell, 2000

[103] Abu Dâwood and Tirmidhi (sound according to Albâni)

[104] Muslim and Tirmidhi

[105] Bukhâri and Muslim

[106] Ursell, 2000

[107] Ursell, 2000

[108] Bukhâri and Muslim

[109] Muslim, Ibn Mâjah, Nasâ'i and Ahmed

[110] Ursell, 2000

[111] Jauziyah, (شمس الدين ابن قيم الجوزية) 2001

[112] Bukhâri and Muslim

[113] Ursell, 2000

[114] Ursell, 2000

[115] Ursell, 2000

[116] Dhahabi, S. (أبي عبد الله شمس الدين بن عثمان الذهبي) 2004

[117] Jauziyah, 2003

[118] Ursell, 2000

[119] Huang et al., 1990

[120] Yamahara et al., 1985

[121] Masuda et al., 2004

[122] Aggarwal & Shishodia, 2004

[123] Young et al., 2005

[124] Nurtjahja-Tjendraputra et al., 2003

[125] Mahady et al., 2003

[126] Note that the Arabic word 'Rayḥân' رَيحان may be translated in a broad sense as 'sweet and delightful smell' or may specifically refer to the herb basil.

[127] Nasâ'i and Abu Dâwood

[128] Ody, 2000

[129] Jayasinghe et al., 2003

[130] Synergy is when two or more drugs or chemical agents interact to produce a new or better effect than their separate effects.

[131] Muslim, Abu Dâwood and Nasâ'i

[132] Satoh & Sugawara, 2003

[133] Jauziyah, 2003

[134] Kapiszewska et al., 2005

[135] Sokmen et al., 2004

[136] Dhahabi, S. (أبي عبد الله شمس الدين بن عثمان الذهبي) 2004

[137] Ody, 2000

[138] Ody, 2000

[139] Bayhaqi, as noted by Adh-Dhahabi in his *Medicine of the Prophet*

[140] Ody, 2000

[141] Ody, 2000

[142] Valenzuela et al., 2003

[143] Moss et al., 2003

[144] Ody, 2000

[145] Ody, 2000

[146] Bremness, 1990

[147] Trickey, 2003

[148] Jauziyah, 2003

[149] Atkins, 2002

[150] Oedema is an excess of watery fluid collecting in the tissues.

[151] Gray, 2003

[152] Atkins, 2002

[153] Katzer, 2005

[154] Katzer, 2005

[155] Bremness, 1990

[156] Gagandeep et al., 2005

[157] Bremness, 1990

[158] Ibn Mâjah and Ḥâkim (a good hadith)

[159] Ody, 2000

[160] Satyanarayana et al.

[161] Aggarwal & Shishodia, 2004

[162] Choi & Hwang, 2004

[163] Puodziuniene et al.

[164] Krishna & Banerjee, 1999

[165] Nostro et al., 2005

[166] Platel et al., 2002

[167] Bukhâri, Muslim, Tirmidhi, Ibn Mâjah and Ahmed

[168] Luetjohann, 1998

[169] Luetjohann, 1998

[170] Thrombosis is a condition in which the blood changes from liquid to solid state, producing a blood clot.

[171] Enomoto et al., 2001

[172] Rchid et al., 2004

[173] Ali & Blunden, 2003

[174] Luetjohann, 1998

[175] Jauziyah, 2003

[176] Bremness, 1990

[177] Jauziyah, 2003

[178] Mucilage is a viscous or gelatinous substance of plant origin and is used in medicines.

[179] Bremness, 1990

[180] Damanik et al., 2004

[181] Saxena & Vikram, 2004

[182] Handa et al., 2005

[183] Thompson-Coon & Ernst, 2003

[184] Seeds such as walnuts are even a richer plant-source of omega-3s; the most common dietary source is fatty fish like sardines and salmon.

[185] Reed, 2002

[186] Xiaoling, 1999

[187] Plants for a Future, 1997-2000

[188] Reed, 2002

[189] Bayhaqi

[190] Jauziyah, 2003

[191] Chevrier et al., 2005

[192] Muslim

[193] A variety of date; ripe dates or date paste

[194] Tirmidhi, Ibn Mâjah and Ahmed (sound according to Albâni)

[195] Muslim

[196] Bukhâri and Muslim

[197] Muslim

[198] Islamweb Fatwa Center, n.d.

[199] Bukhâri, Muslim, Tirmidhi and Abu Dâwood

[200] Bukhâri and Bayhaqi (graded as sound)

[201] Amer, n.d.

[202] Jauziyah, 2003

[203] Gout is the painful condition resulting from the precipitation of uric acid in the joints mainly due to excess meat consumption.

[204] Alabaster, n.d.

[205] Ursell, 2000

[206] Ursell, 2000

[207] From a hadith narrated by both Bukhâri and Muslim

[208] Dhahabi, S. (أبي عبد الله شمس الدين بن عثمان الذهبي) (2004)

[209] Dhahabi, S. (أبي عبد الله شمس الدين بن عثمان الذهبي) (2004)

[210] Jauziyah, 2003

[211] Holford, 2005a

[212] Carper, 2001

[213] Antioxidants are known to help empower the immune system, increase resistance to infection, increase fertility and reduce inflammation as in arthritis; they also protect the DNA (nuclear genetic material) from any possible damage caused by free radicals — seen as the main cause of cancer development. Furthermore, antioxidants play an important role in protecting against atherosclerosis and heart disease; they are also powerful liver tonics and detoxifying agents.

214 Ursell, 2000

215 Horvath, 1999

216 Keevil et al., 2000

217 Cited in Jaret. 2000

218 Jaret. 2000

219 Cited in Jaret. 2000

220 *Doctor's Guide*, 1997

221 *Doctor's Guide*, 1997

222 Gordon, 2005

223 Gil et al., 2000

224 According to this explanation of the verse, the Arabic word *ṭalḥ* refers to banana plants, whereas other explanations suggest other types of trees.

225 Jauziyah, 2003

226 Ursell, 2000

227 Jauziyah, 2003

228 Scrivner, 2003

229 Sayyid, A. (عبد الباسط السيد) 2002

230 Holford, 2005a

231 Quice, n.d

232 Nâsâ'i, noted in Jauziyah 2003

233 Quince, n.d.

234 Jauziyah, 2003

235 Bukhâri, Muslim, Nasâ'i, Abu Dâwood, Tirmidhi, Ibn Mâjah and Ahmed

236 Morton, 1987

237 Morton, 1987

238 Dhahabi, S. (أبي عبد الله شمس الدين بن عثمان الذهبي) 2004

239 Trickey, 2003

240 Glycosides are compounds of a sugar attached to another molecule. A wide variety occurs in plants and some, such as digitalis and rutin, have proven medicinal benefits.

241 Dhahabi, S. (أبي عبد الله شمس الدين بن عثمان الذهبي) 2004

242 BMR is the amount of energy consumed by the body while at rest.

243 Nykamp, 2004, May

244 Bukhâri

245 Dafni, Levy, & Lev, 2005

246 Dafni, Levy & Lev, 2005

247 Chinese Jujube, 2001-2004

248 Amino acids are organic acids containing an amine group which carries a nitrogen atom.

249 Smolin & Grosvenor, 1994

250 Sayyid, A. (عبد الباسط السيد), 2003

251 Smolin & Grosvenor, 1994

252 Smolin & Grosvenor, 1994

253 Dhahabi, S. (أبي عبد الله شمس الدين بن عثمان الذهبي) 2004

254 Muslim

255 A hadith with a chain that stops at 'Umar, narrated by Imam Mâlik

256 Hâkim (a sound hadith according to Albâni)

257 Sources of iron from plants include cereals, beans and dark green leafy vegetables.

258 Duyff, 2002

259 Haas, 2006

260 Duyff, 2002

261 Jauziyah, 2003

262 Jauziyah, 2003

263 Bukhâri, Muslim, Tirmidhi, Nasâ'i, Ibn Mâjah and Ahmed

264 Bukhâri and Muslim

265 Ursell, 2000

266 Duyff, 2002

267 Ursell, 2000

268 Ahmed and Ibn Mâjah (a sound hadith according to Albâni)

269 Smolin & Grosvenor, 1994

270 Duyff, 2002

271 Causing malformation of an embryo.

272 Ursell, 2000

273 Ursell, 2000

274 Peanuts are technically legumes (like peas, they grow in a pod); while they do not grow on trees like almonds or walnuts do, we use them as nuts in our food, so that is why they are mentioned in both contexts in this section.

275 Ursell, 2000

276 The night of 'Isrâ' and Mi'râj is the night of the Prophet's journey from Makkah to Jerusalem and then to the heavens.

[277] Bukhâri and Muslim

[278] Tirmidhi and Abu Dâwood (a good hadith)

[279] Muslim and Abu Dâwood

[280] Duyff, 2002

[281] Duyff, 2002

[282] Duyff, 2002

[283] Duyff, 2002

[284] Fankhauser, 1998

[285] Duyff, 2002

[286] Probiotics are active bacterial cultures that help reintroduce or 'charge' healthy intestinal bacteria (microflora).

[287] Duyff, 2002

[288] Haas, 2006

[289] A ranking system devised to describe the effect of consumed sugars or carbohydrates on the blood sugar level (BSL)

[290] Haas, 2006

[291] Haas, 2006

[292] Duyff, 2002

[293] Bukhâri, Muslim, Abu Dâwood, Tirmidhi and Ibn Mâjah

[294] Ghee is clarified butter obtained by heating the butter to remove milk solids for it to withstand higher cooking temperatures and have a longer shelf life.

[295] Ḥâkim (who graded it as sound) and Bayhaqi

[296] Sayyid, A. (عبد الباسط السيد) 2002

[297] Scrivner, 2003

[298] Bukhâri and Muslim

[299] Ursell, 2000

[300] Waili, 2004

[301] Waili, 2004

[302] O'Connell, 2005; Waili & Boni, 2003

[303] McGuire, 1999; Rajan et al., 2002

[304] Busserolles, et al., 2002; Gross, 2004; Schramm et al., 2003

[305] Mercan, et al., 2007

[306] Molan, 2001

[307] Sanz, et al., 2005

[308] Prebiotics are substances in food that promote the growth of normal healthful bacteria naturally existing in the human colon.

[309] Ustunol & Gandhi, 2001

[310] Somal et al., 1994

[311] Dunford, 2005

[312] Wahdan, 1998

[313] Atkins, 2002

[314] Atkins, 2002

[315] Atkins, 2002

[316] *Royalisin,* is an example of a potent antibacterial protein found only in royal jelly (Fujiwara et al.,1990).

[317] Erem et al., 2006

[318] 10-HDA is another active substance newly discovered. It is a potential antibacterial, antiviral, antifungal and antioxidant agent which strengthens immunity, prevents some forms of cancer and alleviates the symptoms of Rheumatoid Arthritis (Chiangmai Royal Jelly Co., Ltd., n.d.)

[319] Wang et al., 2004

[320] Duyff, 2002

[321] Hensrud, 2006

[322] Homemade mayo is very rich in fats, and its content of raw eggs is not recommended anymore since the bird flu virus outbreak

[323] Ibn Mâjah and Bayhaqi (sound according to Albâni)

[324] Abu Dâwood (a sound hadith)

[325] Duyff, 2002

[326] Duyff, 2002

[327] Muslim

[328] Marieb, 2003

[329] Duyff, 2002

[330] Muslim, Ahmed and Bayhaqi

[331] Ibn Mâjah, Ahmed and Hâkim (a sound hadith)

[332] Nassar, M. (محمود نصار) 1995

[333] The Vinegar Institute, n.d.

[334] The Vinegar Institute, n.d.

[335] Muslim, Abu Dâwood, Tirmidhi, Nasâ'i and Ibn Mâjah

[336] Leeman, et al., 2005, July 20

[337] Ostman et al., 2005, June 29

[338] *Frugal Living*, n.d.

[339] Bukhâri and Muslim

[340] Muslim

[341] Tirmidhi and Abu Dâwood (Albâni graded it as sound)

[342] Weil, 1998

[343] Muslim and Abu Dâwood

[344] Gray, 2003

[345] Gray, 2003

[346] Adh-Dhahabi, 2004

[347] Bukhâri and Tirmidhi

[348] Sears, 1995

[349] Prime Minister of Norway in the 1980s and '90s and later was director general of the World Health Organization (WHO: 1998 - 2003). Trained as a physician, she became identified with public health and environmental issues and with the rights of women. (Encyclopaedia Brittanica Online)

[350] The Asahi Glass Foundation, n.d

[351] Tabari's explanation of the following verse

[352] Abu Dâwood and Bayhaqi (a sound hadith)

[353] Hadith stated as such by Ahmed (with a good chain of narration) and mentioned in a different format by Muslim

[354] Bayhaqi

[355] Nasâ'i (Hâkim graded it as sound)

[356] Bukhâri

[357] Rosenthal, 2001

[358] According to Ibn Mâjah this hadith has a weak chain, but is strengthened by the sound hadith before it in Ibn Mâjah's collection, in which Allah's Messenger r says: "Do not be wasteful, do not be wasteful!"

[359] Muslim, Ibn Mâjah and Ahmed

[360] Bukhâri

[361] Bukhâri

[362] Borysenko, 1998

[363] Weil, 1998

[364] Weil, 1998

[365] Tirmidhi

[366] Bukhâri

[367] Ibrahim, A. S. (أحمد شوقي ابراهيم). 2004

[368] Peters & Woodham, 2000

[369] World Health Organization, 1980

370   Bukhâri and Muslim

371   Abu Dâwood

Chapter 3
Intellectual Body

1   Muslim and Ibn Mâjah

2   Tirmidhi (he graded it as 'good, but at one point in its chain there is a single narrator')

3   Winston, 2004

4   Restak, 1997

5   Dhahabi, S. (أبي عبد الله شمس الدين بن عثمان الذهبي) 2004

6   Bukhâri

7   Tirmidhi and Ahmed

8   Restak, 1997

9   Ibn Mâjah (this is a weak hadith, but Nawawi said that its meaning was true)

10   Muslim

11   Restak, 1997

12   Ahmed, Abu Dâwood, Tirmidhi, and Ibn Mâjah (its chain of narration is good)

13   Winston, 2004

14   Dementia is the deterioration in mental activity that occurs mainly in the elderly.

15   Bukhâri, Tirmidhi, Ibn Mâjah and Ahmed

16   Muslim and Abu Dâwood

17   Bukhâri

18   McManners, 2004

19   Cited in: Restak, 1997

20   Santrock, 2003

21   Santrock, 2003

22   Hobson, et al., 2000

23   Santrock, 2003

24   Empson & Clarke, 1970

25   Santrock, 2003

26   In the past decade scientists have begun to question their knowledge concerning brain cells. The notion that neurons are fully formed by the age of two and start decaying thereafter no longer rang true. In 1999, neuroscientific research carried

out by Princeton University demonstrating the growth of new cells in monkey brains started a whole new era in this highly complicated field. Since that date, mounting evidence has been piling up showing that adult human brain cells can actually regenerate if given the proper conditions. Lindvall, O. and McKay, R. (2003). Brain repair by cell replacement and regeneration. The National Academy of Sciences. http://www.pnas.org/ and Discoveries: Brain cells regeneration. http://www.novusresearch.com/ Retrieved July 2010.

[27] Bukhâri

[28] Ḥâkim (a sound hadith in *Fortification of the Muslim*)

[29] Bukhâri, Muslim, Abu Dâwood and Tirmidhi

[30] A detailed discussion of the subconscious is found in the next section of this chapter.

[31] Muslim

[32] Yahya, 2003b

[33] A hadith mentioned and authenticated by Albâni

[34] Abd Al-Ati, 2003

[35] Santrock, 2003

[36] Campebell et al., 2001; Ramey & Ramey, 1998; Ramey & Campbell, 1984 & Ramey et al., 2001

[37] Muslim and Abu Dâwood

[38] Restak, 1997

[39] Abd Al-Ati, 2003

[40] Holford, 2005b

[41] Jauziyah, (شمس الدين ابن قيم الجوزية) 2003b

[42] Note that I am referring here to yoga as a physical exercise and not as a spiritual practice.

[43] Restak, 1997

[44] Restak, 1997

[45] For more detailed information, a good reference is 'Optimum Nutrition for the Mind' by Patrick Holford

[46] Holford, 2005b

[47] Glycemic index is a measure of how fast glucose is released into the bloodstream after food consumption, with the glucose itself being given the value of 100.

[48] Leeman, et al., 2005, July 20

[49] Holford, 2005b

[50] Holford, 2005b

440   *Healing Body & Soul*

[51] Ibn Mâjah, authenticated by Albâni

[52] Holford, 2005b

[53] Holford, 2005b

[54] Carper, 2001

[55] Imam Mâlik

[56] Holford, 2005b

[57] Restak, 1997

[58] Smolin & Grosvenor, 1994

[59] Carper, 2001

[60] Holford, 2005b

[61] Ibn Mâjah and Ahmed, authenticated by Albâni

[62] Carper, 2001

[63] Ursell, 2000

[64] Homocysteine is an amino acid believed to be a major risk factor in the development of atherosclerosis and circulatory problems.

[65] McCully, 1999

[66] Abu Dâwood, Tirmidhi, Ibn Mâjah, and Ahmed (graded as good)

[67] Holford, 2005b

[68] Winston, 2004

[69] Holford, 2005b

[70] Holford, 2005b

[71] Holford, 2005b

[72] Ahmed and Mâlik, authenticated by Albâni

[73] Dyer, 1990

[74] Murphy, 2000

[75] 'Abd al-Kâfy, 2005-2006

[76] Ibn Sani ابن السن

[77] Murphy, 2000

[78] Murphy, 2000

[79] Murphy, 2000

[80] Muslim

[81] Tirmidhi and Ibn Mâjah

[82] Bukhâri

[83] James, 2005

[84] Holford, 2005b

[85] Holford, 2005b

[86] For an explanation of this concept, please read the explanation of verse 42 of *Soorat az-Zumar* (Qur'an 39: 42).

[87] Bukhâri and Muslim; This and most of the supplications and remembrances of Allah in this book are taken from *Fortification of the Muslim: supplications from the Qur'an and Sunnah,* compiled by Sa'eed ibn 'Ali ibn Wahf Qaḥṭâni, Cairo: Dar Al-Salaam

[88] Ahmed (graded as sound by Albâni)

[89] For more details check: *Fortification of the Muslim, supplications from the Qur'an and Sunnah* compiled by Sa'eed ibn 'Ali ibn Wahf Qaḥṭâni or in Arabic, الوابل الصيب من الكلم الطيب لإبن القيم الجوزية.

Chapter 4
Emotional Body

[1] Santrock, 2003

[2] Santrock, 2003

[3] Martin, 1998

[4] Martin, 1998

[5] Environmental in this context refers to events and circumstances happening in our lives, and does not refer to factors involving the earth's environment (for this latter see the last section of Chapter Two).

[6] Maddi, 1996

[7] Muslim

[8] Landrine & Klonoff, 2001

[9] Alder, 2001

[10] Bukhâri

[11] Santrock, 2003

[12] Santrock, 2003

[13] Marieb, 2003

[14] Brown, 2007

[15] Lazarus, 1993 & 2000

[16] Santrock, 2003

[17] This anecdote, along with several others related in this book, is one of many such stories circulating via email. The author is unknown to me, and I hope I am excused for using it as an illustrative example.

[18] Muslim

442   *Healing Body & Soul*

[19] Jauziyah. (شمس الدين ابن القيم الجوزية) 2003b

[20] Ghazâli the Younger (محمد الغزالي) 2003a

[21] Abu Dâwood, Ahmed and Tirmidhi (who graded it as sound)

[22] Muslim

[23] Jandi, K. (خالد الجندي) 2004

[24] Muslim

[25] Jandi, K. (خالد الجندي) 2004

[26] Ahmed Bukhatir is a singer of Islamic *nasheed* (songs without musical instrumental accompaniment) who is well known in the Arab world.

[27] Carter-Scott, 1999

[28] Muslim

[29] Khaled, A. (عمرو خالد) 2003a

[30] A *hadith qudsi*, or 'sacred hadith', is a hadith of the Prophet r communicated to him by Allah, although the wording of the hadith is usually that of the Prophet, and not necessarily Allah's exact words to him. (Ibrahim & Johnson-Davies, 1980)

[31] Related by Bukhâri, Muslim and Nasâ'i

[32] Williams et al., 1998

[33] Sugarman, 1997

[34] Ghazâli the Younger (محمد الغزالي) 2003a

[35] Cited in: Khaled, A. (عمرو خالد) 2003a

[36] Muslim, Abu Dâwood, Ibn Mâjah and Tirmidhi

[37] Cited in: Khaled, A. (عمرو خالد) 2003a

[38] Dyer, 1990

[39] Bukhâri and Muslim

[40] Cited in Schnebly, 2000

[41] Dyer, 1990

[42] Dyer, 1990

[43] Bukhâri

[44] Schnebly, 2000

[45] Tirmidhi, Ibn Mâjah and Ibn Ḥibbân (a good hadith)

[46] Muslim; This du'â' can also be said in the evening, substituting the word 'evening' for 'morning'. From *Fortification of the Muslim: Supplications from the Qur'an and Sunnah,* compiled by Sa'eed ibn 'Ali ibn Wahf Qaḥtâni, Cairo: Dar Al-Salaam, 2004, pp. 128-129. Unless otherwise noted, all the supplications and remembrances are from this source, and they are from reliable hadiths.

[47] Ibn Mâjah and Ahmed

[48] Abu Dâwood (in *Fortification of the Muslim*)

⁴⁹ Muslim

⁵⁰ Carter-Scott, 1999

⁵¹ Dyer, 1990

⁵² Ghazâli the Younger, (محمد الغزالي), 2003a

⁵³ Khirallah, n.d

⁵⁴ Tirmidhi and Ibn Mâjah (a good hadith)

⁵⁵ Tirmidhi (a sound hadith)

⁵⁶ Bukhâri

⁵⁷ Ahmed (graded as sound by Albâni)

⁵⁸ Muslim

⁵⁹ Can, 2004

⁶⁰ Gulen, 2004

⁶¹ Muslim

⁶² Muslim, Abu Dâwood and Tirmidhi

⁶³ Bukhâri and Muslim

⁶⁴ Tirmidhi (a good, sound hadith)

⁶⁵ This anecdote, along with several others related in this book, is one of many such stories circulating via email. The author is unknown to me, and I hope I am excused for using it as an illustrative example.

⁶⁶ Yahya, 2003c

⁶⁷ Yahya, 2003c

⁶⁸ Bukhâri and Muslim

⁶⁹ 'Abd Al Kâfi, (د. عمر عبد الكافي) n.d.

⁷⁰ Yahya, 2003c

⁷¹ Johnson, 1999

⁷² Bayhaqi (authenticated by Albâni)

⁷³ Rahman and Khaleque, 1996

⁷⁴ 'Ulwân. 2003

⁷⁵ This anecdote, along with several others related in this book, is one of many such stories circulating via email. The author is unknown to me, and I hope I am excused for using it as an illustrative example.

⁷⁶ Myers & Diener, 1995

⁷⁷ Tirmidhi (who said it was 'good, but at one point in its chain there is a single narrator')

⁷⁸ Muslim

⁷⁹ That is, what has been written and decreed cannot be altered. (Ibrahim and Johnson-Davies 1976, p. 68)

[80] Tirmidhi, graded as sound by Albâni

[81] Seymour & Shervington, 2001

[82] Abu Dâwood and Tirmidhi, with a good chain

[83] Seymour & Shervington, 2001

[84] Seymour & Shervington, 2001

[85] Hallowell, 2004

[86] Mubarakpuri, 1995, pp.395-396; this phrase is found in *Qur'an 12: 92.*

[87] Ghazâli the Elder (أبي حامد محمد الغزالي), 2004

[88] Bayhaqi (graded as sound by Albâni)

[89] Ghazâli the Younger, (محمد الغزالي) 2003a

[90] Ghazâli the Elder, 2001

[91] Ghazâli the Elder, (أبي حامد محمد الغزالي) 2004

[92] Ghazâli the Younger, (محمد الغزالي) 2003a

[93] Tirmidhi (a good hadith)

[94] Ghazâli the Elder, 2001

[95] Dyer, 1990

[96] Carter-Scott, 1999

[97] Bukhâri and Muslim

[98] Bukhâri and Muslim

[99] Bukhâri

[100] Muslim

[101] Ahmed, a reliable hadith

[102] Muslim

[103] Bukhâri

[104] This anecdote, along with several others related in this book, is one of many such stories circulating via email. The author is unknown to me, and I hope I am excused for using it as an illustrative example.

[105] Dhahabi, (أبي عبد الله شمس الدين بن عثمان الذهبي), 2004

[106] Holford, 2005a

[107] Holford, 2005b

[108] Tirmidhi (Albâni said that it had a weak chain, but that its correlation with the Hadith was good)

[109] Hâkim (a good hadith)

[110] Abu Dâwood and Ahmed, authenticated by Albâni

[111] Ahmed, authenticated by Albâni

[112] This anecdote, along with several others related in this book, is one of many such stories circulating via email. The author is unknown to me, and I hope I am excused for using it as an illustrative example.

[113] Ghazâli the Elder (أبي حامد محمد الغزالي), 2004

[114] Dyer, 1990

[115] Bukhâri and Muslim

[116] Tirmidhi, Ibn Mâjah and Ahmed (a sound hadith)

[117] Qarni, 2005

[118] Ghazâli the Elder, 2001

[119] Ghazâli the Elder, 2001

[120] Bukhâri and Muslim

[121] Bukhâri

[122] Khan, 2003

[123] Jobs, 2005

[124] Seymour & Shervington, 2001

[125] de Bono, 1996

[126] Ghazâli, 2004 (أبي حامد محمد الغزالي)

[127] Tirmidhi, who graded it 'good, but at one point in its chain there is a single narrator'

[128] Ṭabarâni (its chain of narration is good)

[129] Bukhâri

[130] Carter-Scott, 1999

[131] Carter-Scott, 1999

[132] Ahmed (a good hadith)

[133] Bukhâri and Muslim

[134] Tirmidhi (a good or sound hadith)

[135] Ghazâli, 2001

[136] Jauziyah, (شمس الدين ابن قيم الجوزية) 2001

[137] Tirmidhi and Ibn Mâjah, with a good chain of narration

[138] Ghazâli the Elder, 2001

[139] Muslim, Ahmed and Nasâ'i

[140] Tirmidhi

[141] Tirmidhi and Ahmed

[142] Carter-Scott, 1999

[143] Carter-Scott, 1999

[144] Muslim

[145] Ghazâli the Elder, 2001

146 Hadith authenticated by Albâni
147 Ghazâli, 2001
148 Muslim
149 Bayhaqi (authenticated by Albâni)
150 A sound hadith noted by Albâni
151 'Abd Al Kâfi, (عمر عبد الكافي) n.d.
152 Tirmidhi and Ibn Mâjah
153 Muslim
154 Bukhâri and Muslim
155 This anecdote, along with several others related in this book, is one of many such stories circulating via email. The author is unknown to me, and I hope I am excused for using it as an illustrative example.
156 Bukhâri
157 Schnebly, 2000
158 Schnebly, 2000
159 Bukhâri
160 Anecdote related in Khamees & Mitkees, n.d.
161 Ghazâli the Elder, 2001
162 Muslim
163 Mannion, 2002
164 Saber, 2001
165 Weil, 1998
166 Santrock, 2003
167 Santrock, 2003
168 Bukhâri and Muslim
169 Muslim
170 Santrock, 2003
171 Bukhâri and Muslim
172 Ghazâli the Younger (محمد الغزالي), 2003a
173 Keyes, 1984
174 A sound hadith noted by Albâni
175 Bukhâri and Muslim
176 Bukhâri
177 Bukhâri, Muslim and Abu Dâwood
178 Bukhâri
179 Tirmidhi

180 Winston, 2004
181 Bukhâri, Muslim, Abu Dâwood and Tirmidhi
182 Bukhâri and Muslim
183 Bukhâri
184 Bukhâri
185 Bukhâri
186 Bukhâri and Muslim
187 Muslim
188 Bukhâri
189 Santrock, 2003
190 Bukhâri and Muslim
191 Santrock, 2003
192 Santrock, 2003
193 Bukhâri and Muslim
194 Santrock, 2003
195 Santrock, 2003

Chapter 5
Spiritual Body

1 Hensrud, 2006
2 CTNS, n.d.
3 Ramadan, 2004
4 Hensrud, 2006
5 Hensrud, 2006
6 Ramadan, 2004
7 Ramadan, 2004
8 Ramadan, 2004
9 Bukhâri
10 Abu Dâwood
11 Williams, 2004
12 Bukhâri
13 Hensrud, 2006.
14 Muslim and Tirmidhi
15 Bukhâri and Muslim

[16] Abd Al-Ati, 2003.

[17] Gray, 2003

[18] Bukhâri

[19] The advice given here is based on experiences from the author's own culture and should be understood in that way. It is not recommended to sleep right after a heavy meal but the personal sleeping, eating and working times can be adjusted according to local conditions, day length, season, obligations, etc.

[20] Tirmidhi

[21] Abd Al-Ati, 2003

[22] Bukhâri, Muslim, Ahmed and Tirmidhi

[23] Ibn Mâjah

[24] Khaled, A. (عمرو خالد) 2003c

[25] Abd Al-Ati, 2003

[26] Khaled, A. (عمرو خالد) 2003c

[27] Abd Al-Ati, 2003

[28] Khaled, A. (عمرو خالد) 2003c

[29] Abd Al-Ati, 2003

[30] Abd Al-Ati, 2003

[31] Yahya, 2003b.

[32] Khaled, A. (عمرو خالد) 2004c

[33] Khaled, A. (عمرو خالد) 2004c

[34] Yahya, 2003b

[35] Lazar et al. 2000.

[36] Gillani & Smith, 2001; Tassi & Muzet, 2001

[37] Eppley, Abrams & Shear, 1989; Holmes, 1988; Wallace & Benson, 1972

[38] Tirmidhi, Ahmed and Ibn Mâjah (and Ibn Hibbân noted it in his compilation of sound hadiths, as did Albâni)

[39] Louis, n.d.

[40] Jose Silva UltraMind system, n.d.

[41] More about the spiritual benefits of dhikr can be found in Ibn al-Qayyim Jauziyah's book: الوابل الصيب من الكلم الطيب [*The downpour of good words*]

[42] Bukhâri

[43] Jauziyah, (شمس الدين ابن قيم الجوزية), 2002.

[44] Tirmidhi (a good hadith)

[45] Abd Al-Ati, 2003

[46] Abd Al-Ati, 2003

[47] Bukhâri and Muslim

[48] Abd Al-Ati, 2003

[49] Tirmidhi (a good, sound hadith)

[50] Bukhâri

[51] Bukhâri

[52] Ahmed and Hâkim (a sound hadith)

[53] Bukhâri

[54] According to some scholars' opinions it is the saying of a famous Arab physician.

[55] Bukhâri and Muslim

[56] Chaitow, 2003

[57] Ibn Mâjah and Tirmidhi

[58] Muhammad, H (حامد أحمد حامد محمد) 2002

[59] Mosuli, S. (سامي أحمد الموصلي) 2004

[60] Bukhâri and Muslim

[61] Tirmidhi, Nasâ'i and Hâkim

[62] Ghazâli the Elder (أبي حامد محمد الغزالي) 2004

[63] Ibn Mâjah

[64] Ibn Mâjah

[65] This means that they cause a rapid rise in the blood sugar level (BSL), leading to a hastened insulin surge.

[66] Muslim

[67] Ahmed (a hadith with a strong chain and noted in Albâni's collection of sound hadiths)

[68] Abd Al-Ati, 2003

[69] Myss, 1996

[70] Abd Al-Ati, 2003

[71] A sound hadith

[72] Bukhâri

[73] Bukhâri

[74] Bukhâri

[75] Abd Al-Ati, 2003

[76] Abu Dâwood and Tirmidhi

[77] Ahmed (a sound hadith)

[78] Abu Dâwood, Nasâ'i and Tirmidhi (who called it good and sound)

[79] Hadith cited in Khaled, A.(عمرو خالد) 2003c

80 Tirmidhi

81 Tirmidhi, Abu Dâwood and Ibn Mâjah

82 Bukhâri and Muslim

83 Tirmidhi and Ḥâkim

84 Tirmidhi and Ḥâkim

85 Muslim, Ibn Mâjah and Ahmed

86 Muslim, Tirmidhi and Ahmed

87 noted in *At-Targheeb wat-Tarheeb*

88 MacPhee, 2003.

89 This anecdote, along with several others related in this book, is one of many such stories circulating via email. The author is unknown to me, and I hope I am excused for using it as an illustrative example.

Epilogue

1 'Abd Al Kâfy, (د. عمر عبد الكافي) n.d.

BIBLIOGRAPHY

Sources in English

Abd Al-Ati, H. (2003). *Islam in focus* (4ᵗʰ ed.). Al-Falah Foundation.

Abdul Latif, S. (2002). *The mind al-Qur'an builds* (new edition). Islamic Book Trust.

Abouleish, E. (n.d). Contributions of Islam to medicine. In S. Athar (Ed.), *Islamic medicine*. Retrieved May 16, 2007, from http://www.islam-usa.com/im1.html

Aggarwal, B.B., Shishodia, S. (2004, December). Suppression of the nuclear factor-kappaB activation pathway by spice-derived phytochemicals: reasoning for seasoning. *Ann N Y Acad Sci.*, 1030: 434-41.

Aggarwal, B.B., Takada, Y., and Oommen, O.V. (2004, October). From chemoprevention to chemotherapy: common targets and common goals. *Expert Opin Investig Drugs.* 13 (10): 1327-38.

Alabaster, O. (n.d.). Retrieved February 2004 from: http://www.californiafigs.com/nutrition/dietitians_info.html

Alder, N.E. (2001). A consideration of multiple pathways from socioeconomic status to health. In J.A. Auerbach & B.K. Krimgold (Eds.), *Income, socioeconomic status, and health.* Washington, DC: National Policy Association.

Alexandrovich, I., Rakovitskaya, O., Kolmo, E., Sidorova, T., and Shushunov, S. (2003, July-August). The effect of fennel

(Foeniculum Vulgare) seed oil emulsion in infantile colic: a randomized, placebo-controlled study. *Altern Ther Health Med.* 9 (4): 58-61.

Ali, B.H., Blunden, G. (2003, April). Pharmacological and toxicological properties of Nigella sativa. *Phytother Res.* 17 (4): 299-305.

Alkire, B. (1998). Capers. Retrieved on February 2004 from: http://www.hort.purdue.edu/newcrop/cropfactsheets/caper. html

Amer, W. (n. d). History of Botany Part 1: The Date Palm in Ancient History. Retrieved January 2005 from: http://www.alchemywebsite.com/islam08.html

Amer, W.M. (1994). Taxonomic and documentary study of food plants in Ancient Egypt. Ph.D. thesis, Cairo University.

American Academy of Otolaryngology–Head and Neck Surgery. 2007. Children and Secondhand Smoke. Retrieved 1 October 2007 from: http://www.entnet.org/healthinfo/tobacco/second-hand_smoke.cfm

American Dietitic Association. (2005, April 28). Olive Oil: Fruity, Flavorful...and Confusing. Retrieved February, 2005 from: http://www.eatright.org/cps/rde/xchg/ada/hs.xsl/home_4230_ ENU_HTML.htm

American Medical Association. (2007, June 1). AMA history. Retrieved June 2007 from: http://www.ama-assn.org/ama/pub/category/1854.html

Amin, A., Alkaabi, A., Al-Falasi, S., and Daoud, S.A. (2005, June 1). Chemopreventive activities of Fenugreek against breast cancer. *Cell Biol Int.*

Ann, N.Y., Aggarwal, B.B., Shishodia, S. (2004, December). Suppression of the nuclear factor-kappaB activation pathway by spice-derived phytochemicals: reasoning for seasoning. *Acad Sci.*; 1030: 434-41.

Appendino, G., Mercalli, E., Fuzzati, N., Arnoldi, L., Stavri, M., Gibbons, S., et al. (2004, December). Antimycobacterial coumarins from the sardinian giant fennel. *J Nat Prod.*; 67 (12): 2108-10.

Atkins, R. (2002). *Your Complete Guide to Natural Health.* Pocket Books.

Badria, F.A,, Mikhaeil, B.R., Maatooq, G.T., and Amer, M.M. (2003, July-August). Immunomodulatory triterpenoids from the oleogum resin of Boswellia carterii Birdwood. *Z Naturforsch [C].*; 58 (7-8): 505-16.

Bagamboula, C.F., Uyttendaele, M., and Debevere, J. (2001). Inhibitory effects of spices and herbs towards Shigella sonnei and S. flexneri. *Biol Wet.,* 66 (3b): 523-30.

Bairacli-Levy, J. (1991). *The Complete Herbal Handbook for Farm and Stable.* Boston: Faber.

Barakat, H.N. (1986). Plant life in Douch area: Kharga Oasis, A comparative study of the present and Greaco-Roman period. M.Sc. thesis, Cairo University.

Bender, A.E. & Bender, D.A. (1995). *Oxford Dictionary of Food and Nutrition.* Oxford University Press.

Berberoglu, H. (2003). Retrieved March, 2005 from: http://www.foodreference.com/html/arttruffles.html

Bircher, W.H. (1990). The date palm; A Boon for Mankind. Egypt: Cairo University Herbarium.

Bornstein, M.H. & Bradley, R.H. (Eds.), (2003). *Socioeconomic status, parenting and child development.* Mahwah, NJ: Erlbaum.

Borysenko, J. (1998). *A woman's book of life.* New York: Riverhead

Boskabady, M.H., Khatami, A., and Nazari, A. (2004 July). Possible mechanism(s) for relaxant effects of Foeniculum vulgare on guinea pig tracheal chains. *Pharmazie*, 59 (7): 561-4.

Boskabady, M.H., Shirmohammadi, B., Jandaghi, P., and Kiani, S. (2004, February 25). Possible mechanism(s) for relaxant effect of aqueous and macerated extracts from Nigella sativa on tracheal chains of guinea pig. *BMC Pharmacol.*, 4 (1): 3.

Bremness, L. (1990). *Herbs: Pocket Encyclopedia.* Dorling Kindersley.

Brown, D. (2007). Immunology and infectious diseases. Retrieved May 2007 from: http://www.hhmi.org/cgi-bin/askascientist/highlight.pl?kw=&file=answers%2Fimmunology%2 Fans_011.html

Brown, S. (1991). *Vegetarian Cookery: Pocket Encyclopedia.* Dorling Kindersley.

Bukhâri (1999). *Sahih Al-Bukhari text and translation* vol. I & II. (A. Zidan & D. Zidan, Trans.). Egypt: Islamic Inc.

Burits, M. & Bucar, F. (2000 August). Antioxidant activity of Nigella sativa essential oil. *Phytother Res.*, 14 (5): 323-8.

Burnett, K.M., Solterbeck, L.A., and Strapp, C.M. (2004, October). Scent and mood state following an anxiety-provoking task. *Psychol Rep.*; 95 (2): 707-22.

Busserolles, J., Gueux, E., Rock, E., Mazur, A., and Rayssiguier, Y. (2002, November). Substituting honey for refined carbohydrates protects rats from hypertriglyceridemic and prooxidative effects of fructose. *J Nutr.*,132 (11): 3379-82.

Calzuola, I., Marsili, V., and Gianfranceschi, G.L. (2004, August). Synthesis of antioxidants in wheat sprouts. *J Agric Food Chem.*, 11; 52 (16): 5201-6.

Campanella, L., Bonanni, A., Favero, G., and Tomassetti, M. (2003, April). Determination of antioxidant properties of aromatic herbs, olives and fresh fruit using an enzymatic sensor. *Anal Bioanal Chem.*, 375 (8): 1011-6.

Campebell, F.A., Pungello, E.P., Miller-Johnson, S., Burchinal, M., and Ramey, C.T. (2001). The development of cognitive and academic abilities: Growth curves from an early childhood educational experiment. *Developmental psychology*, 37, 231-243.

Can, S. (2004). *Fundamentals of Rumi's thought.* The Light Inc.

Carter-Scott, C. (1999). *If life is a game, these are the rules* (export ed.). Broadway books.

Chard. n.d. University of Illinois Extension, Urbana program. Retrieved April 2005 from: http://www.urbanext.uiuc.edu/veggies/chard1.html

Chavan, J.K. & Kadam S.S. (1989). Nutritional improvement of cereals by sprouting. *Crit Rev Food Sci Nutr.*, 28 (5): 401-37.

Chevrier, M.R., Ryan, A.E., Lee, D.Y., Zhongze, M., Wu-Yan, Z., and Via, C. S. (2005, May). Boswellia carterii extract inhibits TH1 cytokines and promotes TH2 cytokines in vitro. *Clin Diagn Lab Immunol.*, 12 (5): 575-80.

Chiangmai Royal Jelly Co., Ltd. (n.d.) Royal Jelly. Retrieved September 2007 from: http://www.bee.co.th

Chinese Jujube. (2001-2004). Retrieved March 2005 from: http://www.foodsnherbs.com/new_ page_47.htm

Choi, E.M., Hwang, J.K. (2004, September). Antiinflammatory, analgesic and antioxidant activities of the fruit of Foeniculum vulgare. *Fitoterapia,* 75 (6): 557-65.

Collins, W.A., Maccoby, E.E., Steinberg, L., Hetherington, E.M., & Bornstein, M.H. (2000). Contemporary research on parenting: the case for natural nurture. *American psychologist*, 55, 218-232.

Colome, S., Irvine, C.A., McCunney, R. J., Samet, J. M., & Swankin, D. (1994). Indoor Air Pollution: An Introduction for

Health Professionals. Retrieved 1 October 2007 from: http://www.epa.gov/iaq/pubs/hpguide.html#environmental%20tobacco%20smoke

Cox, J. (2002). *Natural beauty at home* (2nd ed.). Henry Holt & Company.

CTNS. (n.d.). Science and the Spiritual Quest. Retrieved 22 October 2007 from: http://www.ctns.org/ssq/index.html

Dadalioglu, I. & Evrendilek, G.A. (2004 December). Chemical compositions and antibacterial effects of essential oils of Turkish oregano, bay laurel, Spanish lavender, and fennel on common foodborne pathogens. *J Agric Food Chem.*, 29; 52 (26): 8255-60.

Dafni, A., Levy, S., & Lev, E. (2005). The ethnobotany of Christ's Thorn Jujube in Israel. *Journal of Ethnobiology and Ethnomedicine.* 1:8 doi: 10.1186/1746-4269-1-8.

Damanik, R., Wahlqvist, M.L., and Wattanapenpaiboon, N. (2004). The use of a putative lactagogue plant on breast milk production in Simalungun, North Sumatra, Indonesia. *Asia Pac J Clin Nutr.*, 13 (Suppl): S118.

Darshan, S. & Doreswamy, R. (2004, May). Patented antiinflammatory plant drug development from traditional medicine. *Phytother Res.*, 18 (5): 343-57.

Dasgupta, T., Rao, A.R., and Yadava, P.K. (2004, February). Chemomodulatory efficacy of basil leaf (Ocimum basilicum) on drug metabolizing and antioxidant enzymes, and on carcinogen-induced skin and forestomach papillomagenesis. *Phytomedicine*, 11 (2-3): 139-51.

De Bono, E. (1996). *Teach Yourself to Think.* Penguin Books.

De la Lastra, C.A. & Villegas, I. (2005, May). Resveratrol as an anti-inflammatory and anti-aging agent: mechanisms and clinical implications. *Mol Nutr Food Res.*, 49 (5): 405-30.

Delaquis, P.J., Stanich, K., Girard, B., and Mazza, G. (2002, March 25). Antimicrobial activity of individual and mixed fractions of dill, cilantro, coriander and eucalyptus essential oils. *Int J Food Microbiol.*, 74 (1-2): 101-9.

Divisi, D., Di Tommaso, S., Salvemini, S., Garramone, M., & Crisci, R. (2006, August). Diet and cancer. Acta Biomed.;77 (2): 118-23.

Doctor's Guide. (1997, April 8). Study Reveals New Antioxidant; More Potent than C, E and Beta-Carotene. Retrieved January 2005 from: http://www.docguide.com/dg.nsf/PrintPrint/5A24 8D0AAF3A01108525647300683986

Duke, J. A. & Ayensu, E. S. (1985). *Medicinal Plants of China.* Reference Publications.

Dunford, C. (2005, April). The use of honey-derived dressings to promote effective wound management (Review). Prof Nurse., 20 (8): 35-8.

Duyff, R. L. (2002). *American Dietetic Association: Complete food and nutrition guide* (2nd ed.). Hoboken, NJ: Wiley & Sons.

Dyer, W. W. (1990). *You'll see it when you believe it.* Arrow Books.

Edris, A.E., & Farrag, E.S. (2003, April). Antifungal activity of peppermint and sweet basil essential oils and their major aroma constituents on some plant pathogenic fungi from the vapor phase. *Nahrung.*, 47 (2): 117-21.

El-Fiky, I. (1999). *10 keys to ultimate success.* Sales Masters Press.

Empson, J.A.C., & Clarke, P.R.F. (1970). Rapid eye movements and remembering. *Nature*, 227, 287-288.

Enomoto, S., Asano, R., Iwahori, Y., Narui, T., Okada, Y., Singab, A.N., et al. (2001, March). Hematological studies on black cumin oil from the seeds of Nigella sativa. *Biol Pharm Bull.*, 24 (3): 307-10.

Epicenter. (2003). Encyclopedia of spices. Retrieved March 2005 from: http://www.theepicentre.com/Spices/spiceref.html

Eppley, K.R., Abrams, A.I., & Shear, J. (1989). Differential affects of relaxation on trait anxiety. *J. of Clinical Psychology*, 45, 957-974.

Erem C, Deger O, Ovali E, Barlak Y. (2006, Oct). The effects of royal jelly on autoimmunity in Graves' disease. *Endocrine*. 30 (2): 175-83.

Eskander, E.F. & Jun, H. Won. (1995). Hypoglycaemic and hyperinsulinemic effects of some Egyptian herbs used for the treatment of diabetes mellitus (type II) in rats. *Egyptian Journal of Pharmaceutical Sciences*, 36 (1-6): 331-342.

Ezekwe, M. O., Omara, A. T. R., and Membrahtu T. (1999). Nutritive characterization of purslane accessions as influenced by planting date. *Plant Foods for Human Nutrition (Dordrecht)*, 54(3): 183-191.

Facciola, S. (1991). *Cornucopia - A Sourcebook for Edible Plants*. Kampong Publications.

Famuyiwa, O.O., Hazmi, M.A.F., Jasser, S.J., Sulimani, R.A., Jayakumar, R.V. and Nuaim, A.A.A. (1992). A comparison of acute glycaemic and insulin response to date and oral dextrose in diabetic and non-diabetic subjects. *Journal of Medicine and Biochemistry, College of Medicine Riyadh*, 15 (3): 397-402.

Fankhauser, D. B. (1998, July 20). Making Buttermilk. Retrieved January, 2005 from: http://biology.clc.uc.edu/Fankhauser/index.htm

Farah, I.O., Begum, R.A. (2003). Effect of Nigella sativa (N. sativa L.) and oxidative stress on the survival pattern of MCF-7 breast cancer cells. *Biomed Sci Instrum.*, 39: 359-64.

Fil, M.I., et al. (2000). Antioxidant activity of pomegranate juice and its relationship with phenolic composition and processing. *J Agric Food Chem.*, 48: 4581-9.

Fotsis. T., et al. (1997). Flavonoids, dietary-derived inhibitors of cell proliferation and in vitro angiogenesis. *Cancer Research*, 57: 2916-2921.

Frugal Living. (n.d.). Uses of vinegar. Retrieved September, 2006 from: http://groups.msn.com/FrugalLiving/vinegar.msnw

Fujiwara S, Imai J, Fujiwara M, Yaeshima T, Kawashima T, Kobayashi K. (Jul 5, 1990). A potent antibacterial protein in royal jelly: Purification and determination of the primary structure of royalisin. *J Biol Chem*. 265(19):11333-7.

Gagandeep, Dhiman, M., Mendiz, E., Rao, A.R., and Kale, R.K. (2005, June). Chemopreventive effects of mustard (Brassica compestris) on chemically induced tumorigenesis in murine forestomach and uterine cervix. *Hum Exp Toxicol.*, 24 (6): 303-12.

Gajdusek, C. (1976, December 13). Unconventional viruses and the origin and disappearance of kuru. Retrieved March, 2005 from: http://nobelprize.org/nobel_prizes/medicine/laureates/1976/gajdusek-lecture.html

Gandeboeuf, D., Dupre, C., RoeckelDrevet, P., Nicolas, P., and Chevalier, G. (1997). Grouping and identification of (Tuber) species using RAPD markers. *Can. J. Bot.-Rev.*, 75 (1): 36-45.

Gavrankapetanovic, F., Klinika, T. and Sarajevo, K. (1997). Medical aspects of fasting. *Med Arh.*, 51 (1-2): 25-7.

Ghazâli, A.(the Elder) (2001). *The Book of Religious Learning*, vol. I to IV. (F. Karim, Trans.). Islamic Book Service

Gil, M.I., Tomas-Barberan, F.A., Hess-Pierce, B., Holcroft, D.M., and Kader, A. A. (2000). Antioxidant activity of pomegranate juice. *Journal of Agricultural Food and Chemistry*, 48: 4581-4589.

Gillani, N.B. & Smith, J.C. (2001). Zen meditation and ABC relaxation theory. *Journal of Clinical Psychology*, 57: 839-846.

Gordon, S. (2005, March 22). Pomegranate juice reduces cardio-vascular risks. Forbes/ HealthDay News. Retrieved January 2005 from: http://www.wildoats.com/content/Pomegranate.pdf

Gray, J. (2003). *The Mars and Venus diet and exercise solution.* Pan Books.

Greger, M. (2003, December 24). USDA Misleading American Public about Beef Safety. Organic Consumers Association. Retrieved February, 2005 from: http://www.organicconsumers.org/

Gross, H. (2004, March 29). Effect of honey consumption on plasma antioxidant status in human subjects. Abstract presented at the American Chemical Society.

Gulen, F. (2000). *Advocate of dialogue.* The Fountain.

Gulen, F. (2004). *Towards a global civilization of love and tolerance.* The Light Inc.

Haas, E., M. (2006). *Staying healthy with nutrition.* Berkeley: Celestial arts

Haggag, E.G., Abou-Moustafa, M.A., Boucher, W., and Theoharides, T.C. (2003). The effect of an herbal water-extract on histamine release from mast cells and on allergic asthma. *J Herb Pharmacother.,* 3 (4): 41-54.

Hajhashemi, V., Ghannadi, A., Jafarabadi, H. (2004, March). Black cumin seed essential oil, as a potent analgesic and anti-inflammatory drug. *Phytother Res.,* 18 (3): 195-9.

Haas, E., M. (2006). *Staying healthy with nutrition.* Berkeley: Celestial arts

Hakam, J. (1999) 'The Arabic Constituent in Modern English.' Unpublished essay.

Hale, T. (2001). *Breathing Free.* London: Coronet Books, Hodder & Stoughton.

Hallowell, E. M. (2004). *Dare to Forgive*. Health Communications.

Hanafy, M.S. & Hatem, M.E. (1991, September). Studies on the antimicrobial activity of Nigella sativa seed (black cumin). *Ethnopharmacol.*, 34 (2-3): 275-8.

Handa, T., Yamaguchi, K., Sono, Y., and Yazawa, K. (2005, June). Effects of fenugreek seed extract in obese mice fed a high-fat diet. *Biosci Biotechnol Biochem.*, 69 (6): 1186-8.

Hensrud, D. (Ed.). (2006). *The Mayo clinic plan: 10 essential steps to a better body and healthier life*. New York: Time.

Hertog, M.G.L., et al. (1997). Antioxidant flavonols and coronary heart disease risk. *Lancet*, 349:699.

Hills, L. (1984). *The Good Fruit Guide*. HDRA.

Hobson, J.A., Pace Schott, E.F., & Stickgold, R. (2000). Dreaming and the brain. *Behavior and Brain Sciences*, 23, 793-842.

Holford, P. (2005a). *New Optimum Nutrition Bible*. London: Piatkus Books.

Holford, P. (2005b). *Optimum Nutrition for the Mind*. London: Piatkus Books.

Holmes, D.S. (1988). The influence of meditation versus rest on psychological considerations. In M. West (Ed.), *the psychology of meditation*. New York: Oxford University.

Horvath, H. (1999, July 6). Will wine help your heart? Retrieved January 2005 from:
http://unv.net/HEALTH/heart/9907/06/wine.heart/index.html

Hourani, A. (1991) *A History of the Arab Peoples*. New York: Warner Books

Huang, Q., Matsuda, H., Sakai, K., Yamahara, J., and Tamai, Y. (1990, December). The effect of ginger on serotonin induced hypothermia and diarrhea. *Yakugaku Zasshi,* 110 (12): 936-42.

Iacobellis, N.S., Lo Cantore, P., Capasso, F., and Senatore. F. (2005, January 12). Antibacterial activity of Cuminum cyminum L. and Carum carvi L. essential oils. *J Agric Food Chem.*, 53 (1): 57-61.

Ibrahim, E. and Johnson-Davies, D. (1976) *An-Nawawi's Forty Hadith.* Beirut: Holy Koran Publishing House

Ibrahim, E. and Johnson-Davies, D. (1980) *Forty Hadith Qudsi.* Beirut: Dar Al-Koran Al-Kareem

Ingram, S. (2002). The real nutritional value of fungi. Retrieved on February 2004 from: http://www.world-of-fungi.org/Mostly_Medical/Stephanie_Ingram/NUTRITIONAL_VALUE.htm

Islam, M.W., Zakaria, M.N.M., Radhakrishnan, R., Habibullah, M., and Chan, K. (1998). Evaluation of analgesic activity of the aerial parts of Portulaca oleracea v. sativa and its comparison with two related spices. *Journal of Pharmacy and Pharmacology*, 50 (Suppl.): 226.

Islamweb Fatwa Center. (n.d.). Retrieved October 2007 from: http://islamweb.net/ver2/fatwa/ShowFatwa.php?lang=E&Id=89646&Option=FatwaId

Jadayil, S.A., Tukan, S.K., and Takruri, H.R. (1999). Bioavailability of iron from four different local food plants in Jordan. *Plant Foods Hum Nutr.*, 54 (4): 285-94.

James, T. (2005). Some Basic Concepts in Neuro-Linguistic Programming. Tad James and Advanced Neuro Dynamics Retrieved January 2005 from: http://www.nlp.com/whatisnlp.aspx

Jaret, P. (2000, March 31). Wine or Welch's? Grape juice provides health benefits without alcohol. Retrieved January 2005 from: http://archives.cnn.com/2000/HEALTH/alternative/03/31/wine.heart.wmd/

Jauziyah, I. (2003). *Healing with the medicine of the Prophet* (2nd ed.) (J. Abual Rub, Trans.). KSA: Darussalam.

Jayasinghe, C., Gotoh, N., Aoki, T., and Wada, S. (2003, July 16). Phenolics composition and antioxidant activity of sweet basil. *J Agric Food Chem*, 51 (15): 4442-9.

Jobs, S. (2005). *Stanford Report:* You've got to find what you love. 14 June 2005. Retrieved 20 October 2007 from: http://news-service.stanford.edu/news/2005/june15/jobs-061505.html

Johnson, S. (1999). *Who moved my cheese.* Vermillion, Ebury Press.

Johnston, C.S. (2005, June). Strategies for healthy weight loss: from vitamin C to the glycemic response. *J Am Coll Nutr.*, 24 (3): 158-65.

Jolad, S.D., Lantz, R.C., Solyom, A.M., Chen, G.J., Bates, R.B., and Timmermann, B.N. (2004 July). Fresh organically grown ginger (Zingiber officinale): composition and effects on LPS-induced PGE2 production. *Phytochemistry*, 65 (13): 1937-54.

Jose Silva UltraMind system. (n.d.). Silva lessons. Retrieved September 2005 from: http://www.silvaultramindsystem.com/

Kalus, U., Pruss, A., Bystron, J., Jurecka, M., Smekalova, A., Lichius, J.J., and Kiesewetter, H. (2003, December). Effect of Nigella sativa (black seed) on subjective feeling in patients with allergic diseases. *Phytother Res.*, 17 (10): 1209-14.

Kapiszewska, M., Soltys, E., Visioli, F., Cierniak, A., and Zajac, G. (2005, March). The protective ability of the Mediterranean plant extracts against the oxidative DNA damage. The role of the radical oxygen species and the polyphenol content. *Physiol Pharmacol.*, 56 Suppl 1: 183-97.

Kaplan, M., Hayek, T., Raz, A., Coleman, R., Dornfeld, L., Vaya, J., et al. (2001). Pomegranate Juice Supplementation to Atherosclerotic Mice Reduces Macrophage Lipid Peroxidation, Cellular Cholesterol Accumulation and Development of Atherosclerosis. *Journal of Nutrition*, 131 (8): 2082-2089.

Kataria, M. (1999). *Laugh Your Way to Health*. Madhuri International.

Katzer, G. (2005). Gernot Katzer's Spice. University of Graz. Retrieved February 2005 from: http://www.uni-graz.at/~katzer/engl/spice_small.html

Keevil, J.G., Osman, H.E., Reed, J.D., and Folts, J.D. (2000, January). Grape juice, but not orange juice or grapefruit juice, inhibits human platelet aggregation. *J Nutr.*, 130 (1): 53-6.

Kenton, L. (1999). *10 Steps to a New You*. Ebury Press.

Keyes, K. (1984) The Hundredth Monkey. Retrieved 6 November, 2007 from: http://www.hundredthmonkey.net/

Khan, W. (2003). *The moral vision: Islamic ethics for success in life*. Goodword Books.

Khirallah, L.(n.d.) Retrieved 6th July 2003 from: http://membres. lycos.fr/philosophie15/

Kim, M.A., Sakong, J.K., Kim, E.J., Kim, E.H., and Kim, E.H. (2005, February). Effect of aromatherapy massage for the relief of constipation in the elderly. *Taehan Kanho Hakhoe Chi.*, 35 (1): 56-64.

Kim, M.J., Nam, E.S., and Paik, S.I. (2005, February). The effects of aromatherapy on pain, depression, and life satisfaction of arthritis patients. *Taehan Kanho Hakhoe Chi.*, 35 (1): 186-94.

Kimberlin, R. H. (1992). Human Spongiform Encephalopathies and BSE. *Medical Laboratory Sciences*, 49: 216-217.

Kleinman, L., Messina-Kleinman, D. 2001, March 20. What's in Your Smokes? Retrieved 1 October 2007 from: http://nosmoking.org/march01/03-27-01-1.html

Krajvcovivcova-Kudlavckova, M., Ginter, E., Blavzicvek, P., Klvanova, J., and Babinska, K. (2001, March 15). Nutritional status in adults on an alternative or traditional diet. *Cas Lek Cesk.*, 140 (5): 142-6.

Krishna, De M. & Banerjee, A.B. De A. (1999, November). Antimicrobial screening of some Indian spices. *Phytother Res.*, 13 (7): 616-8.

Lai, P.K. & Roy, J. (2004, June). Antimicrobial and chemopreventive properties of herbs and spices. *Curr Med Chem.*, 11 (11): 1451-60.

Landrine, H. & Klonoff, E.A. (2001). Cultural diversity and health psychology. In A. Baum, T.A. Revenson, and J.E. Singer (Eds.), *Handbook of Health Psychology*. Mahwah, NJ: Erlbaum.

Lange, M. & Bayard Hora, F. (1963). *Collins Guide to Mushrooms and Toadstools*. Collins.

Langley, S. (2004). *The Naturopathy Workbook*. College of Naturopathic Medicine (CNM).

Lanska, D. (1992). *The Illustrated Guide to Edible Plants*. Chancellor Press.

Lazar, S.W., Bush, G., Gollub, R.L., Fricchione, G.L., Khalsa, G., and Benson, H. (2000). Functional brain mapping of the relaxation response and meditation. *Neuroreport*, 15, 1581-1585.

Lazarus, R.S. (1993). Coping theory & research: Past, present, and future. *Psychosomatic Medicine*, 55, 234-247.

Lazarus, R.S. (2000). Toward better research on stress and coping. *American Psychologist*, 55, 665-673.

Le, P.M., Benhaddou-Andaloussi, A., Elimadi, A., Settaf, A., Cherrah, Y., and Haddad, P.S. (2004, October). The petroleum ether extract of Nigella sativa exerts lipid-lowering and insulin-sensitizing actions in the rat. *J Ethnopharmacol.*, 94 (2-3): 251-9.

Lee, K.G. & Shibamoto, T. (2002, August 14). Determination of antioxidant potential of volatile extracts isolated from various herbs and spices. *J Agric Food Chem.*, 50 (17): 4947-52.

Leeman, M., Ostman, E., and Bjorck, I. (2005, July 20). Vinegar dressing and cold storage of potatoes lowers postprandial glycaemic and insulinaemic responses in healthy subjects. *Eur J Clin Nutr.*

Leiper, J.B., Molla, A.M., and Molla, A.M. (2003, December). Effects on health of fluid restriction during fasting in Ramadan. *Eur J Clin Nutr.*, 57 Suppl 2: S30-8.

Lindgren, J. (March–April 1997). *Eating raw mushrooms causes problems.* Bulletin of the Puget Sound Mycological Society, 338, Jan. 1998; (Electronic Edition). Retrieved 2 December 2007 from: http://www.psms.org/sporeprints/sp338.html

Lindlahr, H. (2005). *Philosophy of natural therapeutics.* London: Vermilion.

Lipschutz-Robinson. (1996-2005). Holistic Health for People and Animals: Sherley's wellness café. Retrieved February, 2005 from: http://www.shirleys-wellness-cafe.com/greens.htm#a

Lo Cantore, P., Iacobellis, N.S., De Marco, A., Capasso, F., and Senatore, F. (2004, December 29). Antibacterial activity of Coriandrum sativum L. and Foeniculum vulgare Miller Var. vulgare (Miller) essential oils. *J Agric Food Chem.*, 52 (26): 7862-6.

Lorenz, K. (1980). Cereal sprouts: composition, nutritive value, food applications. *Crit Rev Food Sci Nutr.*, 13 (4): 353-85.

Louis, S. (n.d.). EEG waves. Retrieved October, 2006 from: http://www.brown.edu/Departments/Clinical_Neurosciences/louis/eegfreq.html

Lucas, A. & Harris, J.R. (1962). *Ancient Egyptian Materials and Industries*. London: Edward Arnold.

Luetjohann, S. (1998). *The Healing Power of Black Cumin* (1st English ed.). Lotus Light Publications.

MacPhee, M. (2003, January-March). Medicine for the heart: the embodiment of faith in Morocco. *Med Anthropol.*, 22 (1): 53-83.

Maddi, S. (1996). *Personality theories* (6th ed.). Pacific Grove, CA: Brooks/ Cole.

Mahady, G.B., Pendland, S.L., Yun, G.S., Lu, Z.Z., and Stoia, A. (2003, September-October). Ginger (Zingiber officinale Roscoe) and the gingerols inhibit the growth of Cag A+ strains of Helicobacter pylori. *Anticancer Res.*, 23 (5A): 3699-702.

Makenna, P. (2004). *Change Your Life in Seven Days*. Bantam Press.

Manchanda, A. (2004a). *Naturally Beautiful Your Hair* (2nd ed.). International Print-O-Pac Ltd.

Manchanda, A. (2004b). *Naturally Beautiful Your Skin* (2nd ed.). International Print-O-Pac Ltd.

Mannion, J. (2002). *The everything philosophy book*. Massachusetts: Adams Media Corporation.

Marieb, E. N. (2003). *Essentials of Human Anatomy and Physiology* (7th ed.). Pearson Education; Benjamin Cummings.

Marsili, V., Calzuola, I., Gianfranceschi, G.L. (2004, July). Nutritional relevance of wheat sprouts containing high levels of organic phosphates and antioxidant compounds. *J Clin Gastroenterol.*, 38 (6 Suppl): S123-6.

Martin, P. (1998). *The healing mind*. New York: Thomas Dunne Books.

Martinez-Tome, M., Jimenez, A.M., Ruggieri, S., Frega, N., Strabbioli, R., and Murcia, M.A. (2001, September). Antioxidant properties of Mediterranean spices compared with common food additives. *J Food Prot.,* 64 (9): 1412-9.

Marvin, C. (2000). Philosophers: Ibn Sina (Avicenna). Retrieved May 16, 2007 from http://www.trincoll.edu/depts/phil/philo/phils/muslim/sina.html

Masic, I. (1997). The art of therapy in Islamic medicine. *Med Arh.,* 51 (1-2): 5-8.

Masuda, Y., Kikuzaki, H., Hisamoto, M., and Nakatani, N. (2004). Antioxidant properties of gingerol related compounds from ginger. *Biofactors,* 21 (1-4): 293-6.

McCully, K. (1999). *Homocysteine Revolution.* Keates, NTC/Contemporary Publishing group.

McGregor, M. (1991). Psychoneuroimmunology: What Is It and Can It Help Me? New York: Academic Press.

McGuire, M. (1999, April 5). Researcher studying honey as possible allergy remedy. University of Connecticut. Retrieved September 2006 from: http://advance.uconn.edu/1999/990405/04059903.htm

Mcloyd, V.C. (2000). Poverty; In A. Kazdin (Ed.), *Encyclopedia of Psychology.* Washington, DC, & New York: American Psychological Association & Oxford University Press.

McManners, D. (2004). *The Holistic Doctor.* Piatkus Books.

Mercan, N., Guvensen, A., Celik, A., Katircioglu, H. (2007, March) Antimicrobial activity and pollen composition of honey samples collected from different provinces in Turkey. Nat Prod Res., 21 (3):187-95.

Molan, P.C. (2001, November-December) The potential of honey to promote oral wellness. *General Dentistry,* 49 (6): 584-9.

Mondal, D.K., Yousuf, B.M., Banu, L.A., Ferdousi, R., Khalil, M., and Shamim, K.M. (2004, July). Effect of fenugreek seeds on the fasting blood glucose level in the streptozotocin induced diabetic rats. *Mymensingh Med J.*, 13 (2): 161-4.

Moreno, G. F., Montañés, R. M.L., Alvarez, B. J.C., Galve, G. M. 1991 Oct 26. An analysis of the effect of tobacco on glucose metabolism. *Med Clin (Barc)*; 97 (14): 531-2.

Morton, J. (1987). Citron. p. 179–182. In: Fruits of warm climates. Retrieved March 2005 from: http://www.hort.purdue.edu/newcrop/morton/citron.html

Moss, M., Cook, J., Weanes, K., and Duckett, P. (2003, January). Aromas of rosemary and lavender essential oils differentially affect cognition and mood in healthy adults. *Int J Neurosci.*, 113(1):15-38.

Mubarakpuri, S. (1995) *The Sealed Nectar,* Riyadh: Maktaba Darus-Salam

Murphy, J. (2000). *The Power of Your Subconscious Mind.* Bantam Books.

Myers, D., & E. Diener. (1995). Who is Happy? *Psychological Science,* 6: 10.

Myss, C., 1996. *Anatomy of the spirit.* New York: Three Rivers Press.

Nagamia, H. F. (1998, October 1). Islamic medicine: History and current practice. Retrieved May 16, 2007 from http://www.iiim.org/islamed3.html

Naggar, T.B., Gomez-Serranillos, M.P., Carretero, M.E., and Villar, A.M. (2003, September). Neuropharmacological activity of Nigella sativa L. extracts. *J Ethnopharmacol.*, 88 (1): 63-8.

Nair, S., Nagar, R., and Gupta, R. (1998, August). Antioxidant phenolics and flavonoids in common Indian foods. *J Assoc Physicians India.*, 46(8):708-10.

Nakano, Y., Matsunaga, H., Saita, T., Mori, M., Katano, M., and Okabe, H. (1998, March). Antiproliferative constituents in

Umbelliferae plants II. Screening for polyacetylenes in some Umbelliferae plants, and isolation of panaxynol and falcarindiol from the root of Heracleum moellendorffii. *Biol Pharm Bull.*, 21 (3): 257-61.

National Library of Medicine. (1998, April 5). Islamic Culture and the Medical Arts: Prophetic medicine. Retrieved June 6, 2007 from http://www.nlm.nih.gov/exhibition/islamic_medical/islamic_05.html

National Library of Medicine. (n.d.). Retrieved September, 2006 from: http://www.nlm.nih.gov

Nawawi. (2003). *The meadows of the righteous* (vol. I & II). (I. Marouf, Trans.). Egypt: Dar-Al-Manarah.

Ng, S.S. & Figg, W.D. (2003, September-October). Antitumor activity of herbal supplements in human prostate cancer xenografts implanted in immunodeficient mice. *Anticancer Res.*, 23 (5A): 3585-90.

Ninfali, P., Mea, G., Giorgini, S., Rocchi, M., Bacchiocca, M. (2005, February). Antioxidant capacity of vegetables, spices and dressings relevant to nutrition. *Br J Nutr.*, 93 (2): 257-66.

Niven, D. (2000). *The 100 simple secrets of happy people.* San Francisco: Harper Collins.

Nostro, A., Cellini, L., Di Bartolomeo, S., Di Campli, E., Grande, R., Cannatelli, M.A., Marzio, L. and Alonzo, V. (2005, March). Antibacterial effect of plant extracts against Helicobacter pylori. *Phytother Res.*, 19 (3): 198-202.

Nurtjahja-Tjendraputra, E., Ammit, A.J., Roufogalis, B.D., Tran, V.H., and Duke, C.C. (2003). Effective anti-platelet and COX-1 enzyme inhibitors from pungent constituents of ginger. *Thromb Res.*, 111 (4-5): 259-65.

Nykamp, D.L. (2004, May). Possible association of acute lateral-wall myocardial infarction and bitter orange supplement. *Ann Pharmacother.*, 38 (5): 812-6.

O'Connell, N. (2005, November 2). It's all the buzz. *Nurs Stand.*, 8; 20 (8): 22-4.

Ody, P. (2000). *The Complete Guide, Medicinal, Herbal* (2nd ed.). Dorling Kindersley Books.

Oluwatuyi, M., Kaatz, G.W., and Gibbons, S. (2004, December). Antibacterial and resistance modifying activity of Rosmarinus officinalis. *Phytochemistry*, 65 (24): 3249-54.

Opalchenova, G. & Obreshkova, D. (2003, July). Comparative studies on the activity of basil — an essential oil from Ocimum basilicum L. against multidrug resistant clinical isolates of the genera Staphylococcus, Enterococcus and Pseudomonas by using different test methods. *J Microbiol Methods*, 54 (1): 105-10.

Ostman, E., Granfeldt, Y., Persson, L., and Bjorck, I. (2005, June 29). Vinegar supplementation lowers glucose and insulin responses and increases satiety after a bread meal in healthy subjects. *Eur J Clin Nutr.*

Ozbek, H., Ugras, S., Dulger, H., Bayram, I., Tuncer, I., Ozturk, G., et al. (2003, April). Hepatoprotective effect of Foeniculum vulgare essential oil. *Fitoterapia*, 74 (3): 317-9.

Peale, N.V. (2004). *The Power of Positive Thinking*. Vermillion, Ebury Press.

Penalver, P., Huerta, B., Borge, C., Astorga, R., Romero, R., and Perea, A. (2005, January). Antimicrobial activity of five essential oils against origin strains of the Enterobacteriaceae family. *APMIS*, 113 (1): 1-6.

Peters, D. & Woodham, A. (2000). *The Complete Guide: Integrated Medicine*. London: Dorling Kindersley Books.

Plants For A Future. (1997-2000). Retrieved April 2005 from: http://www.ibiblio.org/pfaf/cgi-bin/arr_html?Portulaca+olera cea&CAN=LATIND

Platel, K., Rao, A., Saraswathi, G., and Srinivasan, K. (2002, December). Digestive stimulant action of three Indian spice mixes in experimental rats. *Nahrung.*, 46 (6): 394-8.

Pukalskas, A., Van Beek, T.A., and de Waard, P. (2005, May 13). Development of a triple hyphenated HPLC-radical scavenging detection-DAD-SPE-NMR system for the rapid identification of antioxidants in complex plant extracts. *J Chromatogr A.*, 1074 (1-2): 81-8.

Puodziuniene, G., Janulis, V., Milasius, A., and Budnikas, M. (2004). Development of throat clearing herbal teas. *Medicina (Kaunas)*, 40 (8): 762-7.

Qahtani, S. A. (2004). *Fortification of the Muslim.* (K. E. Abu Zeid, Trans.). Cairo: Dar-us-Salam.

Qahtani, S. A. (2004). *Invocations from the Qur'an and Sunnah* (compiled). (K. E. Abu Zeid, Trans.). Egypt: Dar-Al-Salam.

Qardawi, Y. (1997). *Introduction to Islam.* Egypt: Islamic Inc.

Qardawi, Y. (2002). *The Sunnah: A source of civilization* (2nd ed.). Egypt: Al-Falah Foundation.

Qardawi, Y. (2003). *Hygiene in Sunnah* (2nd ed.). Egypt: Al-Falah Foundation.

Qarni, A. (2005). *Don't be sad.* (Faisal M. Shafeeq, Trans.). Riyadh: International Islamic Publishing House

Qoz, A.A. (2004). *Men and the universe, reflections of Ibn Al-Quayyem* (2nd ed.). Riyadh: Darussalam.

Quince. (n.d). Cydonia oblonga. Retrieved March, 2005 from: http://www.agroforestry.co.uk/ansample.html

Rababah, T.M., Hettiarachchy, N.S., and Horax, R. (2004, August 11). Total phenolics and antioxidant activities of fenugreek, green tea, black tea, grape seed, ginger, rosemary, gotu kola, and ginkgo extracts, vitamin E, and tert-butylhydroquinone. *J Agric Food Chem.*, 52 (16): 5183-6.

Rahman, T., & Khaleque, A. (1996). The purpose in life and academic behaviour problem students. *Social indicators research*, 39:59.

Rajan, T.V., Tennen, H., Lindquist, R.L., Cohen, L., and Clive, J. (2002). Effect of honey on symptoms of rhinoconjunctivitis. *Annals of Allergy, Asthma, and Immunology*, 88: 198-203.

Ramadan, T. (2004). *Western Muslims and the future of Islam*. Oxford University Press.

Ramey, C.T. & Ramey, S.L. (1998). Early Prevention and Early Experience. *American Psychologist*, 53, 109-120.

Ramey, C.T., & Campbell, F.A. (1984). Preventive education for high-risk children: cognitive consequences of the Carolina Abeccedarian Project. *American Journal of Mental Deficiency*, 88, 515-523.

Ramey, C.T., Ramey, S.L., & Lanzi, R.G. (2001). Intelligence and experience. In R.J. Sternberg & E. L. Grigorenko (Eds.), *Environmental effects on cognitive abilities*. Mahwah, NJ: Erlbaum.

Rashidy, H. (2000, March). The poisoned arrow. Unpublished article.

Rchid, H., Chevassus, H., Nmila, R., Guiral, C., Petit, P., Chokairi, M., et al. (2004, October). Nigella sativa seed extracts enhance glucose-induced insulin release from rat-isolated Langerhans islets. *Fundam Clin Pharmacol.*, 18 (5): 525-9.

Reed, D. W. (2002, March 2). Wild flowers of the Southeastern US. Retrieved March 2005 from: http://2bnthewild.com/plants/H186.htm#OtherInfo

Restak, R. M. (1997). *Older and Wiser*. New York: Berkley Books.

Revill, J.(2005). *Bird flu*. Rodale International.

Rosenthal, M. S. (2001). *Stopping cancer at the source*. Canada: Your Health Press

Ruby, B.C., Gaskill, S.E., Slivka, D., and Harger, S.G. (2005, February). The addition of fenugreek extract (Trigonella foenumgraecum) to glucose feeding increases muscle glycogen resynthesis after exercise. *Amino Acids*, 28 (1): 71-6.

Santoyo, S., Cavero, S., Jaime, L., Ibanez, E., Senorans, F.J., and Reglero, G. (2005, April). Chemical composition and antimicrobial activity of Rosmarinus officinalis L. essential oil obtained via supercritical fluid extraction. *J Food Prot.*, 68 (4): 790-5.

Santrock, J. W. (2003). *Psychology 7* (7th ed.). McGraw-Hill.

Sanz, M.L., Polemis, N., Morales, V., Corzo, N., Drakoularakou, A., Gibson, G.R., Rastall, R.A. (2005, April 20). In vitro investigation into the potential prebiotic activity of honey oligosaccharides. *J Agric Food Chem.*, 53 (8): 2914-21.

Satoh, T. & Sugawara, Y. (2003, January). Effects on humans elicited by inhaling the fragrance of essential oils: sensory test, multi-channel thermometric study and forehead surface potential wave measurement on basil and peppermint. *Anal Sci.*, 19 (1): 139-46.

Satyanarayana, S., Sushruta, K., Sarma, G.S., Srinivas, N., and Subba Raju, G.V. (2004). Antioxidant activity of the aqueous extracts of spicy food additives-evaluation and comparison with ascorbic acid in in-vitro systems. *J Herb Pharmacother.*, 4 (2): 1-10.

Savino, F., Cresi, F., Castagno, E., Silvestro, L., and Oggero, R. (2005, April). A randomized double-blind placebo-controlled trial of a standardized extract of Matricariae recutita, Foeniculum vulgare and Melissa officinalis in the treatment of breastfed colicky infants. *Phytother Res.*, 19 (4): 335-40.

Saxena, A. & Vikram, N.K. (2004, April). Role of selected Indian plants in management of type 2 diabetes: a review. *J Altern Complement Med.*, 10 (2): 369-78.

Schnebly, L. (2000). *Nurturing yourself and others*. Fisher books.

Schramm, D.D., Karim, M., Schrader, H.R., Holt, R.R., Cardetti, M., and Keen, C.L. (2003). Honey with high levels of antioxidants can provide protection to healthy human subjects. *Journal of Agricultural and Food Chemistry*, 51 (6): 1732-1735.

Sears, B. (1995). *Enter the Zone*. Regan Books, Harper Collins Publishers.

Seymour, J. & Shervington, M. (2001). *Peak Performance through NLP*. Dorling Kindersley.

Shahidi, F. (2000). Antioxidant factors in plant foods and selected oilseeds. *Biofactors*, 13 (1-4): 179-85.

Sharma, R. S. (2006). *The Monk Who Sold His Ferrari*. Harper-Torch, Harper Collins.

Simon, J.E., Chadwick, A.F. and Craker, L.E. (1984). Caper; In: *Herbs – An Indexed Bibliography*. 1971-1980. Archon Books.

Simonich, M.T., et al. (2007, June). Natural chlorophyll inhibits aflatoxin B1-induced multi-organ carcinogenesis in the rat. Carcinogenesis; 28(6):1294-302.

Singh, G., Kapoor, I.P., Pandey, S.K., Singh, U.K., and Singh, R.K. (2002, November). Studies on essential oils: part 10; antibacterial activity of volatile oils of some spices. *Phytother Res.*, 16 (7): 680-2.

Singh, U.P., Singh, D.P., Maurya, S., Maheshwari, R., Singh, M., Dubey, R.S., and Singh, R.B. (2004). Investigation on the phenolics of some spices having pharmacotherapeuthic properties. *J Herb Pharmacother.*, 4 (4): 27-42.

Sinha, R., Anderson, D.E., McDonald, S.S., and Greenwald, P. (2003, July-September). Cancer risk and diet in India. *J Postgrad Med.*, 49 (3): 222-8.

Sivanada Yoga Vedanta centre. (1998). *Yoga mind and body*. Dorling Kindersley Books.

Smolin & Grosvenor. (1994). *Nutrition science and applications* vol. I & II (2nd ed.). John Wiley & Sons.

Sokmen, M., Serkedjieva, J., Daferera, D., Gulluce, M., Polissiou, M., Tepe, B., et al. (2004, June 2). In vitro antioxidant, antimicrobial, and antiviral activities of the essential oil and various extracts from herbal parts and callus cultures of Origanum acutidens. *J Agric Food Chem.*, 52 (11): 3309-12.

Somal, N., Coley, K.E., Molan, P.C., and Hancock, B.M. (1994, October). Susceptibility of Helicobacter pylori to the antibacterial activity of manuka honey. *J R Soc Med.*, 87 (10): 644.

Stansbry, J. E. (1999, August). Cancer prevention diet. Nutrition Science News. Retrieved June 2005 from: http://www.chiro.org/nutrition/FULL/Cancer_Prevention_Diet.shtml

Stare, F. J. & Whelan, E. (1998). *Fad-free nutrition*. Hunter House Inc.

Steinmann, A., Schatzle, M., Agathos, M., and Breit, R. (1997, May). Allergic contact dermatitis from black cumin (Nigella sativa) oil after topical use. *Contact Dermatitis*, 36 (5): 268-9.

Suboh, S.M., Bilto, Y.Y., and Aburjai, T.A. (2004, April). Protective effects of selected medicinal plants against protein degradation, lipid peroxidation and deformability loss of oxidatively stressed human erythrocytes. *Phytother Res.*, 18 (4): 280-4.

Sugarman, S. (1997). Happiness and population density. Master's thesis, California State University, Long Beach, California.

Suppakul, P., Miltz, J., Sonneveld, K., and Bigger, S.W. (2003, May 21). Antimicrobial properties of basil and its possible application in food packaging. *J Agric Food Chem.*, 51 (11): 3197-207.

Surh, Y.J., Park, K.K., Chun, K.S., Lee, L.J., Lee, E., and Lee, S.S. (1999). Anti-tumor-promoting activities of selected pungent phenolic substances present in ginger. *J Environ Pathol Toxicol Oncol.*, 18 (2): 131-9.

Tassi, P., & Muzet, A. (2001). Defining states of consciousness. *Neuroscience and Biobehavioral Review*, 25, 175-191.

The Asahi Glass Foundation, (n.d.). Profiles of the 2004 Blue Planet Prize Recipients. Retrieved September, 2005 from: http://www.af-info.or.jp/eng/honor/hot/enr-brundtland.html

The Vinegar Institute. (n.d.). retrieved September 2006 from: http://www.versatilevinegar.org/faqs.html

Thompson-Coon, J.S. & Ernst, E. (2003, June). Herbs for serum cholesterol reduction: a systematic view. *J Fam Pract.*, 52 (6): 468-78.

Trickey, R. (2003). *Women, hormones and the menstrual cycle* (2nd ed.). Australia: Allen & Unwin.

Ulwan, A. N. (2003). *Islam and love.* Egypt: Dar Al-Salam.

Ulwan, A. N. (2003). *Islam: the law of life.* Egypt: Dar Al-Salam.

Ursell, A. (2000). *The Complete Guide, Healing Food.* Dorling Kindersley Books.

Ustunol, Z. & Gandhi, H. (2001). Growth and acid production by lactic acid bacteria and bifidobacteria grown in skim milk containing honey. *Journal of Food Science*, 66 (3): 478-481.

Valenzuela, A., Sanhueza, J., and Nieto, S. (2003). Cholesterol oxidation: health hazard and the role of antioxidants in prevention. *Biol Res.*, 36 (3-4): 291-302.

Valero, M. & Salmeron, M.C. (2003, August 15). Antibacterial activity of 11 essential oils against Bacillus cereus in tyndallized carrot broth. *Int J Food Microbiol.*, 85 (1-2): 73-81.

Vijayakumar, M.V., Singh, S., Chhipa, R.R., and Bhat, M.K. (2005, June 27). The hypoglycaemic activity of fenugreek seed extract is mediated through the stimulation of an insulin signalling pathway. *Br J Pharmacol.*

Vinson, J. A. (1999, February). The Functional Food Properties of Figs. *Cereal Foods World*; 44 (2).

Vitaglione, P., Morisco, F., Caporaso, N., and Fogliano, V. (2004). Dietary antioxidant compounds and liver health. *Crit Rev Food Sci Nutr.*, 44 (7-8): 575-86.

Wagner, V., Gais, S., and Born, J. (2001). Emotional memory formation is enhanced across sleep intervals with high amounts of REM sleep. *Learning and Memory*, 8, 112-119.

Wahdan, H.A.L. (1998). Causes of the antimicrobial activity of honey. *Infection*. 26: 30-35

Wallace, R.K. & Benson, H. (1972). The physiology of meditation. *Scientific American*, 226, 83-90.

Wang, X.H., Gheldof, N., and Engeseth, N.J. (2004). Effect of processing and storage on antioxidant capacity of honey. *Journal of Food Science*, 69 (2): 96-101.

Waili, N. S. & Boni, N. S. (2003). Natural honey lowers plasma prostaglandin concentrations in normal individuals. *Journal of Medicinal Food,* summer, 6 (2): 129-33.)

Waili, N.S. (2004). Natural honey lowers plasma glucose, C-reactive protein, homocysteine, and blood lipids in healthy, diabetic, and hyperlipidemic subjects: comparison with dextrose and sucrose. J Med Food., Spring, 7 (1): 100-7.

Weil, A. (1998). *8 Weeks for Optimum Health*. New York: Ballantine Books.

Williams, A., Harber, D., Weaver, G., and Freeman, J. (1998). Altruistic activity. *Activities, adaptation, and Aging*, 22: 31.

Williams, N. (2004). *Powerful beyond measure*. Bantam Books.

Winston, R. (2004). *The Human Mind*. Bantam Books.

Wood, M. (2005). *Vitalism*. California: North Atlantic Books

World Health Organization. (1980). Environmental health criteria 12: Noise. Retrieved September, 2005 from: http://www.inchem.org/documents/ehc/ehc/ehc012. htm#SubSectionNumber:1.1.3

Xiaoling, Z. (1999). A study of scavenging action of purslane aquenous extracts on oxygen free radical. *Hunan Yike Daxue Xuebao*, 24 (2): 133-135.

Yahya, H. (1999). *The importance of conscience in the Qur'an*. Global Publishing.

Yahya, H. (2002). *The basic concepts in the Quran*. Goodword Books.

Yahya, H. (2003a). *An index to the Quran*. Global Publishing.

Yahya, H. (2003b). *Deep Thinking* (4th English ed.). Ta-Ha Publishers.

Yahya, H. (2003c). *Hopefulness in the Qur'an*. Saba Islamic Medica.

Yahya, H. (2003d). *Learning from the Qur'an*. Global Publishing.

Yahya, H. (2003e). *Prayer in the Qur'an*. Al-Saadawi Publications.

Yahya, H. (2004). *Faith: The Way to Happiness*. Global Publishing.

Yamahara, J., Miki, K., Chisaka, T., Sawada, T., Fujimura, H., Tomimatsu, T., Nakano, K., and Nohara, T. (1985, May). Cholagogic effect of ginger and its active constituents. *J Ethnopharmacol.*, 13 (2): 217-25.

Yamamoto, J., Yamada, K., Naemura, A., Yamashita, T., and Arai, R. (2005, May). Testing various herbs for antithrombotic effect. *Nutrition*, 21 (5): 580-7.

Yang, F., Basu, T.K., and Ooraikul, B. (2001, July). Studies on germination conditions and antioxidant contents of wheat grain. *Int J Food Sci Nutr.*, 52 (4): 319-30.

Yang, Y.C., Lee, H.S., Clark, J.M., and Ahn, Y.J. (2004, July). Insecticidal activity of plant essential oils against Pediculus humanus capitis. *J Med Entomol.*, 41 (4): 699-704.

Yoon, J.W., Ham, S.S., and Jun, H.S. (1999). Portulaca oleracea and tumor cell growth. *Official Gazette of the United States Patent and Trademark Office Patents*, 1219 (2): 1472.

Young, H.Y., Luo, Y.L., Cheng, H.Y., Hsieh, W.C., Liao, J.C., and Peng, W.H. (2005, January 4). Analgesic and anti-inflammatory activities of [6]-gingerol. *J Ethnopharmacol.*, 96 (1-2): 207-10.

Zakaria, M.N.M., Islam, M.W., Radhakrishnan, R., Habibullah, M., and Chan, K. (1998). Evaluation of anti-inflammatory activity of Portulaca species. Journal of Pharmacy and *Pharmacology*, 50 (Suppl.): 227.

Zakaria, R., Islam, M.N..M, Ismail, M.W., Habibullah, A., and Chan, M. K. (1998). Neuropharmacological actions of Portulaca oleracea v. sativa. *Journal of Pharmacy and Pharmacology*, 50 (Suppl.): 225.

Zedlitz, S., Kaufmann, R., and Boehncke, W.H. (2002, March). Allergic contact dermatitis from black cumin (Nigella sativa) oil-containing ointment. *Contact Dermatitis*, 46 (3): 188.

Sources in Arabic

'Abd Al-Kâfi, O (عمر عبد الكافي .د). n.d. Interpretation of *Saheeh al-Bukhari*. (audio tapes). Egypt: Al-Noor IslamicRecordings

'Abd al-Kâfi, O. (عمر عبد الكافي) (2005-2006). هذا ديننا *This is our religion* (Audio recordings). UAE: Markaz al-Shareet al-Islami

Abou Al-So'oud, H. (1998) (حسام الدين أبو السعود), December. دواء من القرآن والسنة [*Medicine from the Qur'an and the Sunnah*]. Kitâb al-Yaum at-Tibbi (201). Dâr Akhbâr-Al-Yaum.

'Ammâr, K. (خالد عمار) (2003). الأحاديث القدسية [*The Qudsi Hadiths*]. Al-Fajr.

Aytah, D. (درية العيطة) (n.d.). فقه العبادات على المذهب الشافعي [*The fiqh of worship according to the Shâfi'i School*]. As-Sabah.

Badr, A. Y. (عزيزة ياسين بدر) (2004). فلينظر الإنسان إلى طعامه-مدخل إلى الغذاء في القرآن الكريم [*Introduction to the nutrition in the Glorious Qur'an*]. Lebanon: Ad-Dâr al-'Arabiyyah lil-'Uloom.

Balch, J & Balch, P. (2001) الوصفة الطبية للعلاج بالتغذية [*Prescription for natural healing*]. (2nd ed.). KSA: Jareer

Bar, M. A. (محمد علي البار) (2000). الإعجاز العلمي في أحاديث التداوي بالخمر [*Scientific miracles in the Hadith concerning treatment with alcohol*]. Syria: Dâr al-Kalâm; Lebanon: Dâr ash-Shâmiyyah.

Basha, H. S. (حسان شمسي باشا) (2004). الطب النبوي بين العلم والإعجاز [*Prophetic medicine: between science and miracle*]. Syria: Dâr al-Kalâm; Lebanon: Dâr ash-Shâmiyyah.

Carper, J. (2001). المخ المعجزة [*Your miracle brain*]. KSA: Jareer.

Chaitow, L. (2003). بدائل المضادات الحيوية من الطبيعة [*Natural alternatives to antibiotics*]. KSA: Jareer.

الطب النبوي (2004). (أبي عبد الله شمس الدين بن عثمان الذهبي). Dhahabi, S. [*The Medicine of the Prophet*]. (M. Al-Merashly, محمد تحقيق د. عبد الرحمن المرعشلي editor). Dâr an-Nafâ'is.

Durant, W. (1994). قصة الفلسفة [*The story of philosophy*]. (Trans. A. Shaybani, (أحمد الشيباني). (2nd ed.). Dâr al-Qâri' al-'Arabi.

Dweik, J. A. (جميل القدسي دويك). (2003). القمح والشعير:الغذاء الميزان [*Wheat and barley: the balanced diet*]. Al-Askar.

Dweik, J. A. (جميل القدسي دويك). (2004). الزنجبيل [*Ginger*]. Ad-Dâr al-Waṭaniyyah al-Jadeedah.

Dweik, J. A. (جميل القدسي دويك). (2005). اللبأ معجزة الله في الأرض [*Colostrum: Allah's miracle on earth*]. Ad-Dâr al-Waṭaniyyah al-Jadeedah.

Feqi, I. (إبراهيم الفقي). (2001). البرمجة اللغوية العصبية وفن الاتصال اللامحدود [*NLP and the art of unlimited communication*]. NLP Canadian Center.

Ghazâli, A. M. (the Elder) (أبي حامد محمد الغزالي). (2004). إحياء علوم الدين [*Revival of religious knowledge*]. Lebanon: Dâr al-Ma'rifah.

Ghazâli, M. (the Younger) (محمد الغزالي). (2000). المحاور الخمسة للقرآن [*The five pivots of the Qur'an*]. Egypt: Dâr ash-Shurooq.

Ghazâli, M. (محمد الغزالي). (a2003). جدد حياتك [*Renovate your life*]. (5th ed.). Egypt: Nahdat Miṣr.

Ghazâli, M. (محمد الغزالي). (2003b). نحو تفسير موضوعي لسور القرآن الكريم [*Towards an objective explanation of the Qur'an*]. (6th ed.). Egypt: Dâr ash-Shurooq.

Gray, J. (2002). معجزات عملية للمريخ والزهرة [*Practical miracles for Mars and Venus*]. KSA: Jareer.

Ḥabbal, M. J. & 'Imary, W., R. (محمد جميل الحبال، وميض رمزي العمري). (2004). الطب في القرآن [*Medicine in the Qur'an*]. (2nd ed.). Dâr an-Nafâ'is.

Ḥakeem, S. (سعاد الحكيم) (2004). إحياء علوم الدين في القرن الواحد والعشرين [*Revival of the religious sciences in the 21ˢᵗ century*]. Egypt: Dâr ash-Shurooq.

Ibrahim, A.S. (أحمد شوقي ابراهيم) (2004). -موسوعة ما فرطنا في الكتاب من شيء [*Encyclopaedia of "We have neglected nothing in the Book"*]. المعارف الطبية في ضوء القرآن والسنة (Parts I to IV). Dâr al-Fikr al-'Arabi.

Jandi, K. (خالد الجندي) (2004). شهد الكلمات في رحاب سورة الفاتحة [*Beauty of the words in Soorat Al-Fâtiḥah*]. Lebanon: Dâr al-Ma'rifah.

Jauziyah, I. (شمس الدين ابن قيم الجوزية) (2001). الطب النبوي [*Prophetic medicine*]. (S. Oweda, تحقيق صلاح عويضة - editor). Dâr al-Aqeedah lit-Turâth.

Jauziyah, I. (شمس الدين ابن قيم الجوزية) (2002). الوابل الصيب من الكلم الطيب [*The downpour of good words*]. (A. Sa'd, تحقيق أبي عبد الرحمن عادل بن سعد - editor). Dâr Ibn Haytham.

Jauziyah, I.(شمس الدين ابن قيم الجوزية) (2003b). مفتاح دار السعادة [*The key to the house of happiness*]. Lebanon: Al-Maktaba al-'Aṣriyyah.

Jauziyah, I.(شمس الدين ابن قيم الجوزية) (2005). عدة الصابرين وذخيرة الشاكرين [*Tools of the forbearing and the provision of the grateful*]. (A. Enayat, تحقيق أحمد عناية - editor). Dâr al-Kitâb al-'Arabi.

Jumu'ah, M. L. (محمد لطفي جمعة) (1999). تاريخ فلسفة الإسلام [*History of Islamic philosophy*]. 'Âlam al-Kutub.

Khaled, A. (عمرو خالد) (2002). الصبر والذوق [*Patience and decency*]. Egypt: 'Areej.

Khaled, A. (عمرو خالد) (2003a). فعل الخير من مجموعة: فاستبقوا الخيرات [*Good deeds from "So hasten towards all that is good"*]. (Tape recording). Dâr al-Balâgh.

Khaled, A. (عمرو خالد) (2003b). أخلاق المؤمن [*Ethics of the believer*]. (3ʳᵈ ed.). Egypt: 'Areej.

Khaled, A. (عمرو خالد) (2003c). عبادات المؤمن [*The acts of worship of the believer*]. Egypt: 'Areej.

Khaled, A. (عمرو خالد) (2004a). إصلاح القلوب [*Remedying hearts*]. Egypt: 'Areej.

Khaled, A. (عمرو خالد) (2004b). خواطر قرآنية [*Reflections on the Qur'an*]. Lebanon: Ad-Dâr al-'Arabiyyah lil-'Uloom.

Khaled, A. (عمرو خالد) (2004c). عبادة التفكر [*Worship using deep thinking*]. Egypt: 'Areej.

Khamees, M. A. & Mitkees, A. محمد عطية خميس وعبد الوهاب ميتكيس (n.d.). مفاتيح الفرج *Keys of relief* (Abu al-Maa'ti ed.) 10th ed. Egypt: Dâr ar-Rawda

Maḥmoud, M. (مصطفىٰ محمود) (1998, August). علم نفس قرآني جديد [*New psychology from the Quran*]. Kitâb al-Yaum. Dâr Akhbâr-Al-Yaum.

Maḥmoud, M. (مصطفىٰ محمود) (2002). القرآن-محاولة لفهم عصري [*The Quran: An attempt at contemporary understanding*]. Dâr Mâyu al-Waṭaniyyah.

Ma'roof, N. (نايف معروف) (1995). الإنسان والعقل [*Human being and the mind*]. Sabeel ar-Rashâd.

Mosuli, S. (سامي أحمد الموصلي) (2004). الإسلام طبيب أمراض العصر [*Islam: the physician of modern diseases*]. Dâr an-Nafâ'is.

Muhammad, H.A.H. (حامدأحمد حامد محمد) (2002). رحلة الإيمان في جسم الإنسان [*Journey of faith through the human body*]. (3rd ed.). Syria: Dar al-Kalâm; KSA: Dar al-Basheer.

Musṭeehy, M. R., Jassem, A. A., Yâseen, I. A., Jandi, A. R., and Shukri, L. (محمود رجائي المصطيهي، أحمد عبد العزيزالجاسم، إبراهيم المهلهل الياسين، أحمد رجائي الجندي، لاحسان شكري) المجلة الإسلامية الشهرية لطب الأسنان (n.d.) مجلد ٣٦، ١٩١٨ ص ٣٦٢-٣٦٦ [*Islamic monthly magazine of dentistry*]. Kuwait.

Mu'ṭi, M. M. (موسى محمد المعطي) (2002). الطب البديل [*Alternative medicine*]. (2ⁿᵈ ed.). At-Tawba.

Najjâr, Z. (زغلول النجار) (2003a). الإعجاز العلمي في السنة النبوية [*The miraculous scientific nature of the Sunnah*]. Part I. (4ᵗʰ ed.). Egypt: Nahdat Miṣr.

Najjâr, Z. (زغلول النجار) (2003b). الإعجاز العلمي في السنة النبوية [*The miraculous scientific nature of the Sunnah*]. Part II. (2ⁿᵈ ed.). Egypt: Nahdat Miṣr.

Naṣṣâr, M. (محمود نصار) (1995). صفة طعام وشراب النبي [*Characteristics of the Prophet's food and drink*]. Dâr al-Fadheelah.

Qardawi, Y. (2002a). *The Sunnah: A source of civilization* (2ⁿᵈ ed.). Egypt: Al-Falaḥ Foundation.

Qardawi, Y. (يوسف القرضاوي) (2002b). الرسول والعلم [*The Prophet and the science*]. (7ᵗʰ ed.). Ar-Risâlah.

Qardawi, Y. (يوسف القرضاوي) (2002c). السنة مصدر للمعرفة والحضارة [*The Sunnah: A source of knowledge and civilization*]. (3ʳᵈ ed.). Egypt: Dâr ash-Shurooq.

Quṭb, S. (سيد قطب) (2005). في ظلال القرآن [*In the shade of the Qur'an*]. (35ᵗʰ ed.). Egypt: Dâr ash-Shurooq.

Râwi, H. (حسام الراوي). (1999). الرسول الطبيب [*The Prophet, the healer*]. Al-Intishâr al-'Arabi.

Sabki, (السبكي تاج الدين الطبقات الشافعية الكبرى) [*Major categories of the Shâfi'i School*]

Sâbir, H.A. نظرات في تاريخ الخلفاء الراشدين. (2001). حلمي عبد المنعم صابر [*Glimpses of the history of the Rightly-guided Caliphs*]. Egypt: The American Open University.

Ṣabooni, M. A. (محمد علي الصابوني) (2005). شرح رياض الصالحين للإمام النووي [*Interpretation of the meadows of the righteous*]. Al-Maktaba al-'Aṣriyyah.

Scrivner, J. (2003). تخلص من السموم [*Detox yourself*]. KSA: Jareer.

Sayyid, A. (السيد الباسط عبد). (2000). النبوي والطب بالأعشاب التداوي [*Healing with herbs and Prophetic medicine*]. Egypt: Longman.

Sayyid, A. (السيد الباسط عبد). (2002). سلسلة شرائط ،التغذية -النبوي الطب النبوية السنة في النبوي الإعجاز [*Prophetic medicine: Nutrition*] (tape recordings). Egypt: Misk.

Sayyid, A. (السيد الباسط عبد). (2003). أسابيع ثمانية في النبوية التغذية [*Prophetic nutrition in eight weeks*]. Egypt: Alfa.

Sayyid, A. (السيد الباسط عبد). (2004). الوقائي الطب [*Prophylactic medicine*]. (3rd ed.). Egypt: Alfa.

Shareef, A. (الشريف عدنان) (1990). القرآني الطب علم من [*From the medical science of the Qur'an*]. Dar al-Ilm lil-Malayin.

'Ulwân, A.N. (علوان ناصح الله عبد) (1984). في وأثرها الإسلام في الحضارة معالم الأوروبية النهضة [*Islamic civilization and its effects on European renaissance*]. (2nd ed.). Egypt: Dâr as-Salâm.

Table of Health Problems and Suggested Dietary Intervention

How to use this table

1. $\mathcal{L}$ook up the health problem or condition you are concerned about (the list is in alphabetical order).
2. In the column next to it you will find a list of recommended or suggested useful food or herbs.
3. Then use the index at the back of this book to find the page number(s) for each item.
4. Turn to those pages to find more detailed information about the suggested food or herb.

Note that the recommended herbs and foods are mere preventive measures that should be implemented along with a holistic healthy life style as discussed in this book. It should be taken into consideration also that no food is in any way like a 'magic pill' that shows its result as soon as it is administered; beneficial foods and herbs should be part of a regular, healthy eating routine that builds a strong, healthy organism over time. It should also be noted that the use of a combination of different foods and herbs causes a synergistic effect, so it would be very useful to vary your diet and experiment with new flavours and combinations of flavours every now and then.

The suggested foods here are not in any way meant to take the place of professional medical advice.

Health concern	Useful foods & herbs
Allergy	Black seed, fennel, honey
Anaemia	Capers, dates, pomegranates, iron-rich food as red meat and organs (caution for people with high cholesterol and pregnant women)
Aphrodisiac	Truffles, ginger, thyme, dates with milk and cinnamon, banana, watermelons
Appetite loss	Citrons, bitter orange (in small amounts)
Arthritis/ rheumatoid arthritis	Capers, ginger, rosemary infusion (ti-sane), fennel, frankincense (luban); topically: oil of thyme and eucalyptus essential oil, mustard seed poultice
Asthma	Ginger, eucalyptus essential oil inhalation, black seeds, fennel, frankincense (lubân)
Atherosclerosis (blocked/hardened arteries)	Capers, chard (or silq), onion, pumpkins, gourds and squashes, ginger, grapes, bananas, foods rich in Omega-3 fatty acids as pumpkin seeds, purslane and fish; honey
Athlete's foot and nail fungus	Soak feet in vinegar
Bacteria, fungi, yeast, mould	Garlic, onions, basil and marjoram essential oils, Aloe vera, umbelliferous fruits (dill, cumin, fennel...), black seeds, honey and bee propolis

Health concern	Useful foods & herbs
Blood circulation (poor)	see microcirculation
Blood clots *(preventive measures, not treatment)*	Garlic, foods rich in omega-3 fatty acids, like pumpkin seeds, purslane and fish; ginger, black seeds, figs, purple and red grape juice, quince
Blood pressure (high)	see hypertension
Blood sugar (high): *see diabetes*	
Breast milk (reduced flow)	Cumin seeds, fennel, dill, fenugreek, dates, figs
Bronchitis (and cough)	Onion, ginger, basil, marjoram and thyme infusion, eucalyptus essential oil (topical rub or inhalation), fennel, black seed, fenugreek, bananas, bitter orange, frankincense (lubân), decoction of dates, grapes, candied citron peel
Burning urination	Vinegar
Burns (on skin)	Aloe vera, purslane, honey
Cancer (breast, ovarian, colon, prostate)	High fibre foods and food rich in lignan and lignin, such as whole grain barley and wheat; carrots, ginger, fenugreek, dates, figs, quince, citrons with rind, soya beans, chickpeas and lentils
Cancer, skin	Olive oil

Health concern	Useful foods & herbs
Cancers (in general)	Plants rich in chlorophyll such as wheat & barley grass, and dark green leafy vegetables; anti-oxidants and variety of coloured vegetables and sulphur-containing foods (see toxins and free radicals); foods rich in omega-3 fatty acids as purslane, nuts and fish; onion, black seed (& its oil), garlic, ginger, Aloe vera, mustard seeds, fenugreek, purslane, dates, figs, red grapes, citrons, *probiotic* such as buttermilk, *prebiotic* such as honey; royal jelly
Central nervous system (CNS) disorders	Foods rich in omega-3 fatty acids such as purslane, nuts and fish
Chills (in common cold)	Ginger infusion with cinnamon
Cholesterol (high)	Foods rich in fibres as whole grains especially barley and oat; blue, purple or red foods like beets, blackberries, blueberries, cherries, purple and red grapes, and purple cabbage; carrots, garlic, pumpkin seeds, Aloe vera, fennel, black seed oil, fenugreek, dates, figs, purple and red grape juice, pomegranate juice, bananas, quince, nuts like almonds, peanuts, walnuts, hazelnuts and cashews (in small amounts as they are high in fats), *probiotic* such as buttermilk, *prebiotic* such as honey, vinegar, royal jelly, olive oil

Health concern	Useful foods & herbs
Cold sore	Vinegar (topically)
Cold virus	Ginger, infusion (tisane) of marjoram and rosemary, eucalyptus infusion (w/ lemon & honey), watermelons
Colic	Cumin, fennel, anise, caraway, thyme
Colitis	Frankincense (lubân), decoction of dates
Constipation	High fibre foods as whole grain barley and wheat (as preventive and bowel regulator not treatment for existing constipation); dates, figs, aloe Vera, grapes, olive oil
Convalescence	Chard and barley
Cough	See *bronchitis*
Depression	*Talbeenah* (barley soup), basil, foods rich in omega-3 fatty acids as purslane, nuts and fish; grapes, banana, lean turkey aromatherapy: rosemary and basil essential oils
Dermatitis (see also *dry skin*)	Cucumber, pumpkin seeds topically: Aloe vera gel
Diabetes	Onion, ginger, basil, Aloe vera, black seed, fenugreek, purslane, chromium-rich food such as whole grain barley
Diarrhoea	Fenugreek, black seed, banana, pomegranates, honey

Health concern	Useful foods & herbs
Diverticulosis (gastric disorder)	Foods rich in fibers such as whole grain wheat, figs
Dysmenhorroea	Lemongrass, ginger
Eye disease (cataracts, poor night vision)	Vitamin A-rich food: yellow/orange vegetables like carrots, watermelons; ginger
Fertility, male	see *infertility*
Flatulence	Capers, ginger, basil, thyme, rosemary, cumin seeds, fennel, dill, fenugreek, citron peel
Gout	Capers, figs
Gum disease	Siwâk (as toothbrush)
Hair, dandruff	Rosemary infusion as a rinse; olive oil
Hair, dry	Olive oil and avocado applied topically; olive oil w/ shampoo
Headache	Marjoram infusion
Heart disease	Barley, chard or silq (beetroot leaves), onion, yellow/orange vegetables, pumpkins, gourds and squashes, ginger, purple and red grape juice, pomegranate juice, quince marmalade, bitter orange, foods rich in omega-3 fatty acids like pumpkin seeds, purslane and fish; flax seeds, almonds, peanuts, walnuts, hazelnuts and cashews, soya beans, chickpeas and lentils, honey

Health concern	Useful foods & herbs
Heartburn and hyperacidity	Carrots, Aloe vera, banana, pomegranate
Haemorrhoids	Whole grain wheat, dates, figs
Health concern	Useful foods & herbs
Hypertension	Cucumber, carrots (diuretics), garlic, basil, black seed oil, dates, banana, pomegranates, foods rich in omega-3 fatty acids like pumpkin seeds, purslane and fish
Immune system deficiency	Bean and seed sprouts; wheat and barley grass; mushrooms, yellow/orange vegetables as carrots; truffles, pumpkins, ginger, basil infusion (tisane), rosemary, Aloe vera, foods rich in omega-3 fatty acids like pumpkin seeds, purslane and fish; dates, bananas, watermelons, pecans, peanuts and cashew nuts, *probiotic* like buttermilk, *prebiotic* like honey; royal jelly
Indigestion	Lemongrass, ginger, basil, Aloe vera, fenugreek, thyme, rosemary infusion (tisane), black seed, cumin seeds, fennel, dill, bananas, bitter orange, *probiotic* such as buttermilk, *talbeenah* (barley soup)
Infertility, male	Pumpkin seeds, garlic, red meat, pecans, peanuts and cashew nuts

Health concern	Useful foods & herbs
Insect bites	Basil, purslane, Aloe vera, vinegar (as a local rub)
Intestinal lining inflammation	Quince
Intestinal problems and spasms	Ginger, thyme, umbelliferous fruits (dill, cumin, fennel, anise, caraway…), fenugreek, citrons
Intestinal parasites	Purslane, pomegranate rind decoction
Kidney problems	Capers, black seeds, dates, figs, grapes and raisins, bananas, watermelons, honey dissolved in warm water
Labour (childbirth) / contractions	Dates
Liver toxins	Wheat grass, barley grass, capers, ginger, Aloe vera (bitters in general), black seed, fennel essential oil, figs, quince marmalade, honey
Malnutrition: beri-beri	Whole grains for vitamin B_1 (thiamine)
Memory and mental concentration problems	Rosemary essential oil, raisins, bananas
Menstrual cramps and PMS	Whole grains (vitamin B_6), lemongrass, ginger, citron rind, soya beans, chickpeas and lentils

Health concern	Useful foods & herbs
Microcirculation problems & capillary fragility	Sulphur-containing foods including garlic, onion, pineapple and the crucifer family (which includes broccoli, Brussels sprouts, cabbage, cauliflower, mustard greens, radishes and turnips); ginger, foods rich in rutin such as rye, capers and bee pollens; citrons, bitter orange and other citrus fruits with rind; foods rich in omega-3 fatty acids such as pumpkin seeds, purslane and fish
Mucus (excess)	Ginger, liquorice, fennel and thyme herbal tea; aloe Vera, black seed, vinegar in warm water,
Nausea, morning sickness	Lemongrass, ginger, basil, Aloe vera, fenugreek
Night blindness	see *eye disease*
Obesity	Fibre-rich food as whole grain barley, cucumbers, fenugreek, citrons and vitamin C-rich food
Osteoporosis	Canned oily fish with their soft bones; milk and dairy, vinegar added during preparation of soup stocks
Postpartum bleeding	Fenugreek, figs
Respiratory tract problems	Ginger, thyme infusion, fennel tisane, black seed oil, grapes & raisins, banana, citrons, bitter orange; eucalyptus topically or as steam inhalation

Health concern	Useful foods & herbs
Rheumatism	see *arthritis*
Salmonella bacteria	Garlic, thyme
Skin, dry (see also *dermatitis*)	Olive oil, wheat grass, barley grass, cucumber
Skin, oily	Lemongrass
Sore throat	Ginger, thyme, fennel, eucalyptus gargle with lemon and honey, quince, jujube (*nabq*), vinegar gargle
Sunburn	Cucumber (topically)
Teeth (plaque formation)	Siwâk (as toothbrush)
Thrombosis	see *blood clot*
Thrush (a fungal infection)	Vinegar added to drinking water
Toxins and free radicals	Antioxidant-rich foods such as: sprouts, wheat & barley grass; dark green leafy vegetables like chard and spinach; beta-carotene rich foods such as carrots and sweet potatoes; *lycopene*-rich foods like tomatoes; blue, purple or red foods such as beets, blackberries, blueberries, cherries, purple and red grapes, and purple cabbage; sulphur-containing foods including garlic, onion, pineapple and the crucifer family (broccoli, Brussels

Health concern	Useful foods & herbs
	the crucifer family (broccoli, Brussels sprouts, cabbage, watercress, cauliflower, mustard seeds, mustard greens, radishes and turnips); cucumber, capers, pumpkins, gourds and squashes, ginger, basil, marjoram, rosemary, umbelliferous fruits (dill, cumin, fennel...), black seed, fenugreek, purslane, dried fruits especially raisins; red grape juice, pomegranates, watermelon (and its seeds), citrons, bitter oranges, honey
Ulcer (mouth and local ulcers)	Purslane, honey
Ulcer (peptic and duodenal)	Ginger (not used on active ulcer), thyme, Aloe vera, cumin, figs, banana, pomegranate, honey
Water retention	Rosemary, thyme, purslane
Worms	see *intestinal parasites*

MICRONUTRIENTS:
VITAMINS AND MINERALS

$\mathcal{V}$itamins are organic compounds that do not provide energy but are needed in small amounts to perform important functions in the body. If you study this table closely, you will notice that the ones that are needed most frequently by the body (vitamin C, E and B vitamins) are widely spread in common and different food sources, and they are not stored in the body, so that if we consume more than we need, the excess will just be excreted, causing no toxic symptoms. (This will not be the case if you obtain them from supplements). On the other hand, the fat-soluble vitamins like A and D, which can be stored in the body, are less available in our foods. Nevertheless, to avoid deficiency, Allah made your body able to synthesise these vitamins, only when needed, from other available sources (vitamin A from beta-carotenes and vitamin D by the action of sunlight on your skin). Another fat-soluble vitamin, K, is needed in a tiny amount: it is found in few food sources, and any additional need for it is provided by the action of intestinal bacteria, so deficiency is not common except as a result of human interference like the long-term use of antibiotics.

Minerals are elements needed in the diet to perform important chemical reactions or act as structural components and regulators of different body processes. Trace minerals are minerals required in very small amounts but they perform crucial functions in the body.

As a general rule, it is better to obtain vitamins and minerals from natural dietary sources rather than from supplements.

Micronutrient[1]	Source	Main function
	Water soluble vitamins	
Vitamin C Ascorbic acid	Citrus fruits, vegetables of the cabbage family, strawberries, cantaloupe, green leafy vegetables	Antioxidant, collagen synthesis, hormones, bile acids, and neurotransmitter synthesis; maintains connective tissue, immune system and capillary integrity; aids iron and folate absorption, detoxifies the body and plays an important role in releasing stress hormones from the adrenal glands; restores vitamin E
The B vitamins		
Vitamin B_1 Thiamine	Whole grains, legumes, seeds, organ meat	Nerve function, energy production, metabolism of sugars, synthesis of neurotransmitters
B_2 Riboflavin	Milk, whole grains, leafy greens, broccoli	Energy production, fat metabolism

[1] The information in this table is compiled from: Smolin & Grosvenor, 1994; Duyff, 2002; Haas, 2006

Micronutrient	Source	Main function
B_3 Niacin	Peanuts, tuna, chicken, beef, whole grains except corn; part is synthesized in the body from amino acid tryptophan	Energy production, fat and sugar metabolism, enzyme functions
B_5 Pantothenic acid	Whole grains, meat and organs, legumes, eggs, milk, vegetables and fruits	Energy production, cholesterol and fatty acid synthesis, metabolism of fats, proteins and carbohydrates
B_6 Pyridoxine	Whole grains, meat, legumes, nuts and seeds, leafy greens	essential for metabolism & synthesis of amino acids, neurotransmitters, white blood cells (immune system cells) and haemoglobin
B_{12} Cyanocobalamin	Animal products (meat and dairy)	Essential for proper nerve function and folate metabolism, works with folate to form haemoglobin
Biotin	Liver, egg yolk, nuts and seeds; synthesized by bacteria in the gut	essential for energy production, glucose synthesis, and metabolism of fatty and amino acids

Micronutrient	Source	Main function
Folate	Green leafy vegetables, organ meat, legumes, pith of oranges & other citrus	Essential for synthesis and integrity of RNA and DNA (the genetic materials in every cell) and amino acids metabolism, works with B_{12} to form haemoglobin; protects the heart

Fat soluble vitamins

Vitamin A Retinol	All liver, fish liver oil, egg yolk, butter; synthesized in the body from Beta-carotenes: yellow, orange and red vegetables and fruits like carrots, sweet potatoes, peaches, squash; leafy greens, broccoli	Vision, growth, tissue healing, cell differentiation, reproduction, immune function, maintenance of epithelial tissue and healthy skin, regulation of genetic processes; Beta-carotenes are powerful antioxidants.
Vitamin E Alpha-tocopherol	Vegetable oils (cold pressed), leafy greens, nuts and peanuts, seeds, wheat and other whole grain germs	Antioxidant, protects cell membranes, red blood cells, and cells of the nervous and immune systems; protects from environmental pollutants and toxins

Micronutrient	Source	Main function
Vitamin D Cholecalciferol	Egg yolk, organ meat, fatty fish and cod liver oil; synthesized in the skin by the action of sunlight	Regulates absorption and metabolism of calcium and phosphorus; helps normal calcification of bones
Vitamin K	Beef liver, dark leafy greens, alfalfa and kelp, egg yolk. Synthesized by intestinal bacteria (helped by yogurt and buttermilk)	Essential for blood clotting; role in synthesis of some proteins in the blood, bones and kidneys

Major minerals

Sodium	Table salt, processed foods	Nerve transmission, regulation of fluid balance, muscle relaxation – including the heart; regulation of blood pressure
Potassium	Fruits, vegetables, whole grains	Nerve transmission, regulation of fluid and mineral balance, maintenance of normal blood pressure, muscle contraction

Micronutrient	Source	Main function
Calcium	Milk and dairy, canned fish, leafy green vegetables	Structuring of bones and teeth, nerve transmission, muscle contraction, blood clotting
Chloride	Table salt	Regulation of fluid, food digestion, transmission of nerve impulses
Phosphorus	Meat, dairy, cereals, bran, nuts, fish, eggs	Structuring of bones, teeth, and membranes, energy production; forms part of DNA structure
Magnesium	Nuts, seeds, greens, whole grains, bananas	Bone structure, enzyme function, energy production and nerve and muscle function
Sulphur	Proteins non-dietary source: inorganic food preservatives	Part of some amino acids needed for protein synthesis and cell protection from oxidative damage; regulates acid/base balance

Trace minerals

Iron	Animal source: meat, poultry, fish (well absorbed by the body) plant	Forms part of haemoglobin in red blood cells essential for oxygen delivery, and part

Micronutrient	Source	Main function
	source: leafy green vegetables, legumes, whole grains, dried fruits (addition of vitamin C from limes or lemons aids absorption) non-dietary source: iron cookware	of myoglobin in the muscles which stores oxygen for muscle contraction; energy production, antioxidant enzyme function, drug metabolism and immune system
Zinc	Animal source: red meat, liver, eggs, dairy, some seafood (well absorbed by the body) plant source: vegetables, legumes, whole grains	Tissue growth and repair, wound healing, regulation of protein synthesis; development of sex organs, bones, immune function; storage and release of insulin, stabilization of cell membranes
Iodine	Fish, seafood, seaweed, dairy, iodized salt	Essential component of thyroid hormone which regulates metabolic rate and growth and promotes protein synthesis

Micronutrient	Source	Main function
Copper	Organ meat, whole grains, nuts and seeds, chocolate	Important for iron, cholesterol, and fat metabolism; synthesis of neurotransmitters and connective tissue, maintenance of heart muscle, immune and central nervous system function
Manganese	Whole grains, nuts and seeds	Important for metabolism of carbohydrate and fat, brain function
Selenium	Seafood, organ meat, eggs	Antioxidant, spares vitamin E; needed for synthesis of thyroid hormone
Fluoride	Marine fish with bones, water, tea non-dietary source: Teflon cookware, toothpaste	Prevents tooth caries, strengthens bones
Chromium	Organ meat, whole grains, nuts and seeds, brewer's yeast	Necessary fro glucose tolerance and glucose transport into the cells.
Molybdenum	Organ meat, milk and dairy, whole grains, legumes	Works with many enzymes, involved in the formation of red blood cells

Micronutrient	Source	Main function
Boron	Fruits, leafy vegetables, legumes, nuts and seeds	Involved in calcium and magnesium metabolism, maintenance of cell membrane and bone integrity (still under investigation)
Arsenic	Fish, whole grains (occurs in food in an organic, non-toxic form)	Role in heart function and cell growth (still under investigation)
Nickel	Whole grains, nuts and seeds, legumes, chocolate	Involved in metabolism of some fatty and amino acids, affects function of other nutrients like calcium, iron, zinc and vitamin B_{12} (still under investigation)
Silicon	Whole grains, root vegetables	Involved in collagen synthesis and bone calcification

GLOSSARY OF ISLAMIC TERMS[1]

abu, (or *abi*)	أبو، أبي	father (of)
adhân	أذان	the call to prayer
'ajwah	عجوة	a variety of dates; ripe dates or date paste
alḥamdulillâh	الحمد لله	all praise is for Allah
Allâhu akbar	الله أكبر	Allah is the Greatest
Anṣâr	أنصار	'helpers': the Muslim citizens of Madinah
'aṣr	عصر	mid-afternoon; the obligatory prayer at that time
astaghfir Allâh	أستغفر الله	i seek Allah's Forgiveness
âyah (pl. *âyât*)	آية	verse of the Qur'an or signs of Allah
dhikr Allâh	ذكر الله	remembrance of Allah
dhuhr	ظهر	afternoon; the obligatory prayer at that time

---

[1] The Arabic words are transliterated according to the conventions of the Transliteration Chart found in this book. If a word has become part of the English language (i.e. is found in a standard English dictionary), that spelling is used in this book and appears first in this Glossary, with the transliterated form in brackets after it.

du'â'	دعاء	supplication; invocation
ḍuḥâ'	الضحا	mid to late morning; the optional prayer at that time
Eid ('eed)	عيد	festival; the two celebrations: one at the end of Ramadan and the other at the culmination of the Hajj
fajr	فجر	dawn; the obligatory prayer at that time
fiṭrah	فطرة	the natural inclination (of humans) instilled by Allah
ghusl	غسل	ritual shower necessary after a major impurity
Hadith (ḥadeeth)	حديث	the collected sayings and actions of Prophet Muhammad (ﷺ) that with the Qur'an form the basis of Islamic law
hadith (ḥadeeth)	حديث	a saying or action of Prophet Muhammad (ﷺ) that was remembered and recorded by his Companions and followers
hadith qudsi	حديث قدسي	'sacred hadith': a hadith communicated to Prophet Muhammad (ﷺ) by Allah

Hajj (ḥajj)	حج	the major pilgrimage to the Sacred Mosque, site of the Ka'bah at Makkah, to be undertaken by every able Muslim once in his/her lifetime
halal (ḥalâl)	حلال	permitted according to Islamic law
ḥarâm	حرام	forbidden according to Islamic law
Hijrah	هجرة	migration: *esp.* the migration from Makkah to Madinah by Prophet Muhammad (ﷺ) and his Companions that marks the start of the Islamic calendar
'ibâdât (sg. *'ibâdah*)	عبادات	acts of worship
ifṭâr	إفطار	the meal eaten at sunset to break the fast
iḥrâm	إحرام	the state of consecration for Hajj or 'umrah; the special clothing worn by the pilgrim in such a state
'ishâ'	عشا	evening; the obligatory prayer at that time
isrâ' and *mi'râj*	الإسراء والمعراج	the night journey of the Prophet (ﷺ) from Makkah to Jerusalem and then up to visit heaven

istikhârah	استخارة	a prayer by which one seeks guidance from Allah
janâbah	جنابة	a state of impurity due to sexual activity or emission
jumu'ah	جمعة	Friday; *also*, the midday congregational prayer of that day
Kaaba (Ka'bah)	الكعبة	the House of Allah built by Prophets Ibrâheem and Ismâ'eel
khabâ'ith	خبائث	evil deeds
Khaleefah (pl. *Khulafâ'*)	خليفة	Caliph; head of the Islamic state
Al-Khulafâ' ar-Râshidoon	الخلفاء الراشدون	the four 'Rightly-guided Caliphs' who governed after the death of the Prophet (ﷺ)
lâ ilâha illâ Allâh	لا إله إلا الله	there is none worthy of worship other than Allah
maghrib	مغرب	sunset; the obligatory prayer at that time
maytatah	ميتة	dead animal; meat from an animal that was not slaughtered according to Islamic law
muhâjiroon (or *muhâjireen*)	مهاجرون	the Muslims who migrated with Prophet Muhammad (ﷺ) from Makkah to Madinah
mujâhid	مجاهد	one who strives in Allah's cause

raḥm	رحم	womb
raka'ah (pl. *raka'ât*)	ركعة	a unit of the formal prayer (ṣalât)
Ramadan (*Ramaḍân*)	رمضان	the ninth month in the Islamic calendar; the month of obligatory fasting
rukoo'	ركوع	the act of bowing (in prayer)
ṣabr	صبر	patient, steadfast
ṣadaqah	صدقة	voluntary charity
sajdah	سجدة	the act of prostration (in prayer)
ṣalât	صلاة	formal prayer: a combination of physical postures, recitation and supplication
Sharia (*shari'ah*)	شرعة	Islamic law derived from the Qur'an and the Sunnah
siwâk	سواك	a small twig (*usu.* of the Arâk tree) used as a toothbrush
soorah or *soorat*	سورة	chapter of the Qur'an
suḥoor	سحور	the pre-dawn meal eaten before the start of a fasting day
Sunnah	سَنَة	the practice and collected sayings of Prophet Muhammad (ﷺ) that together with the Qur'an forms the basis of Islamic law

tahajjud	تَهَجُّد	night prayer offered between 'ishâ' and fajr
takbeer	تكبير	the act of saying *Allâhu akbar*
tasleem	تسليم	the act of saying *as-salâmu 'alaykum wa raḥmat Allâh* to end the prayer
'uboodiyah	عبوديَّة	servitude, slavery
Ummah	أُمَة	community or nation: *usu.* used to refer to the entire global community of Muslims
'umrah	عمرة	a minor, non-obligatory pilgrimage to Makkah
wuḍoo'	وضوء	ablution usually required before prayer or touching the Qur'an
zakât (zakâh or *zakât)*	زكاة	obligatory charity: an 'alms tax' on wealth payable by Muslims and to be distributed to other Muslims who qualify as recipients

INDEX

A